Hamlet in Iceland
Being the Icelandic Romantic
Ambales Saga

CW01019975

Israel Gollancz

Alpha Editions

This edition published in 2020

ISBN : 9789354154331 (Paperback)

ISBN : 9789354151736 (Hardback)

Design and Setting By
Alpha Editions
www.alphaedis.com
email - alphaedis@gmail.com

HAMLET IN ICELAND

BEING THE ICELANDIC ROMANTIC AMBALES SAGA,
EDITED AND TRANSLATED, WITH EXTRACTS FROM
FIVE AMBALES RIMUR AND OTHER ILLUSTRATIVE
TEXTS, FOR THE MOST PART NOW FIRST PRINTED,
AND AN INTRODUCTORY ESSAY

BY

ISRAEL GOLLANCZ, M.A.

CHRIST'S COLLEGE, CAMBRIDGE; UNIVERSITY
LECTURER IN ENGLISH; EXAMINER IN ENGLISH
TO THE UNIVERSITY OF LONDON; EDITOR OF
"PRE-TUDOR TEXTS," ETC.

*"And if you intreate him faire in a frostie morning, he will
afoord you whole Hamlets. . . ."*—NASH'S *Preface to* GREENE'S
"Menaphon."

LONDON
DAVID NUTT, 270–71 STRAND
1898

Printed by BALLANTYNE, HANSON & Co.
At the Ballantyne Press

EIRÍKI MAGNÚSSYNI

OG

HINRIKI L. D. WARD

með þakklætis-kveðju

" Viðrgefendr ok endrgefendr erosk lengst vinir."

TABLE OF CONTENTS

ix

PREFACE

SCHOLARS are variously infected by the "*morbus Hamleticus.*"
Many years ago, in his boyhood, the present writer fell a
victim, the ailment, in his case, taking the form of an unhealthy
curiosity anent Hamlet's pedigree. He naturally turned to
the land of the Sagas, and although a certain feeling of disappointment attended the quest, the investigator soon became
keenly interested in diagnosing Iceland's long and painful
struggle for a Hamlet Saga. The story of that struggle is
told in the accompanying volume. There is something almost
pathetic in Iceland's effort to compensate itself for its depriva-
tion or loss of ancient story and song concerning the mythical
hero, whose name, first recorded in Scaldic verse, has lived
on the lips of the people for probably the greater part of a
thousand years.

Soon after the composition of the "Ambales Saga," the
possibilities of the Hamlet-story were recognised elsewhere.
In later times, all unconscious of England's triumph, Iceland's
ballad-poets be-rhymed their favourite "Ambales" or "Amloði."
Six independent versions, each in all probability extending to
more than six thousand lines, testify to the attractiveness of
the theme. Of these versions five are represented by parallel
extracts in the Appendices at the end of the book; the sixth
has so far not been discoverable: even the last resource of
patient research has failed, to wit, a public appeal to Icelanders
in the columns of their "*Ísafold*" and "*Dagsskrá.*" *

* "**Saga** eða **Rímur** af *Ambáles kongi* (Amlóða), handrit, verða keypt á skrifst.
Ísafoldar og vel gefið fyrir."—Ísafold, Reykjavik, laugardaginn, 29 ágúst, 1896,
59 blað.

PREFACE

In the Introductory Essay an attempt has been made to throw some new light upon the development of the legend. If the new facts and theories prove acceptable, these studies may have advanced the problem, and may, it is hoped, serve as the basis of future investigation.

Finally, the writer desires to express his sincerest thanks to several kind helpers: to the patriotic Icelander Mr. Thorsteinn Erlingsson, who some ten years ago procured for him MSS. and transcripts of MSS.; to Dr. Jón Thorkelsson, the distinguished author of "Digtningen på Island i det 15 og 16 Arhundrede," who more recently has put at his disposal unique copies of two "Rimur," and has afforded valuable information on many points; to Dr. Jón Stefansson, who has kindly read the proofs of all the Appendices, and has made clear many dark allusions in the extracts from the "Rimur;" lastly, and more especially, to Mr. Eirikr Magnússon, who with zealous generosity familiar to all Cambridge students of Northern lore has encouraged the work from its inception in undergraduate days afar off: to say that he has read the proofs of the Saga is to refer to the least of his many kindly services. The volume is fittingly associated with his name, and with that of another scholar, whose "Catalogue of the Manuscript Romances in the British Museum" deserves some tribute from every worker in the field of inquiry illumined by his learning. "'Give' and 'Give back' make the longest friends," quoth Odin.

> "Ambolis Sögu enda eg hier,
> er eg í fyngrum brenn :
> betra seint en aldrei er,
> su einhvörn tíma er buen."
> —MS. Brit. Mus. 11, 158.

> "Ambales Saga end I here.
> How my fingers burn !
> Better late than never :
> It is done at last ! "

I. G.

viii

INTRODUCTION

I.

Sem Snæbjörn kvað:
"**Hvatt** kveða hræra Grotta
hergrimmastan skerja
út fyrir jarðar skauti
Eylúðrs níu brúðir;
þær er, lungs, fyrir laungu,
lið-meldr, skipa hliðar
baugskerðir ristr barði
ból, Amlóða mólu."
—*Hér er kallat haft Amlóða kvern.*

"'Tis said," sang Snæbjörn, "that far out, off yonder ness, the Nine
Maids of the Island Mill stir amain the host-cruel skerry-quern—
they who in ages past ground Hamlet's meal. The good Chieftain
furrows the hull's lair with his ship's beaked prow."*

TO Snorri Sturlason, the glory of Icelandic historiography, we
are indebted for the preservation of these lines, containing
the earliest known reference to the legendary hero destined to
play so important a part in later literary history. The strange
verse occurs in Snorri's "Skaldskapar-mál," or Gradus to the
Northern Parnassus, the second section of his famous hand-
book of the Art of Poetry, known as "The Prose Edda," composed about the year 1230. The illustrative extracts found in

* *i.e.,* " Kveða níu brúðir eylúðrs hræra hvatt hergrimmastan skerja grotta út
fyrir jarðar skauti, þær er fyrir löngu mólu Amlóða lið-meldr; baugskerðir ristr
skipa hliðar ból lungs barði."

xi

the Gradus (some two hundred and fifty from sixty-five named poets, besides anonymous lays) are in many instances the only remains of the ancient poems quoted. The work is in catechetical form, and in answer to the question, "Hvernig skal sæ kenna?" i.e., "What are the names for the Sea?" a long list of synonyms and epithets is given, together with descriptive passages from various poets, some of them clearly sailor-poets; among these is the extract from Snæbjörn. The lines, though laboured, are evidently from some poem of adventure in Northern waters, "hatched in the storms of the ocean, and feathered in the surges of many perilous seas." The passage presents many difficulties, and various interpretations have been advanced, but the underlying reference is certainly to the great World-Mill deep down in the sea, the great cosmic force, which the ancient Northerners and other races conceived as the cause of storms and showers, and of all the disintegrating changes wrought on mountains, rocks, and shores. The fierce whirlpools and currents of the Arctic Ocean may easily explain this great idea of a gigantic World-Machine, its terrific funnel ever ready to gorge, its cruel mill-stones, huge as islands, ever ready to grind whatsoever the mighty swirl has seized. This great World-Mill must be distinguished from what is called "the Lesser Mill," which the two captured giant-maidens, the Valkyries Menja and Fenja, were forced to grind for greedy King Frothi, singing awhile their "Grotta-söngr," or Mill-song. First they ground for him peace and gold :—"May he sit on riches; may he sleep on down; may his waking be happy! It were well ground then!" But the king's greed would not let them rest, and in anger they prophesied evils to come :—"The tokens of war are waking, the beacons are kindled. On a sudden a host shall come hither, and burn the hall over the king's head." . . . "The maids ground on, putting forth all

INTRODUCTION

their strength, the young maids in giant fury. The huge
props flew off the bin,—the iron rivets burst. . . . The shaft-
tree shivered, the bin shot down, the massy mill-stone rent in
twain. But the Mountain-giant's bride spake this word:—
"We have ground, O Frothi, to our mind's liking. We have
stood full long at the mill." The maidens tell the story of
themselves and of their mill:—"Never had this mill come out
of the grit mount, nor the massy mill-stone out of the earth,
nor were the Mountain-giants' maids thus grinding here, if
thou, O king, knewest our kindred! We two playmates were
brought up under the earth for nine winters. We busied our-
selves with mighty feats; we hurled the cleft rocks out of
their places; we rolled the boulders over the giant's court, so
that the earth shook withal. We hurled the stones so fast
that the massy rocks were split in twain." * This "Grotta-
söngr" would have been lost had not Snorri inserted it in
his Gradus, where he explains why gold was called "Frothi's
meal." There is a prose introduction to the poem not altogether clear, for it confuses the story of Frothi with the
familiar tale, "How the Sea Became Salt."

And now to return to Snæbjörn's verse. It is clear from
the Prose Edda that "the Nine Maidens of the Island-Mill"
are the nine daughters of Ægir, the Ocean-god. These Nereids
are thus enumerated by Snorri:—"Himinglæfa, Dúfa, Blóðug-
hadda, Hefring, Uðr, Hrönn, Bylgja, Bára, Kólga." One of
these, at least, to judge by her name, "the Dove," must have
had kinship with the gentle daughter of Ægir's Celtic brother-
monarch, the much-harassed Lear. The compound, "ey-lúðr,"
translated "Island-Mill," may be regarded as a synonym for
the father of the Nine Maids. "Lúðr" is strictly "the square
case within which the lower and upper quernstones rest,"

* Cp. *Corpus Poeticum Boreale*, vol. i. pp. 184–188.

hence the mill itself, or quern; "ey-lúðr" is "the island quern," *i.e.*, "the grinder at islands," the Ocean-Mill, the Sea, the Sea-god, and, finally, Ægir.

"Ægir's daughters" are the surging waves of Ocean; they work Grotti, "grinder," the great Ocean-Mill (here called "Skerja-Grotti," the grinder of skerries, the lonely rocks in the sea) "beyond the skirts of the earth," or perhaps, better, "off yonder promontory." The latter meaning of the words "út fyr iarðar skauti" would perhaps suit the passage best, if Snæbjörn is pointing to some special whirlpool. Indeed, one cannot help thinking of a possible reference to the marvellous Maelström, the greatest of all whirlpools, one of the wonders of the world; "*umbilicus maris*," according to the old geographers, — "*gurges mirabilis Norvegiæ omnium totius orbis terrarum celeberrimus et maximus*," as Athanasius Kircher describes it in his fascinating folio "*Mundus Subterraneus*." And one recalls, too, Poe's thrilling narrative of the old man's descent into the Maelström, or the Moskoe-ström, as the Norwegians call it, "from the island of Moskoe in the midway." "Just opposite the promontory upon whose apex we were placed," wrote Poe, as though commenting on the Eddaic passage under discussion, "and at a distance of some five or six miles out at sea, there was visible a small, bleak-looking island; or, more properly, its position was discernible through the wilderness of surge in which it was enveloped. About two miles nearer the land arose another of smaller size, hideously craggy and barren, and encompassed at various intervals by a cluster of dark rocks."* The whole story should be re-read in this connection.

---

* According to Kircher, it was supposed that every whirlpool formed round a central rock: a great cavern opened beneath; down this cavern the water rushed; the whirling was produced as in a basin emptying through a central hole. Kircher gives a curious picture illustrative of this theory, with special reference to the Maelström.

INTRODUCTION

The real difficulty in Snorri's extract from Snæbjörn is, however, in its last lines; the arrangement of the words is confusing, the interpretation of the most important of the phrases extremely doubtful. "Lið-meldr" in particular has given much trouble to the commentators: "meldr," at present obsolete in Icelandic, signifies *flour* or *corn in the mill;*" but the word "lið" is a veritable crux. It may be either the neuter noun "lið," meaning "a host, folk, people," or "ship;" or the masculine "liðr," "a joint of the body." The editors of the *Corpus Poeticum Boreale* read "meldr-lið," rendering the word "meal-vessel;" they translate the passage, "who in ages past ground Amloði's meal-vessel = the ocean;" but "mala," to grind, can hardly be synonymous with "hræra," to move, in the earlier lines, and there would be no point in the waves grinding the ocean. There seems, therefore, no reason why "meldr-lið" should be preferred to "lið-meldr," which might well stand for "ship-meal" (? "sea-meal," to be compared with the Eddaic phrase "græðis meldr," *i.e.*, sea-flour, a poetical periphrasis for the sand of the shore). Rydberg,* bearing in mind the connection of the myth concerning the cosmic Grotti-Mill with the myth concerning the fate of Ýmir and other primeval giants, more especially of Ýmir's descendant Bergelmer, who, according to an ingenious interpretation of a verse in Vafþruðnis-mál,† "was laid under the mill-stone,"

---

* *Teutonic Mythology*, pp. 388–392.

† In the poem found in the Elder Edda, the giant tells Odin that, countless ages ere the earth was shapen, Bergelmer was born: "the first thing I remember is when he *á var lúðr um lagiðr.*" The meaning, according to Rydberg, was not clear even to Snorri, who in the Gylfaginning interprets the verse with reference to the drowning of the frost-giants in Ymir's blood:—"One escaped with his household: him the giants call Bergelmer. He with his wife betook himself upon his *ludr* and remained there, and from them the races of giants are descended"—a sort of giant Noah. The Resenian edition of the younger Edda (Copenhagen, 1665) actually reads "*fór á bát sinn*" (went on to his boat) instead of

advanced the theory that "liǒ-meldr" means "limb-grist."
According to this view, it is the limbs and joints of the primeval
giants, which on Amloǒe's mill are transformed into meal.
Allowing, for the nonce, that there is something to be said for
"liǒ-meldr" in the sense of "limb-grist," one finds it difficult
to get Rydberg's interpretation out of the words as they stand
in the text. The Nine Maidens of the Ocean-Mill grinding
Amloǒe's limb-grist, *i.e.*, his bones, might be plausible enough,
suggestive of some story of a brave prince who sailed too near
their dread abode, and received less kindly treatment than did
young Macphail of Colonsay at the hands of the maiden of
Corrivrekin. Snorri does not help us. The note following
Snæbjörn's verse merely adds that here the sea is called
"Amloǒe's kvern." * No explicit explanation is to be found
in early Northern poetry or saga. "Hamlet's mill" may
mean almost anything; if, as the editors of the *Corpus* state,
Hamlet is here an Ocean Giant, his mill seems to be identical
with the great World-Mill, unless the Ocean Giant was himself
ground by the Nine Maidens. All this seems unlikely; indeed,
though at first sight it looks as though some ancient sea-
hero is alluded to in Snæbjörn's phrase, yet the later Icelandic
poets were capable of such fatal ingenuity in the matter of
poetical periphrases, that even so much consistency must not
be expected of them. All that can be said at this point in
the investigation is that the verse quoted in the Prose Edda
gives us a reference to some old legend concerning "Amloǒi,"
whose name is identical with that of the hero known to us
as Hamlet.

It is worthy of note that a few more lines of Snæbjörn's

"fór upp á lúǒr sinn." C. P. B. translates the passage in the poem, "when this
wise giant was laid in the Ark."

* Björn of Skarǒsá, in A.M. 742, writes: "Her er hafid kallad Amlöǒa melldur,"
i.e., "Here the sea is called Amloǒe's meal."

xvi

verse have been preserved; they may well all be fragments of the same poem.*

From the passages preserved it is evident that Snæbjörn was a sailor-poet, and the lost poem must have been descriptive of some voyage in the Arctic seas. In *Landnáma Bók, i.e.*, " The Book of Iceland Settlements," there is a vivid picture of a tenth-century Arctic adventurer, Snæbjörn by name, who went on a perilous expedition to find the unknown land, " Gunn-björn's Reef," after having wrought vengeance, as became a chivalrous gentleman of the period, on the murderer of a fair kinswoman. It is generally accepted, and there can be little doubt, that this Snæbjörn is identical with the poet Snæbjörn.

His family history is not without interest. His great-grand-father, Eywind the Easterling, so called because he had come to the Hebrides from Sweden, married the daughter of Cearbhall, Lord of Ossory, who ruled as King of Dublin from 882 to 888, " one of the principal sovereigns of Europe at the time when Iceland was peopled by the noblemen and others who fled from the tyranny of Harold Harfagr." † Cearbhall was descended from Connla, the grandson of Crimhthann Cosgach, the vic-

---

* The fragments are (1) four short lines, or two long lines, found in Snorri's Edda, edit. 1848, p. 460; and (2) four short lines in A.M. 742, 4to (not A.M. 738, as Edd. Corp. P. B. state, p. 54; *cp.* Bugge, *Arkiv for Nordisk Filologe*, iii. pp. 335–338); the lines are there attributed to þorðr Sjareksson, and not to Snæbjörn, by the writer of the MS., viz., Björn of Skarðsá. þorðr lived in the first half of the eleventh century. Björn was probably mistaken in ascribing the lines to him. They certainly closely resemble Snæbjörn's, and Bugge agrees with the Edd. Corp. P. B. in assigning them to him, and not to the later poet; he reads the lines as follows :—

> " Sváð ór fitjar fjötre,
> flóðs ásynju blóðe
> (röst byrjask römm) systra,
> rýtr, eymylver snýter."

i.e., "the island-mill pours out the blood of the flood goddess's sisters (*i.e.*, waves of the sea), so that (it) bursts from the feller of the land : *whirlpool begins strong.*" In no other *dróttkvætt* verse does eymylver occur : *cp.* " eylúðr," above.

† *Cp. Landnáma Bók*, § 1 ; Todd's *War of the Gœdhill with the Gaill*, pp. 297–302 ;

torious King of Ireland, who is said to have flourished about a century before the Christian era. Lann or Flann, the half-sister of Cearbhall, was married to Malachy I., King of Ireland, whose daughter Cearbhall had married. Flann was the mother of King Sionna and of the Lady Gormflaith. Snæbjörn could certainly boast of a noble pedigree. His family sagas must have had much to tell of the ancient glories of the race: he may often have heard the sad story of the poetess Gormflaith, whom a cruel fate pursued; a king's daughter, the wife of three kings, forced at last to beg for bread from door to door. We may perhaps have more to tell of her later on. Before letting the *Landnáma Bók* tell its own story of Snæbjörn's life, it may be mentioned that, about the date of his Arctic expedition (*circa* 980), his cousin, Ari Marson, is said to have landed on "White Man's Land," or "Great Ireland,"—that part of the coast of North America which extends from Chesapeake Bay, including North and South Carolina, Georgia, and Florida,—and became famous as one of the earliest discoverers of the New World.

Here follows the tragic story of Snæbjörn the Boar:—

"Snæbjörn, son of Eyvind the Easterling, the brother of Helgi the Lean, took land between Mjovafjord (Narrow Firth) and Langadals-á (Langdale River); he had his dwelling at Vatnsfjord (Waterford). His son was Holmstein, the father of Snæbjörn Galti (the boar); the mother of Snæbjörn was Kjalvör; he and Tungu-Odd were sons of sisters. Snæbjörn was fostered in the house of Thorodd at Thingness (but at times he was with Tungu-Odd or his mother). Hallbjörn, the son of Odd of Kiðjaberg, the son of Hallkel, the brother of Ketilbjörn the

---

the history of Cearbhall and his many descendants (he had four sons and four daughters) illustrates the close connection between Ireland and Iceland. For Cearbhall's pedigree, cp. Donovan's *Tribes and Territories of Ancient Ossory*.

Old, took to wife Hallgerð, daughter of Tungu-Odd. The couple were with Odd during the first winter after their marriage; Snæbjörn Galti was there at the same time. Now there was no love lost between the newly wedded folk, and Hallbjörn gat him ready to depart in the springtime, about the flitting season. While he was making his preparations, Odd went from home to the baths at Reykjaholt, where he had his sheep-folds. He had no wish to be present at Hallbjörn's departure, for he doubted whether Hallgerðr would be willing to accompany her husband. Odd had previously done his best to improve matters between them.

"Hallbjörn, having saddled the horses, went to the room where the women kept. Hallgerðr was sitting on the high-seat, combing her hair; the hair fell all about her to the very floor. She had the best hair of all women in Iceland, save only Hallgerð, whom folk named 'Twisted Tartan.' Hallbjörn bade his wife get up and come with him; but she sat silent. He then clutched at her; she moved not from her place. Thrice he seized her, but she moved not. Hallbjörn stood still, and said thus :—

> 'Here stand I as a laughing-stock
>   Before her flowing tresses ;
> The linen goddess dares to mock,
>   While grief my bosom presses.
> O brewer of the sparkling ale,
>   No good for me thou brewest ;
> My heart is sore with bitter bale.
>   O bride, this thing thou ruest.'

Thereupon he wound her hair around his arm, and would have pulled her from her seat, but she sat and flinched not. Then he drew his sword, and struck the head from off her; and so went out and rode away. His comrades were two in number, and they had with them two pack-horses.

"Now there were but few men at the house when this

thing befell, yet the news thereof was forthwith sent to Odd
Snæbjörn was then at Kjalvararstaðir ; Odd sent a messenger to
him, and bade him look to the pursuit ; he himself would not go.

"Snæbjörn went in pursuit of Hallbjörn, eleven men with
him ; and when Hallbjörn was aware that he was approaching,
his comrades bade him hurry on, but he would not yield to
them.   Anon Snæbjörn and his men caught them up near the
hills now called Hallbjörn's Cairns.   Hallbjörn and his two
comrades betook themselves to the hill-top to defend themselves, and there for a time they held out.   Three of Snæbjörn's
men fell there, and both the companions of Hallbjörn.   As for
Hallbjörn, Snæbjörn struck off his foot at the ankle, and he
was forced to hobble along to another hill ; there he slew two
more of Snæbjörn's men, but he himself was slain.   Wherefore
there are three cairns on that hill, and five on the other.
Then Snæbjörn went home.

"Snæbjörn had a ship at the mouth of the river Grims-á ;
Hrolf of Redsand bought half-rights in the vessel ; the crew
were twelve on each side.   Snæbjörn had Thorkel and Sumarliði,
the sons of Thorgeir the Red, who was the son of Einar of
Stafholt.   He took with him also Thorodd of Thingness, his
foster-father, and his wife.   Hrolf took with him Styrbjörn,
who made this ditty after a dream he had :—

> ' I see the bane
> Of both us twain,
> North out at sea
> All piteously :
> Horrors untold,
> Dire frost and cold :
> From these I gain
> Our Snæbjörn slain.'

"They went in search of Gunnbjörn's Reef ; they found land ;
but Snæbjörn would not let them explore at night.   Styrbjörn

went ashore, and found there a treasure-trove in a cairn; he concealed it about his person. Snæbjörn struck him with his axe, and the treasure fell to the ground. Thereafter his men made a hut, but it was soon buried deep in the snow. One day, however, Thorkel, the son of Rauð, found that water was running along the pole which projected from the hut; they knew that spring was near, and they dug themselves out of the snow. While Snæbjörn repaired his ship, Thorodd and his wife stayed in the hut on his behalf; Styrbjörn and his comrades stayed on behalf of Hrolf. The rest of the party had gone out hunting. Styrbjörn then up and slew Thorodd, and then turned and, with the help of Hrolf, slew Snæbjörn. The sons of Rauð and all Snæbjörn's men were put under oath, and were allowed their lives. Thereafter they landed at Halogaland, and thence went to Iceland, and came to Vaðil. Thorkel the Muffler guessed what had befallen the sons of Rauð. Hrolf set up defences to protect himself at Strand-heath. Thorkel sent Sveinung to bring him Hrolf's head. Sveinung first went to Hermund, who dwelt at Myri; then he went to Olaf at Drangar; and finally came to Gest at Hagi: Gest sent him to his friend, Hrolf. Sveinung slew both Hrolf and Styrbjörn, and then returned to Hagi. Gest exchanged with him sword and axe, and gave him two horses black of mane, and he ordered a man to ride round Vaðil all the way to Kollafirth, and asked Thorbjörn the Strong to claim the horses for him from Sveinung. But Thorbjörn slew Sveinung at Sveinungseyri; Sveinung's sword had broken at the hilt. Wherefore Thorkel often bragged to Gest, when their wits were matched, that he had so got round Gest that he had sent his man to bring him the head of his friend." *

* *Cp.* Appendix, ix. Concerning "Gunnbjörn's Reef," *cp.* "*Grönlands Historiske Mindesmærker*," vol. i.

II.

SOME two hundred years after the events recorded in the foregoing story, "Saxo Grammaticus," the learned Dane, emulous of the great Roman historians, took upon himself, at the bidding of Absalon, "Chief Pontiff of the Danes," the task of compiling into a chronicle the history of his country. The labour was a heavy one—too heavy for his weak faculty, as he modestly puts it, for the materials to hand must have been very slight: his Danish predecessors had hitherto done but little "to vaunt the glory of their nation's achievements." His materials, apart from the influence exercised upon him by the Latin classical writers, were mainly drawn from Latin historical writers (such as Bede, Adam of Bremen, and Dudo, "*rerum aquitanicarum scriptor*"), from Danish traditions, and from Icelandic sagas and poems. As regards his indebtedness to Iceland, we know that he had at least one Icelandic friend, Arnoldus Tylensis, Arnold of Thule, a skilful narrator, learned in ancient lore. In his Preface Saxo makes handsome acknowledgment of his obligations to Arnold's countrymen.* "Nor may the

---

* "Nec Tylensium industria silencio obliteranda, qui cum ob nativam soli sterilitatem luxurie nutrimentis carentes, officia continuæ sobrietatis exerceant, omniaque uite momenta ad excolendam alienorum operum noticiam conferre soleant, inopiam ingenio pensant. Cunctarum quippe nacionum res gestas cognosse memorieque mandare voluptatis loco reputant, non minoris gloriæ iudicantes alienas uirtutes disserere quam proprias exhibere. Quorum thesauros historicarum rerum pignoribus refertos curiosius consulens, haut paruam presentis operis partem ex eorum relacionis imitatione contexui; nec arbitros habere contempsi quos tanta uetustatis pericia callere cognoui."—*Saxo*, Ed. Müller and Velschow, pp. 7–8.

pains of the men of Thule be blotted in oblivion; for though
they lack all that can foster luxury (so naturally barren is the
soil), yet they make up for their neediness by their wit, by
keeping continually every observance of soberness, and by de-
voting every instant of their lives to perfecting our knowledge
of the deeds of foreigners. Indeed, they account it a delight
to learn and to consign to remembrance the history of all
nations, deeming it as great a glory to set forth the excellences
of others as to display their own. Their stores, which are
stocked with attestations of historical events, I have examined
somewhat closely, and have woven together no small portion
of the present work by following their narrative, not despising
the judgment of men whom I know to be so well versed in the
knowledge of antiquity." *   Even more explicit in this respect
was Saxo's Norwegian contemporary, Theoderic the Monk, according to whom the men of Thule, the Icelanders, were the
only Northerners who had preserved the ancient history of their
race; their writings were the only available sources for Northern
historians.†   There can be little doubt, however, that among
the Norwegians and Danes, popular legend, a mass of mythic
and traditional lore, still preserved, however obscurely, the
memory of the ancient gods and heroes. In the matter of
Northern mythology, the first nine books of Saxo's History are

---

* Elton's *First Nine Books of the Danish History of Saxo Grammaticus.*

† *Cp.* Langebek's *Script. Rer. Dan.,* vol. v. The passages in question are fully
discussed in "Safn til Sögu Íslands og Íslenzkra Bókmenta að fornu og nýju gefið
út af hinu íslenzka bókmentafélagi," vol. i. pp. 143–148. Theoderic repeatedly
refers to his debt to the Icelanders; *e.g.,* "Operæ pretium duxi, vir illustrissime,
pauca hæc de antiquitate regum Norvagiensium annotatare, et prout sagaciter
perquirere potuimus ab eis, penes quos borum memoria præcipue vigere creditur,
quos nos Islendingos vocamus, qui hæc in suis antiquis carminibus percelebrata
recolunt . . . Veritatis vero sinceritas in hac nostra narratione ad illos omni
modo referenda est, quorum relatione hæc annotavimus, quia non visa sed audita
conscripsimus." In another passage Theoderic writes of Norway as "illa terra,
ubi nullus antiquitatum unquam scriptor fuerit."

of supreme interest, and it has been well said that " the gratitude due to the Welshman of the twelfth century, whose garnered hoard has enriched so many poets and romancers from his day to now, is no less due to the twelfth-century Dane, whose faithful and eloquent enthusiasm has swept much dust from antique time." * Geoffrey's priceless gift of Arthurian romance has not proved richer than Saxo's wild barbaric tale of Hamlet's fate. " Had fortune been as kind to him as nature," so wrote the historian, " he would have equalled the gods in glory." Fortune had even greater glory in store for Hamlet than his panegyrist could have hoped for.

The story of Amlethus, or Hamlet, as told by Saxo, divides clearly into two periods—the first dealing with his early career, and the consummation of his vengeance; the second with his accession to power, and the subsequent events of his life. The former is to be found at the end of Book III., the latter at the beginning of Book IV. The division is noteworthy. Divested of Saxo's eloquence, the story may be thus epitomised :—Horwendil and Feng succeed their father, Gerwendil, as governors of Jutland. Horwendil's valour gains the favour of King Rorick, who gives him his daughter Gerutha to wife. They have a son who is named Amleth. Feng is jealous of his brother's good fortune, murders him, and takes his wife, alleging that Horwendil had treated her badly. Amleth, fearing lest too shrewd a behaviour may make his uncle suspect him, chooses to feign dulness, and pretends an utter lack of wits. He is altogether listless, and unclean in his habits, and seems to be a very freak of nature. At times he sits over the fire and fashions wooden crooks, shaping at their tips certain barbs.

---

* *Cp.* Professor York Powell's Introduction to Elton's translation of Saxo's Nine Books. The Introduction gives a valuable summary of the sources, together with an excellent analysis of Saxo's folk-lore. &c.

He says he is preparing sharp javelins to avenge his father. The courtiers grow suspicious, and try various tests; more especially they make use of his foster-sister for the purpose. A foster-brother warns him of the trap, and he baffles them. He gives cunning answers to all their questions; "he mingles craft and candour in such wise that, though his words do not lack truth,* yet there is nothing to betoken the truth and betray how far his keenness goes." Thus, as he passes along the beach, his companions find the rudder of a ship, and say they have discovered a huge knife. "This," says he, "is the right knife to carve such a huge ham;" by which he means the sea. *Also, as they pass the sandhills they bid him look at the meal, meaning the sand; he replies that it has been ground small by the hoary tempests of the ocean.*† A friend of Feng suggests that Amleth be spied upon while closeted with his mother. But Amleth has his antidote for the treachery. Afraid of being overheard by some eavesdropper, he at first resorts to his usual imbecile ways, and crows like a noisy cock, beating his arms together to mimic the flapping of wings. Then he mounts the straw and begins to swing his body and jump again and again, wishing to try if aught lurks there in hiding. Feeling a lump beneath his feet, he drives his sword into the spot, and impales him who lies hid. He drags him from his concealment and slays him. He cuts the body into morsels, seethes it in boiling water, and flings it through the mouth of an open sewer for the swine to eat, bestrewing the mire with the hapless limbs. He then returns, upbraids his mother, and

---

* Mr. Elton, on whose excellent rendering this epitome is for the most part based, renders Saxo's words "though his words did lack truth," omitting the negative; but the original runs—"ita astutiam veriloquio permiscebat, *ut nec dictis veracitas deesset*, nec acuminis modus verorum indicio [Madvig, iudicio] proderetur."

† "Arenarum quoque præteritis clivis, sabulum perinde ac farra aspicere jussus, eadem albicantibus maris procellis permolita esse respondit."

explains to her his passion for vengeance. Feng cannot find his friend the spy. Jestingly, folk ask Amleth whether he knows aught; he answers that maybe the man has fallen through the sewer, and, stifled by the filth, has been devoured by swine. His uncle at last determines to send Amleth to the King of Britain with a message that he should slay him. Before his departure Amleth gives secret orders to his mother to hang the hall with knotted tapestry, and to perform pretended obsequies for him a year hence.

Two retainers of Feng accompany him to Britain, bearing a letter graven on wood—" a kind of writing material frequent in old times; " this letter enjoins the king to put to death the youth who is sent to him. Amleth obtains the letter, and substitutes for this the death of his companions, adding an entreaty that the king grant his daughter in marriage to the youth of great judgment whom he sends to him. The king receives the guests and treats them all hospitably and kindly. Amleth disdains the rich food placed before him, much to the king's annoyance. A man is sent into the sleeping-room to take note of Amleth's talk. He reports how Amleth told his companions that the bread was flecked with blood and tainted, and further, that the king had the eyes of a slave, and that the queen had in three ways shown the behaviour of a bondmaid. All this, on special investigation, turns out to be true, and the king adores the wisdom of Amleth as though it were inspired, and gives him his daughter to wife. Moreover, in order to fulfil the bidding of his friend, he hangs Amleth's two companions. Amleth, feigning offence, treats this piece of kindness as a grievance, and receives from the king, as compensation, some gold, which he afterwards melts in the fire, and secretly causes to be poured into some hollowed sticks. After a year he returns to his own land, carrying away of all his wealth only the sticks containing the gold. He then again puts on a grotesque demeanour, and, covered with filth, enters the banquet-room where his own obsequies are being held. The guests jeer at one another, and are right merry. They ask him concerning his comrades; he points to the sticks, saying, " Here is both the one and the other." Then he plies the company with drink, and, to prevent his loose dress hampering his walk, he girds his sword upon his side, and purposely drawing it several times, pricks his fingers with its point. The bystanders accordingly have both the sword and scabbard riveted across with an iron nail. The lords drink so heavily that they fall asleep within the palace. Anon, Amleth takes out of his bosom the stakes he has long ago prepared, and goes into the room where the ground is covered with the bodies of the sleeping lords. Cutting away its supports, he brings down the hanging his mother has knitted, which covers the inner as well as the outer walls of the hall; this he flings upon the sleepers, and then applying the crooked stakes, he knots and binds them up in such insoluble intricacy that not one of the men beneath, however hard he may struggle, can manage to escape. After this he sets fire to the palace, which is soon enveloped in flames. He hurries to his uncle's chamber, and awakening him, tells him that Amleth is come, armed with his old crooks, to help him. Seizing his uncle's sword, and placing his own in its stead, he easily exacts the vengeance, long overdue, for his father's murder.

This is the story told in Book III. In Book IV. it is related how Amleth eloquently harangues the assembled Jutlanders, who appoint him Feng's successor by prompt and general acclaim; how he returns to Britain in magnificent array, with a wondrous shield whereon all his exploits are depicted; how his father-in-law discovers that it is his bounden

duty to avenge Feng's death on his own son-in-law, and hopes
to spare himself the task by deputing him to go and woo for
him a fierce unwedded queen reigning in Scotland, whose
suitors have invariably paid for their insolence with their lives;
how the queen, becoming enamoured of the young prince, plays
on him the very trick he had himself erewhile used, changing
the purport of the letter so that it reads as a commission
from the king that she should wed the bearer; how he yields
to her pressing solicitations that he should transfer his wooing,
and make over to her his marriage vows, and learn to prefer
birth to beauty. It is further told how he returns to Britain
with a strong band of Scots, and is met by his much-injured
wife, who, in spite of her wrongs, reveals to him her father's
plot to entrap him. An under-shirt of mail saves him from
the king's cunning blow. He is, however, anxious to exonerate
himself from the guilt of treachery towards his father-in-law,
and wishes to make the whole blame recoil on his Scotch queen,
Hermutrude; but the king pursues him, and so reduces his
forces that he resorts to a device in order to increase the
apparent number of his men. He puts stakes under some of
the dead bodies of his comrades to prop them up, sets others
on horseback like living men, and ties others to neighbouring
stones. The plan succeeds, and the Britons, terrified at the
spectacle, flee without fighting; the king is killed, and Amleth,
having seized the spoils of Britain, goes back with his wives to
his own land.

Meanwhile Rorick has died, and his successor Wiglek,
regarding Amleth as a usurper, has cruelly harassed Amleth's
mother. This evil treatment Amleth takes at first with much
forbearance, and even gives Wiglek the richest of his spoils;
but soon he seizes a chance of taking vengeance, attacks him,
subdues him, and becomes his open foe. Fialler, the governor

of Skaane, he drives into exile; and the tale is, that "*Fialler retired to a spot called Undensakre, which is unknown to our peoples.*" * Wiglek, recruited with the forces of Skaane and Zealand, sends envoys to challenge Amleth to a war. Amleth foresees that the war will prove fatal, but he is more anxious about the future widowhood of Hermutrude, so greatly does he love her, than about his own death. She protests; the woman who would dread to be united with her lord in death was abominable. But ill she keeps her boast; for when Amleth is slain by Wiglek in battle in Jutland, she yields herself to be the conqueror's spoil and bride.

This, then, is the story of Amleth as told by Saxo towards the end of the twelfth century. Whence did he obtain it? His closing words, that "a plain in Jutland is to be found famous for Amleth's name and burial-place," seem to indicate that the local traditions were somewhat limited, and in all probability Saxo's debt to Jutland sources was but slight.†
It is certainly interesting that a Jutland folk-tale, *De Kloge Studenter*, "The Clever Students," has much in common with Hamlet's wisdom in disdaining the King of Britain's banquet, and in discovering the secret of his mother's low origin.‡ This very episode must have been one of the most popular of the legends fathered on to Hamlet, for Saxo tells us distinctly that

---

* "Quem ad locum, cui Undensakre nomen est, nostris ignotum populis, concessisse est fama."

† Müller points out that two places in Jutland are still called Ammelhede. Olrik, in *Sakses Oldhistorie Norröne sagaer og Danske Sagn*, refers to *Jyske Folkeminder*, viii. No. 152. The story told is that two petty kings lived by Virring, half-a-mile from here (Ammel and Krog); they quarrelled and slew each other. One, hight Ammel, lived by Ammelhede; he is buried in a little mound right east of it. "Ammel-hede" may perhaps = Amlæðæ-heðæ (Amlæðæ, according to Olrik, would be the West Danish form of the name Amlóði; hence Saxo's Amlethus), but when once the legend had become localised in Jutland, the identification would soon follow.

‡ *Cp. Jyske Folkeminder*, vii.–viii. p. 156; and Olrik, p. 165.

INTRODUCTION

" others relate " a slightly different version of the incident, but it is certainly no intrinsic part of the Hamlet story.

As far as Iceland is concerned, we have no trace of the Hamlet story in the sagas and poems belonging to the two centuries intervening between Snæbjörn's verse and Saxo's History; but it seems probable that some account of " Amlođi " was given in the lost " Sciöldunga Saga," that part of it which contained the Lives of the Kings of Denmark from the earliest times.* Internal evidence does not conclusively connect Saxo's story with an Icelandic source, but one statement seems to point to some original document containing a reference to Northern heathendom, such as would have been easily understood by a twelfth-century Icelander; the force of the expression has seemingly been missed by Saxo. " Fialler," he writes, " retired to a spot called *Undensakre*, which is unknown to our people." Surely this represents Saxo's rationalising of a poetical periphrasis for Fialler's departure from the world. " Ódáinsakr," the Land of the Undying, the Northern Elysium, was familiar enough to the Icelanders of the twelfth century; the Danes had evidently forgotten their pagan Paradise.†

---

* Cp. *Prolegomena, Sturlunga Saga*, p. lxxxix. : "Among others we have here to mourn the loss of the Icelandic Saga of Hamlet (Amlođi), Hagbard and Signy, King Frodi, &c., which we take all to have been included in the mythical part. The Skioldunga is mentioned as late as 1462 in the inventory of the church of Modruvalla." Professor York Powell, *Saxo Grammaticus*, p. 411, is of opinion that a brief chapter on Amlođi may have formed an episode in the early part of Scioldunga; there may even have been a scrap or two of verse of an old Amlođi's lay in this chapter.

† Vedel, in his Danish translation of Saxo, places Undensakre in Skaane, the south-west province of Sweden. I cannnot follow Olrik in his suggestion that Undensakre = Undornsakrar (*i. e.*, the south-eastern fields), cp. *Sakses Oldhistorie*, p. 159. Rydberg ingeniously identifies Fialler with Falr, *i.e.*, Balder, "the single person who by an enemy was transferred to *Ódáinsakr*." Cp. sections 44–53, 93 : the former sections give a valuable analysis of Eric Vidforle's Saga (who, one Christmas Eve, made a vow to seek out Odainsaker), where the older pagan myth has become Christianised. E. Mogk, *Grundriss der Germanischen Mythologie*,

xxx

INTRODUCTION

It may be fair to assume that Saxo's source for this passage was some Icelandic lay; similarly, Hamlet's riddling answers to the courtiers, more especially his poetical metaphor concerning the sand of the shore, "ground small by the hoary tempests of the ocean," may well have been derived from some Icelandic original in prose or verse; at all events, the latter passage gives us the twelfth-century explanation of Snæbjörn's reference to "Hamlet's meal,"* whatever may have been Snæbjörn's own interpretation. The solution of the problem found in Saxo is certainly a disappointment. It surely required no dissimulating Solomon, "*stulti sapiens imitator*," to discover for folks accustomed to the conception of the Ocean-kvern the analogy between the sands of the sea and the grist of the mill. Here, too, the passage in Saxo's History gives the impression of representing some more subtle myth rationalised.

But whatever Northern elements may be detected in Saxo's Hamlet story, there can be no doubt that some important incidents have been borrowed from legendary Roman history. The merest outline of the plot cannot fail to show the striking likeness between the tales of Hamlet and Lucius Junius Brutus. Apart from general resemblances (the usurping uncle; the persecuted nephew, who escapes by feigning madness; the journey; the oracular utterances; the outwitting

gives a careful summary of "Life after Death" as conceived by the Northerners (vol. i. p. 1115–6).

* I do not deny that the sand-downs on the west coast of Jutland, to which Olrik refers, seem to be closely associated with Hamlet's famous answer, and may well have helped the localising of the legend; the Icelandic words *mjöl*, meal or flour, *melr*, a sandhill, *meldr*, flour, together with the old myth of the Grotti-mill, are more than enough to explain the not very remarkable simile. Olrik holds a brief for Denmark in his excellent study of Saxo; some of his alleged Danish characteristics seem doubtful, but his comment on Hamlet's resting upon "the hoof of a beast of burden, upon a cockscomb, and also upon a ceiling," is distinctly ingenious, if one of these proves to be a plant-name peculiarly Danish, not found in Icelandic. *Cp.* O. F. Hjaltalin, *Grasafrodi*, pp. 223–224, 230.

INTRODUCTION

of the comrades; the well-matured plans for vengeance), there
are certain points in the former story which must have been
borrowed directly from the latter. This is especially true of
Hamlet's device of putting the gold in the sticks. This could
not be due to mere coincidence; and moreover, the evidence
seems to show that Saxo himself borrowed this incident from
the account of Brutus in Valerius Maximus; one phrase at
least from the passage in the *Memorabilia* was transferred from
Brutus to Hamlet.* Saxo must have also read the Brutus
story as told by Livy, and by later historians, whose versions
were ultimately based on Dionysius of Halicarnassus, Dio Cassius,
&c.; he may have seen some such epitome of Roman history
as that of his contemporary Zonaras, who has preserved a com-
pendium of the early part of Dio's lost Roman history. One
must dwell on this point, for while Livy, Valerius, and others
make mention of Tarquin's murder of the elder brother of
Brutus, Zonaras, as well as Dionysius of Halicarnassus, gives
the important additional statement that the father of Brutus
had also, from motives of jealousy, been put to death by his
brother-in-law, Tarquinius Superbus.† In order that the reader
may be enabled to place in juxtaposition the twin-brothers
Hamlet and Brutus, the earlier portion of the tale of Brutus as
told by Livy is here added; the subsequent events connected

---

* Stephanius first called attention to Saxo's borrowing of the phrase *obtusi
cordis esse*. Valerius Maximus gives the following version of the story : "Quo
in genere acuminis [vafritiæ] in primis Junius Brutus referendus est, nam cum a
rege Tarquinio, avunculo suo, omnem nobilitatis indolem excerpi, interque ceteros
etiam fratrem suum, quod vegetioris ingenii esset, interfectum animadvertet,
obtunsi se cordis esse simulavit eaque fallacia maximas suas virtutes texit, profectus
etiam Delphos cum Tarquinii filiis, quos is ad Apollinem Pythium muneribus et
sacrificiis honorandum miserat, aurum deo nomine doni clam cavato baculo
inclusum tulit, quia timebat ne sibi cæleste numen aperta liberalitate venerari
tutum non esset."

† Cp. *The Credibility of Early Roman History*, by Sir G. C. Lewis, vol. i.
p. 518.

with the rape of Lucrece are too well known to need recapitulating.*

"While Tarquin was thus employed (on certain defensive measures), a dreadful prodigy appeared to him: a snake sliding out of a wooden pillar, terrified the beholders, and made them fly into the palace; and not only struck the king himself with sudden terror, but filled his breast with anxious apprehensions: so that, whereas in the case of public prodigies the Etrurian soothsayers only were applied to, being thoroughly frightened at this domestic apparition, as it were, he resolved to send to Delphi, the most celebrated oracle in the world; and judging it unsafe to entrust the answers of the oracle to any other person, he sent his two sons into Greece, through lands unknown at that time, and seas still more unknown. Titus and Aruns set out, and, as a companion, there was sent with them Junius Brutus, son to Tarquinia, the king's sister, a young man of a capacity widely different from the assumed appearance he had put on. Having heard that the principal men in the state, and among the rest his brother, had been put to death by his uncle, he resolved that the king should find nothing in his capacity which he need dread, nor in his fortune which he need covet; and he determined to find security in contempt, since in justice there was no protection. He took care, therefore, to fashion his behaviour to the resemblance of foolishness, and submitted himself and his portion to the king's rapacity. Nor did he show any dislike to the surname of Brutus, content that, under the cover of that appellation, the genius which was to be the deliverer of the Roman people should lie concealed, and wait the proper season for exertion.

"He was, at this time, carried to Delphi by the Tarquinii,

* Livy, Book I. chap. lvi.

INTRODUCTION

rather as a subject of sport than as a companion ; and is said to
have brought, as an offering to Apollo, *a golden wand inclosed in a
staff of cornel wood, hollowed for the purpose*, an emblem figurative
of the state of his own capacity.   When they were there, and
had executed their father's commission, the young men felt a
wish to inquire to which of them the kingdom of Rome was to
come ; and we are told that these words were uttered from the
bottom of the cave:—' Young men, whichever of you shall first
kiss your mother, he shall possess the sovereign power at
Rome.' . . . Brutus judged that the expression of Apollo had
another meaning, and as if he had accidentally stumbled and
fallen, he touched the earth with his lips, considering that she
was the common mother of all mankind." *

It is clear from this, that however much the Hamlet story
may have already resembled the Brutus story before its appearance in the Danish History, Saxo must have recognised the
kinship of the two stories, and added to their common traits.
These points of contact, however, belong only to the earlier
career of Hamlet, as narrated in Saxo's Third Book.   An ingenious theorist † has even gone so far as to maintain that the
Hamlet story is nothing more than a Northern transformation
of the Roman Brutus saga.   He deepens the likeness between
the two tales by suggesting that Tarquinia, the mother of
Brutus and sister of Tarquin, was regarded as the wife of
Tarquinius, and became identified with the wicked Tullia ; after
the murder of her husband, Tarquin's brother, who might easily
have been identified with the father of Brutus, she became
Tarquin's wife, aiding and abetting him as an accomplice in all
his wickedness.   According to this view, the name "Amloði"

* George Baker's translation, 1797.
    † Dr. Detter, *Zeitschrift für Deutsches Alterthum u. Deutsche Litteratur,*
vol. xxxvi., 1892.

was merely a translation of the Latin "Brutus," *i.e.*, "The Dullard." * Even as it has been suggested that the story of Brutus' pretended idiocy was invented to explain the fact of so wise a man being called by such a name, so, according to this view, the name "Amloði" was originally a common noun, meaning "simpleton," or "fool," which became the descriptive nickname of the hero. It is strange, however, that the original worker of the story should have chosen, as the Northern equivalent of the Latin "*brutus*," so strange a word as "*amlodi*," which is not found in oldest Scandinavian; its modern and mediæval uses in the Icelandic, Swedish, and Danish dialects are all suggestive of the name of the hero of some popular legend; the etymology proposed does not carry any more conviction than the other suggestions put forward by Northern scholars.†

Livy's influence on Saxo is unmistakeable, even in the very arrangement of the materials. Thus the story of Brutus fills the last chapters of Book I. and the earlier chapters of Book II., the former ending with Brutus' election to the consulship, the latter beginning with the consul's address to

---

* *Cp.* Dion. Hal. iv. 67 :—"εἴη δ' ἂν ἐξερμηνευόμενος ὁ βροῦτος εἰς τὴν Ἑλληνικὴν διάλεκτον, ἠλίθιος."

† Dr. Detter proposes "*aml + óði*": the first component (which is not found in old Icelandic, but according to Erik Jonsson is used in modern Icelandic) is said to mean "labour, or toil, without much progress" (*cp.* Icelandic *amstr*, toil ; *ama*, to annoy, vex) ; the compound is rendered "verdruss-wütend," *i.e.*, "annoyingly mad." Other compounds in -*óði* are compared, *e.g.*, *málóði*, mad in speech ; *handóðr*, mad with one's hands ; *steinóði*, stone-mad (*cp.* stone-deaf) : all these latter compounds are easily explained ; *amlóði* stands by itself, isolated. The explanation seems to me an excellent folk-etymology ; in all probability the ending of the word (*óði*=mad) helped to fix the popular usage of the name "*Amlóði*." Similarly, Carl Säve (*Aftryck ur Nord. Univ. Tidsk.* 10 *Årg.* 4 *Häft*) suggested an untenable derivation of the name from "*and-blauðr*" = "*hinn and-blauði*," *i.e.*, "the crack-brained, crazy person."

Dr. Vigfusson rightly withdrew his suggestion that "*amlóði*" might be connected with the Anglo-Saxon word "*homola*," one whose head has been mutilated or shaved ; adding in his "Corrigenda " : "No one knows the origin of this name."

the excited people; similarly, Saxo's Hamlet story, as regards its division between Books III. and IV., seems modelled after Livy's pattern. There is, however, this great difference between the matter distributed over the two books of the Danish history: the earlier incidents of Hamlet's life, found in Book III., have their analogues in Livy, while the later events, described in Book IV. (viz. the chapter of Hamlet's adventures in England, the story of Hermutrude), find no parallels in the Latin story. It seems clear that even were Dr. Detter's contentions altogether acceptable, his theory would only apply to the Hamlet of Saxo's Third Book, though even here a number of elements would have to be accounted for.

It must indeed be admitted that Saxo's Hamlet-tale has but few links connecting it definitely with Northern mythology. The reference to "Ódáinsakr" at the end of the whole story has already been considered; a more important link is to be found in the name of Hamlet's father, Horwendillus, the Scandinavian "Örvandill," the German "Orendel," the English "Éarendel," whose myth was Christianised by Germanic Europe, and whose star was glorified as "the true Light, which lighteth every man that cometh into the world;" as the old English poet sang, in almost Miltonic strain :—

> "Eala, earendel, engla beorhtast,
> Ofer middan-geard monnum sended,
> And soð-fæsta sunnan leoma,
> Torht ofer tunglas, þu tida gehwane
> Of sylfum þe symble inlihtes." *

---

* *Cp.* Cynewulf's Crist, ed. Gollancz, pp. 10, 159.

In the Prose Edda it is told how Thor carried Orwendel from Jotunheim in a basket on his back; Orwendel's toe stuck out of the basket, and got frozen; Thor broke it off, and flung it at the sky, and made a star of it, which is called

INTRODUCTION

"Hail, heavenly Light, brightest of angels thou,
sent unto men upon this middle-earth !
Thou art the true refulgence of the sun,
radiant above the stars, and from thyself
illuminest for ever all the tides of time."

In the stories of Orwendel found in the Eddas, there is
nothing strongly suggestive of Saxo's Hamlet story, though
Rydberg attempted, without success, to identify Hamlet with
Orwendel's famous son Svipdagr, whose adventures in giant-
land to win the giant-guarded maiden are told so dramatically
in the fine Eddaic "Lay of Swipday and Menglad." If, how-

Orvandels-tá. In Anglo-Saxon glosses "earendel" (*cp.* Épinal gloss.), or
"oerendil" (*cp.* Erfurt gloss.), is interpreted *jubar*, but "dawn" or "morning-
star" would probably be a better rendering, as in the only other passage known
in old English literature, viz. *The Blickling Homilies*, p. 163, l. 30: "Nu seo
Cristes gebyrd at his æriste, se niwa eorendel Sanctus Johannes; and nu nu se
leoma þære soþan sunnan God selfa cuman wille;" *i.e.* "And now the birth of
Christ (was) at his appearing, and the new day-spring (or dawn) was John the
Baptist. And now the gleam of the true Sun, God himself, shall come.'
Örvandill, Éarendel, &c., are probably rightly compared with Sanskrit *usrá*, the
morning-red; Latin, *aurora;* Greek, ἠώς. It is interesting to note that the old
Germanic spring-goddess "Austrô" (whose existence has been evolved from Bede's
"Eostra," *i.e.* West Saxon "Eastre"; *cp. De Temporum Ratione*, c. xv.) must have been
identical with *usrá, aurora*, &c.; as Kluge points out (*v.* Ostern, *Etymologisches
Wörterbuch*), the old Indo-Germanic *Aurora* became among the Germans a spring-
goddess in place of a dawn-goddess: the Christian festival commemorating
Christ's resurrection coincided with the pagan festival of Easter, which was
celebrated at the vernal equinox, whence the transference of the pagan name to
Christian purposes. "Earendel" and "Easter" have evidently the same root,
and both illustrate the same interesting compromise between Old and New (*cp.*
Kluge; Paul's *Grundriss*, vol. i. pp. 1099, 1111). On the other hand, Symons
(Paul's *Grundriss*, vol. ii. p. 65) supports the older view of Müllenhoff, and rejects
the theory that *Orwendel*=dawn-god, and points to its oldest form *Auriuuan-
dalus* (gen. *Auriuuandali*, found in Lombardic, anno 720) as connected with old
Norse *aurr*, moisture; Anglo-Saxon *éar*, sea; he holds that the hero's name=the
wanderer on the sea, the seafarer; a sort of Germanic Ulysses. It is certainly
difficult from this standpoint to explain the Anglo-Saxon use of "earendel,"
and recent Northern philologists (*e.g.* Noreen, *cp. Abriss der Urgermanischen
Lautlehre*, p. 89) equate *ear-* with the root signifying "to burn" in Greek εὔω,
Latin *uro*, *Ves*-uvius, &c.

ever, in spite of the absence of evidence to support the view, it be maintained that the Hamlet-tale was originally connected with the Orwendel myth, those who favour nature-myths have here an excellent opportunity for the display of their ingenuity. "The first hero ever born," as Orwendel is described in the preface to the old German "Spielmanns Gedicht," was certainly, as his name implies, a radiant god of dawn or of spring; and does not Saxo make him battle with and ultimately slay King Collerus, *i.e.* King Cold? He kills him in "a spring-tide wood," and in due course is himself slain by his own brother, and avenged by his own son. The hapless Gerutha, the giant-mother "Groa" of the Edda, is Mother Earth, who in the forced embraces of cruel Winter longs for the return of her beloved Spring. Some twenty years ago, Zinzow,* in an elaborate treatise, advanced some such interpretation of the Hamlet story as a nature-myth; and more recently, the distinguished mythologist Mogk has adduced the above theory in dealing with Orwendel's share in Saxo's story; while Dr. Symons, writing in the same work, maintains that Saxo's Danish legend is associated only in name, and not essentially, with the Orwendel myth. Even so, the Hamlet story may very well have borrowed certain elements from the ancient Northern myth of the struggle between Spring and Winter; from this point of view, the most difficult element of the whole story— the part played by the hero's mother—becomes illumined.

Summing up, then, we have in Saxo's "Hamlet" a general framework probably derived from Northern mythology (or rather from Northern mythology which had passed through the various stages of heroic-myth and pseudo-history); we have in Book III. a story presenting remarkable analogues to

---

* *Die Hamletsage: an u. mit verwandten Sagen erläutert: ein Beitrag zum Verständniss nordisch-deutsche Sagendichtung.* Von Dr. A. Zinzow. Halle, 1877.

the Brutus story, and indebted to it for many of its most striking details; while in Book IV. we have a series of incidents which seem to belong to an entirely different stratum of legendary lore. A consideration of this latter portion of the narrative may throw light on the time, place, and origin of Saxo's materials.

III.

OTHER mediæval legends suggest contact with the legendary history of early Rome. One instance must be considered side by side with the Brutus element in "Hamlet." While Hamlet may be regarded as a sort of Northern counterpart of the Roman Brutus, another Danish prince, whom the elder Grundtvig aptly styled "Hamlet's mythical half-brother," [*] recalls the most striking element in the legend of Servius Tullius. Prince Havelok, degraded to the servile condition of scullion and buffoon, reveals his high lineage, during sleep, by the flame-breath issuing from his mouth. "*Caput arsisse Servio Tullio dormienti, quæ historia non prodidit?*" as Cicero puts it in "*De Divinatione.*" There are other parallel incidents in the careers of Servius and Havelok, more especially the rôle played by their respective wives in firing their ambition. The influence of Latin legend on both "Hamlet" and "Havelok" suggests at least the possibility of finding other links in the two stories, and some evidence as to the time and place of their origin.

In dealing with the Anglo-Danish romance of "Havelok," three versions must be differentiated :—(i.) Gaimar's version, found at the beginning of "*Lestorie des Engles ;*" probably originally inserted between the lost "*Lestorie des Bretons*" and the

---

[*] *Cp. Nordens Mythology*, 1832, p. 365.

xl

extant history; (ii.) an Anglo-Norman *Lai de Havelok* found at the end of a copy of *Lestorie* in the College of Arms, Gaimar's version being omitted; (iii.) " *Havelok the Dane*," an English poem belonging to the thirteenth century, probably based on popular legends, and more especially on the local legends accounting for the origin of Grimsby; the Grimsby seal, which may go back to the date of the poem, epitomises the story. This English romance is independent of the French versions, though the author was evidently acquainted with the Anglo-Norman poem. It is of least importance for the present investigation. As regards the *Lai*, it is almost certainly derived from Gaimar's terser version,* which may safely be assigned to the first half of the twelfth century. Its source is unknown; it was possibly in one of the manuscripts borrowed for Gaimar by his patron's friend, Walter Espec, the noble founder of the Abbeys of Kirkham, Rievaulx, and Wardon, from Robert, Earl of Gloucester. Gildas is vaguely referred to immediately before the account of Havelok, but Gaimar certainly did not find any account of the Dane in any lost work of the sixth century historian. Gaimar tells how, in the days of Constantine, Arthur's successor, King Adelbrict, a Dane, rules in Norfolk, while Edelsi, a Briton, rules in Lindsey; the kings are brothers-in-law; Edelsi's sister, Orwain, has been married to the Dane. Adelbrict and Orwain die, leaving Argentille, an only child, to the care of her uncle, who proves to be the proverbially cruel uncle of popular story. Hear what this felon king does! For the inheritance which he covets, he

---

* *Cp.* Ward's *Catalogue of MS. Romances*, pp. 437–439, and the whole section where the whole evidence concerning *Havelok* is dealt with; also, *Lestorie des Engles* (Hardy and Price Martin), (ed. Rolls Series), 1889; Madden's *Havelok the Dane* (Roxburghe Club); Skeat, *Havelok* (E.E.T.S.); Michel, *Le Lai d'Havelok le Danois;* Köster, *Sagnet om Havelok Danske;* G. Storm, *Christiania Videnskabssel-skabs Forhandlinger*, 1879, &c.

mismarries his niece. He gives her to a lad named Cuheran, to abase her.

> *This Cuheran though a scullion*
> *was a comely lad to see,*
> *of beauteous face, and beauteous hands,*
> *of graceful form and mien;*
> *of cheery mood, whate'er befell;*
> *good legs, good feet, were his;*
> *and brave he was, and thereto bold,*
> *and willingly he fought;*
> *and oft it chanced that some vile groom*
> *would play with him in sport,*
> *would hustle him, yet soon he sprawled*
> *with legs high in the air,*
> *but if the groom grew wrath thereat,*
> *he tied him with his belt,*
> *and if no other folk were nigh,*
> *would beat him with a rod:*
> *and yet withal he was so frank,*
> *he soon released his foe,*
> *if he the word of promise gave*
> *to bear him no ill grudge,*
> *and when they had embraced again,*
> *then Cuheran was glad.*

He is the most popular among all the king's servants, and Edelsi, who knows him but as "quistrun," *i.e.* a scullion, has made him his fool ("*de lui son jugleur feseit*"). Argentille sorely feels her disgrace, until one night she sees a marvellous flame coming from Cuheran's mouth. She questions him concerning his birth, and he tells her all he knows, namely, that he is the son of poor fisher-folk at Grimsby. They hasten thither. His "father," Grim, is dead; but Grim's daughter is still living. She knows the whole secret of his birth, though at first she is reluctant to confide it to him, lest harm should befall him therefrom, owing to his "folly" (*par son folage*). At length, however, she reveals that he is the son of Gunther, king of Denmark, who had been killed when King Arthur conquered the land.

> *The queen in sore dismay of the fight*
> *fled thence with the rightful heir;*
> *and you are he, Dan Havelok,*
> *King Gunther's son and heir.*
> *My father had a right good ship;*
> *he took the queen away;*
> *toward this land he steered his course;*
> *but God willed otherwise.*
> *Fierce outlaws met us on the seas,*
> *they pillaged and plundered all;*
> *the knights and all our folk they slew,*
> *nor e'en the queen they spared;*
> *no man but father mine was spared,*
> *no woman but my mother,*
> *for friendship's sake they spared them both,*
> *them, and the children eke,*
> *both me and you, my brothers too,*
> *e'en as my father begged.*
> *And when at length we landed here,*
> *we cut our ship in twain;*
> *shattered and battered were sides and stern,*
> *in that fight when the queen was killed:*
> *of our stout ship we made our home,*
> *by a boat we got our bread.*

So Kelloc, Grim's daughter, describes the early history of the hero, who subsequently behaves with anything but "folage." He and his wife visit Denmark, where various adventures befall them. He is ultimately discovered by his father's seneschal, who soon, by various tests, recognises him as the true heir to the throne. The usurper King Edulf is defeated; Havelok is acclaimed as king. Anon he calls together all his ships, and defies King Edelsi. He fights a drawn battle, but Argentille teaches him a trick by which he wins the second day. All night they fix stakes in the earth; they fix thereon the dead men in two squadrons. The next morning, when

Cuheran's men see that the host of the enemy is so great, all their flesh shuddered, they lose courage, and make the king surrender :—

> *To fight is now of no avail,*
> *yield thou the lady's right,*
> *make peace lest things fare worse.*

Argentille thus gains her heritage; and soon after, on Edelsi's death, Havelok, king of Denmark, succeeds to Lindsey as well as Norfolk. Twenty years was he king.

The briefest summary of the romance suffices to show that we have here a story of the Hamlet type, though the characters of the two heroes stand apart in many important respects. "They may fairly be called foster-brothers," writes Dr. Ward, in an excellent and summary analysis of the two stories; * "they both grow up at the court of a 'usurping uncle,' and are both famous for their quaint sayings. But there the first resemblance ends. In the case of Havelok, the usurper is not the uncle of Havelok himself, but of Argentille. Havelok's simplicity is real. He is quite content with playing pranks before the court at Lincoln, where the king treats him as a sort of jester. He is aware of the marvellous flame-breath, but it never makes him dream of being the heir of kings, or of having any wrongs to avenge; † indeed, he is ashamed of it until Argentille becomes his Valkyria (even the crowning war trick is her device, for it is done *par conseil de la reine*, l. 773); and she informs his splendid body with the spirit of a hero.

---

* *Cp. English Historical Review*, 1895.

† On the other hand, as Dr. Ward points out elsewhere (*Catalogue*, p. 441), in the English poem of Havelok "the hero is never unconscious of his real position. His character is light and thoughtless before his marriage, but then it changes; he withdraws Goldeburgh from Lincoln to Grimsby of his own accord; he has dreams of ambition, remembers his wrongs, and prays for revenge. This brings Havelok in some respects a little closer to Hamlet."

Hamlet, on the other hand, schemes for revenge; and his sayings are in character with his assumed madness. But the course of the two stories often brings the same incident to the front. Thus each of the heroes is a disinherited Danish prince; each marries an English princess, and regains his power in Denmark; each returns to Britain, and marches against an English king; each is accompanied by his own Valkyria (the English Argentille and the Scottish Hermuthruda); each of them half loses the first day's battle, and each wins the second day by staking up the dead men in squadrons. These are marks of the same workshop, at the very least."

But the workshop in which Havelok was wrought is unmistakeable; the mark is graven on the workmanship. The researches of Köster, Storm, and Ward make it certain that "Havelok Cuheran" * is identical with the name of the famous Viking, perhaps the greatest warrior of the house of Ivar, Anlaf Curan, the vanquished hero of Brunanburgh and Tara.

Anlaf Curan, or Olaf o' the Sandal, was the son of Sihtric Gale, or Caoch, a Viking chief of the house of Ivar, who first came to Dublin in 888, and who subsequently gained and lost the kingship of Dublin, and died as king of Northumbria in 925; a year before his death he had married the sister of King Athelstan. Sihtric's son Anlaf was the child of another wife, but the Wessex king stood very much in the relationship of uncle towards his sister's stepson. It was, however, the policy of Alfred's ambitious grandson to make himself king of all England, and Northumbria was to be added to his rule.

---

* The English romance does not mention the name Cuheran at all; the author of *Lai de Havelok* has perhaps misunderstood Gaimar, and explains "*Cuheran*" as equivalent to "*quistron*" (*i.e.* scullion); "*car ceo tenoient li Breton en sur language quistron;*" Gaimar's merely states that "*Cuheran estait quistrun.*" *Cuheran, Kvaran*=Irish *cuarán*, a sock; Welsh *curan* (*cp.* W. Stokes, *Revue Celtique*, iii. p. 189).

He drove thence Godfrey, Sihtric's brother, Godfrey's son Anlaf, and his nephew Anlaf; the latter was destined, as Anlaf Curan, to cause much trouble to the English. Expelled from Northumbria, Anlaf took refuge at the court of Constantine III., king of Scotland, whose daughter he eventually married. Athelstan resented Constantine's alliance with the Hiberno-Danes, and in 934 sent an expedition to waste his kingdom. In 937 a mighty coalition of British and Danish chiefs was formed against Athelstan; Constantine, together with his son-in-law Anlaf, now king of the Northmen in Ireland, were at the head of the league, which soon numbered many chiefs of the west and east; the Danes and British formed a confederacy against their common West Saxon foe. Anlaf, with his cousin Anlaf Godfreyson, came to the Humber with a fleet of 615 sail, and seized York. At Brunanburgh, probably somewhere in the north-west, the opposing forces met, and the English king gained a great and decisive victory; "never had huger slaughter of heroes hapt in this isle." The importance of the issue may be gathered from the noble war-song enshrined in the Anglo-Saxon chronicle :—

> "*Five young Kings put asleep by the sword-stroke,*
> *Seven strong Earls of the army of Anlaf*
> *Fell on the war-field, numberless numbers,*
> *Shipmen and Scotsmen.*" *

But though the Saxon poet was so exultant in his song, we may infer that the poets of the other camp sang a different song, lauding their leader's valour, telling of the havoc he had wrought on the foe, and refusing to recognise the decisive character of the contest. At all events, on the death of Athelstan in 940, or perhaps sooner, Anlaf came again to York, and was received as king. The Danes of Mercia and East Anglia,

* Tennyson's translation of the Anglo-Saxon poem.

xlvi

with Wulfstan, archbishop of York, accepted his kingship, and according to Simeon of Durham, King Edmund was forced to make terms whereby the kingdom was divided between them, the English taking the south, Anlaf the north, the boundary between them being Watling Street. At this time (943), Anlaf, who had hitherto been a pagan, received the rite of baptism. It would seem that he divided Northumbria with his cousin Anlaf Godfreyson, whose life-story is so closely interwoven with his that the old historians are constantly confusing the two. Constantine's abdication made a great difference in Anlaf's position in Northumbria, and at last, in 952, he was driven thence for the last time. His marvellous career as king of Dublin culminated in 980 in his utter defeat at the battle of Tara, which shattered the power of the Scandinavians in Ireland. After the battle Anlaf left the world of action, and became a monk of the monastery at Iona, where he died the following year. His son Sitric became king of Dublin in his stead. It is worthy of note that Sitric's mother, Gormflaith, married Malachy II., the victor of Tara; Gormflaith must be distinguished from Anlaf's other wife, the daughter of Constantine of Scotland; she was the sister of Maelmordha, king of Leinster, daughter of Murchadh, and granddaughter of Finn, Lord of Offaly. She is "Kormlöð" of *Njals saga*, which describes her as "the fairest of all women, and best gifted in everything that was not in her own power," *i.e.* in all physical and natural endowments; but "she did all things ill over which she had any power," *i.e.* in her moral conduct. She was divorced or repudiated by Malachy, and subsequently married his dispossessor, Brian, by whom she was also put away.*

---

* Todd's *War of the Gaedhil with the Gaill* (London, 1867) is the great source for all this Hiberno-Danish history. *Cp.* also Ward, Keary, Steenstrup, Robertson, who are all indebted to Todd.

d

INTRODUCTION

Many legends naturally clustered round Anlaf's heroic career. One of these has been preserved by William of Malmesbury in his "Gesta Regum" and "Gesta Pontificum." It tells how, at the battle of Brunanburgh, Anlaf, disguised as a harper, entered Athelstan's camp, and was brought before the king to display his minstrelsy. He marked well the situation of the king's tent; but the king, warned by a soldier, removed his tent to another part of the camp. A bishop unwittingly took possession of the vacant place, and was slain in the assault which was made that night. We are acquainted with a similar story of an English king's visit to the Danish camp. There can be no doubt that the romance of "Havelok Cuheran" is little more than a romance of the life of "Anlaf Curan," or rather of the many legends fathered upon him, some belonging to ancient story, some derived from various episodes in Hiberno-Anglo-Danish history. The romance must have originally been developed among a Welsh-speaking population, for "Abloec," or "Abloyc" (*with voiced* b, *i.e.* Avloc; *cp.* "Habloc," the form on the Grimsby seal), is the name given to "Anlaf" in the oldest Welsh annals. It is not to be explained, as Todd suggested, as a Welsh form of "Anlaf," but rather, as Dr. Ward has pointed out, as a native Welsh heroic name (Aballach, or Avallach, otherwise Abloyc, the sixth son of the semi-mythical Cunedda) transferred to the Northern hero, its sound being nearly identical with what would have been the Welsh form of some Scandinavian variant of Anlaf. The Welsh kingdom of Strathclyde must be thought of in connection with the Welsh origin of the romance. King Owen, who ruled there during Anlaf's life, was nephew to Constantine of Scotland, Anlaf's father-in-law, and one of his allies at Brunanburgh. The events of the romance clearly belong to Constantine's reign, though by an error Gaimar confuses this tenth-century Constantine with Constantine, "the nephew of Arthur, who had the sword Calidure."

Gaimar's "Havelok" and Saxo's "Hamlet" have many traits in common, as has already been shown. "Havelok" is but a romance of "Anlaf Curan." Is any light thrown on the legendary "Hamlet" when viewed side by side with what is known of the historical Anlaf? As regards the earlier career of Hamlet, there is nothing much more strikingly parallel than the part played by Anlaf's usurping uncle. Unfortunately, the story of Anlaf's youth has not come down to us; there is a blank of ten years in the annals, from the death of his father in 927. But the Hamlet of Saxo's Fourth Book, who journeys to Scotland to woo the fierce virago Hermutrude,* whose cruel arrogance made her always loathe her wooers, may be identified with the son-in-law of Constantine of Scotland. It has been well said that while Hermutrude resembles Anlaf's first wife in her country, she resembles his second wife, Gormflaith, in her character; for though, according to Saxo, she had previously resisted all offers of marriage by reason of her chastity, yet at Hamlet's death "she yielded herself unasked to be the conqueror's spoil and bride."

The most remarkable parallel in the "Havelok" and "Hamlet" stories is perhaps the stratagem of setting up the dead men and so gaining the battle; this incident seems to belong peculiarly to Anglo-Danish or Hiberno-Danish history. A similar expedient is mentioned by Saxo Grammaticus as practised by Fridlevus, king of Denmark, who invades Britain after conquering Dublin; in the Book of the "Wars of the

---

* The whole subject of the Hermutrude-type of woman in mediæval literature is very fully treated of by Olrik (pp. 172–179); Mr. A. Nutt (*Folk-lore*, 1892, 26–48) dwells on its points of contact with Marie de France's "*Eliduc.*" The name "Hermutrude" is evidently a Danish borrowing of the German "Hermintrude.'

Gaedhil with the Gaill," * the same device is resorted to in one of the last episodes of that long struggle. The statement in Saxo and Gaimar must be referred to the traditional exploits of Anlaf Curan.

In the case of " Havelok," the Welsh annals come to our aid in clinching the alleged identification of " Havelok " with " Anlaf." Do we find any similar evidence bearing out the alleged influence of Anlaf's story on Saxo's Hamlet-tale ? The supposed absence of all such evidence must, I think, be answerable for the scant attention hitherto given to the whole subject of the " Havelok-Hamlet " problem, so that in so recent a study as Mr. Elton's valuable Appendix to " Saxo Grammaticus," the possibility of the equation is not even referred to. But there does exist in ancient annals a clue of the greatest possible importance, strangely overlooked by previous workers. Its neglect can easily be explained ; owing to a very simple but unfortunate blunder, the translators have obscured the value of their document, while the historians have naturally followed the translators. In the "Annals of Ireland by the Four Masters," † under the year 917 (= 919), a striking account is given of the great battle of Ath-Cliath, i.e. Kilmashogue (near Rathfarnham, in the county of Dublin). A mighty victory was gained by the Northerners under Imhar and Sitric Gale; twelve Irish kings and princes were struck down in the fight. Chief among these was Niall Glundubh, son of Ædh Finnliath, king of Ireland, " after he had been three years in the sovereignty." " Concerning this battle," adds the annalist, " several songs were made. Fierce and hard was the Wednesday, is the burden of one ; Where is the chief of the western world ? of another. Niall said before the battle :—'Whoever wishes for a speckled boss, and a sword

* Cp. Todd, p. 215.
† " Annals of Ireland by the Four Masters," ed. O'Donovan ; cp. also " Three Fragments, copied from Ancient Sources," &c. (Irish Arch. and Celt. Soc.), 1860.

1

of sore-inflicting wounds, and a green javelin for wounding wretches,
let him go early in the morning to Ath-Cliath.' Celedabhaill,
son of Scannall, successor of Comghall, and confessor of Niall
Glundubh, was he who had requested of Niall to come to the
battle; and it was he who gave the viaticum to Niall, after
having refused to give him a horse to carry him to the battle."
Then follows a strange fragment of song, which the annalist
had already quoted under the year 904. This, however, is its
proper place. Its author was none other than Niall Glundubh's
widow, Queen Gormflaith, daughter of Flann (who must not
be confused with Gormflaith, daughter of Murchadh, Anlaf's
wife, already referred to). These words are quoted from her
lament :—

> "Olc ꝼoꝛm commaoın aɴ ꝺa Ȝhall
> 2)aꝛbꝛac Nıall, aȝuꝛ Ceaꝛball,
> Ceaꝛball la hUlb coṁal ɴȝlé
> Nıall Ȝluɴꝺuḃ la h2lṁhlaıꝺe ;"

> " Ill for me the compliment of the two foreigners,
> Who slew Niall and Cearbhall ;
> Cearbhall was slain by Ulf, a mighty deed ;
> Niall Glundubh by Amhlaide."

The last word, "Amhlaide," is certainly the Irish form of
"Amloði" or Hamlet.* O'Donovan, the editor of the Annals,
mistook the name for "Amhbaeibh," *i.e.* the Irish form of
Áleifr, or Óláfr, and renders it so in his translation of the
passage. The historians, including Steenstrup, have all followed him, and state that Niall Glundubh was slain at the
battle by one of the enemy whose name was Olaf. The confusion of "Amlaidhe" (*i.e.* Amlóði) with Amlaibh (*i.e.* Áleifr,

---

* Mr. Whitley Stokes duly gives the name in his list of " Norse Loan-words
in Irish Annals," Bezzenberger's *Beiträge,* 1892.

Óláfr) was natural enough; the *dh* was taken to be a mere variant of *bh*. That this is not the case is proved by the metrical system of Gormflaith's song, which requires that "Amhlaide" should be a trisyllabic word—the final *-e* cannot be ignored.* This passage in the Irish annals yields us the earliest instance of the name "Amloði" or "Hamlet" to be found anywhere in literature. The Irish queen Gormflaith, about the year 919, introduces it into her verse as the name of one of the Northern heroes at the battle of Ath-Cliath. Who was this "Amlaidhe," the slayer of Niall Glundubh? Though "*The Annals of the Four Masters*" name Imhar (*i.e.* Ivar) and Sitric as the leaders of the Northmen, it is probable that Imhar is an error for Clann Ivar, "the children of Ivar," † and that Sitric, the father of Anlaf Curan, was at the head of the enterprise.‡ Under these circumstances, he was certainly the cause of Niall's death. But it would seem that he was the actual slayer of the Irish king. The Saxon Chronicle (*E.* and *F.*), Simeon of Durham, Henry of Huntingdon, Gaimar, and other authorities, all state that "Sitric slew Niel," though they make the strange mistake of calling him Sitric's brother, king of Northumberland. Hodgson Hinde (Hodgson's *Northumberland*, vol. i.) has shown that this Niel was no other than Niall Glundubh, "who never was king of Northumberland, and was no Dane, nor brother of Sitric, but a genuine Irishman of the race of the Northern Hy Neill."§ Perhaps the chroniclers have confused this Sitric with Sitriucc

* Professor Kuno Meyer has kindly given me his opinion on the point: "From the metre and rhyme we see that Amlaidhe makes three syllables."

† The Ivar were probably of Norse, and not Danish, origin. *Cp.* Steenstrup, *Normannerne*, ii. iii.

‡ *Cp.* Todd.

§ Keary (*Catalogue of English Coins: Anglo-Saxon Series*) states definitely, in his biographical note on SIHTRIC GALE: "slew, in battle of Kilmashogue, 919, King Njel Glundubh, K. of Dublin."

(one of the sons of Ivar of Limerick), who slew his brother Sichfrith. In the *Ulster Annals*, anno 888, it is stated that "Sichfrith Mac Imair rex Nordmannorum a fratre suo per dolum occisus est." The only brother we know of is Sitriucc, Lord of Limerick.

If, then, it can be shown that Sitric, the father of Anlaf Curan, was the slayer of Niel, it follows that "Amlaidhe," the Irish form of "Hamlet," in Gormflaith's song, must have reference to him; yet nowhere else, so far as is discovered at present, is Sitric referred to under this name. Two nicknames of his are well known, viz., "Caoch," an Irish word meaning blind or one-eyed, and "Gale" or "Gaile," a word which, as Todd says, if it be Irish, may signify "the champion" or "hero"; but it cannot well be an Irish word, and Celtic scholars tell me "this epithet wants explanation." I would hazard the suggestion that "gaile" is the Norse *galiðr = galinn*, "bewitched," or, more commonly, "mad" (the past participle of *gala*, "to enchant"). May it not be that "*amlaidhe*," as used by Gormflaith, was synonymous with "*gaile*"? But if Sitric's career recalled the story of "Amloði," how was it that his own Northern countrymen did not apply to him this expressive nickname? As a matter of fact, we know nothing of Sitric's early career. The annals are silent as to his father, and the circumstances under which he first came to Dublin in 888.*

* There is a curious story told by Suhm, in his *Critisk Danmarks Historie*, about the alleged discovery of some coins bearing the inscription, "Amleth Rex Anglorum." Suhm casts doubt on the authenticity of the reading, derived from "Resenii Descr. Jutiæ MSS. in Atlante." The MSS. of Resenius in the Arni-Magnæan Collection have been summarily investigated, but no such note has been discovered. Suhm probably quoted directly from Pontoppidan's *Marmora Danica*, where the following statement is made :—

"In boreali regione paræciæ Törringensis portio terræ in Lymicum se inferens sinum insulam efficit *Hellere* dictam, in qva Amlethus Rex munimentum quondam extruxisse fertur. In medio hujus collis surgit sepulchralis, quem annis abhinc

Again, so far as the legend of "*Amloði*" is concerned, it must be borne in mind that we find no Northern reference to the name before the time of the Icelander Snæbjörn, probably some twenty or thirty years after Gormflaith's reference to "Amlaidhe." Whatever Northern elements there may be in the story of Hamlet, it has not yet been conclusively proved that the name "Hamlet" is of Northern origin. As a Teutonic word "amloði" stands absolutely isolated, and no etymology hitherto advanced by Teutonic philologists commends itself to serious consideration. The word has not yet been connected with Celtic vocables, but future investigations on the part of Celtic scholars may perhaps resolve the name into its component parts; "amhlair," "amadon," and "amlaidhe" may once have been synonyms in Irish speech for that most popular character among all folk, and more especially the Irish, to wit, "the fool;" the nickname "amlaidhe" may perhaps represent the confluence of the characteristic Northern name "Amlaibh" and some such Celtic word as "amhaide," sour, sulky, surly (*cp.* "amaideac," silly, absurd, fantastic, foolish, idiotic).

Anyhow, it would seem that among the Irish, in the Scandinavian kingdom of Dublin, Anlaf Curan's father was known as "Amlaidhe," or "Hamlet." Later on, the father and the more famous son were no doubt blended in popular story, the confusion being greatly helped by the likeness in sound between "Amlaibh," the Irish form of "Anlaf," [*] and "Am-

---

sex cum perfodisset Andreas qvidam Lundius, magnam vim nummorum invenit, partim ex corio clavulis argenteis confixo, partim ex auro cum imagine Viri & inscriptione: Amleth Rex Angliæ."

Probably, as Suhm suggests, if there is any truth at all in the story, Lund found some coins of "Anlaf." Keáry (p. 235) gives several specimens of his coins, one bearing inscription, "Anlaf Rex Tod" (probably = totius Britanniæ). The British Museum has at least one coin of Anlaf's father, Sihtric Gale (*cp.* p. 231).

[*] Many Irish forms of this name are given from the Annals in Whitley Stokes' article, Bezzenberger's *Beiträge*, xviii. 116.

laidhe," the Irish form of " Amloði." In later times the two words, following phonetic law, would become absolutely identical in form.* The story of "Hamlet" in Saxo certainly owed a great debt to this Hiberno-Danish history; and the accretions from this source grafted upon the older mythical story, especially the late matter to be found in Saxo's Fourth Book, may now easily be accounted for. Indeed, the evidence here adduced seems to point to the Celtic West, more particularly the Scandinavian kingdom of Ireland, as the locality where the Northern tale of " Hamlet," as we know it from Saxo, was finally developed some time in the eleventh century—about the same time that the Welsh minstrels of Strathclyde were forging their tale of "Havelok." † The tenth-century Icelander Snæbjörn must have known the tale at an earlier stage of its development, before the legends of the house of Ivar had been added thereto; but it may be inferred (if the interpretation of Gormflaith's "*amlaidhe*," as equivalent

* Professor Kuno Meyer has kindly given me the benefit of his learning on this matter :—"The ending *aidhe* is what Irish grammarians call a 'slender,' *i.e.* a palatal-sound combination, represented in English by *ie* or *ey*, as you actually find in *Auley*, which might come either from *Amlaibh* or *Amlaidhe*, though the former also makes *Auliff*, with the labial preserved."

† Dr. Ward (*Cat. MSS.*, p. 860) calls attention to the curious fact that a word almost the same in sound as Amloði formed the name of one of the old Welsh heroes. This was Amlaudd, of whom nothing is known except that he was the father of three or four heroines, one of whom was Eigr, the mother of Arthur. Lady Charlotte Guest states in a note that he was married to Gwen, a daughter of Cunedda (*Mabinogion*, ii. 319). Dr. Ward ingeniously makes the following observation :—"This forms, at all events, some sort of connection between him and Abloyc (or Avallach), the son of Cunedda, whose name was transferred to Anlaf Curan. We think it quite possible that both names were used for Anlaf by different romancers, and that whilst one became Havelok, the other became Hamlet." This is rather too ingenious : the similarity of Amlóði to Welsh "Amlawdd" is probably purely accidental. Professor Meyer tells me that the older form of anlawdd, viz. "anblaud," is against the theory.

While writing of Wales in connection with Hamlet, it may be well to call attention to *Trev Amlodd* in Pembrokeshire ; this seems to point to the settlement of a Norseman.

INTRODUCTION

to *galinn, i.e.* mad, be accepted) that the hero's stupidity, assumed or otherwise, was the important element of the tale as known to him. Even this earlier and simpler form of the story may have been brought to Iceland from Ireland, whither the Vikings had originally taken the story of Orwendil's son. No Scandinavian family illustrates more strikingly than Snæbjörn's the close connection between the Northerners and the Celts from the ninth to the eleventh centuries;* the greatest names in Hiberno-Scandinavian history figure in his pedigree; even the poetess Gormflaith, whose husband, Niall Glundubh, was slain by Amlaidhe, was among his kinsfolk; she probably died when he was a youth. It is indeed a curious coincidence that the earliest instances of the name "Hamlet" should be found in Gormflaith's Irish lament, and in Snæbjörn's Icelandic poem of adventure in Arctic Seas.

In view of the evidence adduced tending to associate the

---

* The mutual influence of the Celts and the Scandinavians both received increased attention at the hands of scholars. Vigfusson boldly recognised the non-Icelandic character of many of the Eddaic songs (*cp. Corpus Poeticum Boreale*, vol. i. p. lxii.). In the Prolegomena to "The Sturlunga Saga" occurs the following statement : — " We may therefore take the Lays to be a *parallel* development in the Western Isles to the Saga in Iceland, composed for the same purpose, popular entertainments, after the initiative of some great poet who arose among the Norse emigrants somewhere in the West (Ireland, Man, Northumberland, or Scotland, we know not which)." Professor Bugge is the chief exponent of the influence of Irish Christianity on Scandinavian mythology; and as regards Northern poetry, he has recently worked out his theory that the "Helgi" poems belong originally to the West. In an article on "Gaelic Words and Names in the Icelandic Sagas" (*Zeitschrift für Celtische Philologie*, 1897), Mr. Craigie re-asserts his previous contention (*Arkiv för nordisk Filologi*, x.) that "there is abundance of evidence in the Gaelic vocabulary to show that the Celt learned much from the Scandinavian, while there is scarcely any similar evidence to prove an Irish influence on the Norsemen." The test of vocabulary in this case is to my mind not altogether conclusive. The case of Olaf Pá, who was taught Irish by his mother, and "spoke it as well as any man" (*Laxdœla Saga*), was probably not an isolated instance. E. Mogk's *Kelten und Nordgermanen im 9. u. 10. Jahrbundeste*, 1892, emphasises the Celtic influence on Northern (and more especially Icelandic) literature.

development of the Hamlet story with the British Isles, it is a
matter of surprise that English folk-lore or folk-speech has not
so far yielded one slight trace of the story independently of
modern literary influences.   It is possible that Middle English
poetry may give us some such trace—a valuable confirmatory
clue to the theory previously propounded.   Alliterative poetry
of the West and North-West has preserved for us many fossil-
remains of ancient legend, and so rich a treasury of archaic
speech, that the student will be prepared to consider carefully
the following problem.   In "The Wars of Alexander," an alliterative romance, translated for the most part from the famous
"Historia de Preliis," * and composed somewhere in the North
of England about the beginning of the fifteenth century, we
find a strange word, "amlaʒe" or "amlaugh," twice used as a
term of reproach, Alexander the Great being scoffed at by
Porrus of Inde as "Amlaʒe out of Grece" :—

> "I, Porrus, that as principall possessed am in Ynde,
>   To this michare † out of Messedoine this mandment I write.
>   Thou, Alexander, thou ape, thou Amlaʒe out of Grece,
>   Thou little thefe, thou losangere,‡ thou lurkare in cites . . .
>   *Madding marred has thi mode* § and thi mynd changid."—(3540–3545.)

While Darius, inquiring about Alexander's appearance, is shown
by his courtiers a caricature thus graphically described :—

> "And thai in parchment him payntid, his person him shewid,
>   Ane amlaʒe, ane asaleny,¶ ane ape of all othire,
>   A wirling,** a wayryngle, †† a wawil-eʒid ‡‡ shrewe,
>   The caitifeste creatour, that cried §§ was evire."—(1707.)

---

* Re-edited from MS., Ashmore 44, and Trinity College, Dublin, MS., by
Professor Skeat, E.E.T.S., 1886 ; the former MS. was edited for the Roxburghe
Club, in 1849, by Stevenson.

† Petty thief.   ‡ Liar.   § Mind.   ¶ Little ass.
** Dwarf.   †† Little villain.   ‡‡ Wall-eyed.   §§ Created.

INTRODUCTION

In disdain Darius sends him a ball to play with, a golden headpiece, and a hat made of twigs, together with a letter, bidding him abandon his folly, and bethink him that he is but ' a dwinyng, a dwaȝe, and a dwerȝe "—a dwarf and a grub; he must learn to "*feign with fairness.*" *

Have we in these passages some reminiscence of a popular tale of "Hamlet"? or rather, is the word "Amlaȝe" not merely a synonym used much in the same way as "Amlóðï" in modern Icelandic, but actually its Middle English equivalent? It is a curious fact that the first editor of "The Wars of Alexander" misread the text and printed "Amlair," evidently recalling the Irish "amhlair," a fool. Professor Skeat, in his great edition of the two texts, rightly prints "amlaȝe," "amlaugh," explaining the words in the glossary as equivalent to "imbecile, weak person," and adding without comment "Icelandic, *amlóði.*" The difficulty of deriving the Middle English form from the Scandinavian is probably answerable for the omission of the word from Middle English lexicons, as well as from that noble survey of English speech, the New English Dictionary. The phonological aspects of the word must first be considered. It is difficult to determine whether the guttural in "amlaȝe" was of any phonetic or etymological value. The poem in which the word occurs belongs to a Northern district, and was composed at so late a period that it may safely be assumed that in most cases the guttural

---

* The Latin original of the two passages has been elaborately worked up by the English poets. The letter of Porrus begins with these words :—"*Porus Indorum rex latroni Alexandro, qui latrocinando obtinet civitates, precipiendo mandamus. Cum sis mortalis homo, quid prevales facere deo?*" &c. The drawing of the caricature is described in section 29 :—"*Illi vero ostenderunt ei staturam Alexandri depictam in membrana. Videns autem illam Darius despexit eam propter parvitatem forme ejus et statim direxit ei pilam lubricam,*" &c. (cp. *Historia de Preliis*, ed. O. Zingerle, Breslau, 1885).

symbol, even when of etymological significance, was unsounded in pronunciation.* In consequence of its non-phonetic value, the symbol was often used erroneously, or as a mere scribal mannerism. It may well be that the final syllable of " Amlaȝe " does not etymologically represent a guttural letter, and that the ending -laȝe was due to the influence of the common word " out-laȝe," outlaw—an attempt to Anglicise some Gaelic vocable with an undefined vowel in the second syllable. At all events, if the word should prove to be ultimately identical with the Scandinavian " amlóˣi," it can only be accounted for by derivation from the Celtic form " amlaidhe." In later Irish and Gaelic the endings -dh(e), -bh(e), -gh(e) were not sounded, though scribes continued to write them,† too often erroneously. Hence, however, results the following conclusion :— If the Middle English *Amla[e]* may be traced to the Gaelic *Amlaidhe*, and thence to the Norse *amlóði*, it may similarly also represent the Gaelic *amlaibh, i.e.* Old Norse *Anleifr* (*Olaf*).

It may be that the linguistic problems of the form " *Amlaȝe* " illustrate in an interesting manner the literary problems, already discussed, of the fusion of the legendary story of " Amlóˣi " with the romantic legendary history of Anlaf Curan. It comes to this, that, from a philological point of view, the

---

* " The Wars of Alexander " is probably half a century later than " Gawayne and the Grene Knight," " Cleanness," " Patience," and " Pearl "; these latter poems (more especially the first and last, owing to their rhymes) clearly demonstrate the loss of the guttural in such words as *might, light,* rhyming with non-guttural words ; hence such spellings as *sorquidryȝhe, fayryȝe,* and such forms as *ȝolȝe* (= *ȝolwe*) by false analogy with the correct Middle English *sorȝe* (= *sorwe*).

The writer of " The Wars of Alexander " belonged, in all probability, to a more northernly district than the Gawayne-poet, whose disciple he seems to have been, if we may judge from vocabulary and characteristics of style.

† Such a text as Kuno Meyer's *Vision of MacConghle* gives abundant illustration of this ; *cp.* also the etymology of " ban-*shee*," given as from *sidhe,* instead of *sighe* (*v.* Skeat's *Student's Pastime*).

modern Gaelic name "MacAulay" may be interpreted as "Hamlet's son," or "Olaf's son." *

* As a matter of fact, the name "Amlaidhe" (Amlóði) took no root in the Highlands ; there are, as Mr. MacBain, the author of the *Gaelic Dictionary*, kindly points out to me, two M'Aulay clans in Scotland : the Argyleshire branch is from (1) *Amalgaid*, which appears in charters of the thirteenth century as Amelec, Ameleus, and even Saxonised as Hammelin ; the Lewis M'Aulays from (2) *Amhlaibh*, *i.e.* Norse Anláfr (Áleifr, Óláfr). There is no distinction in modern Gaelic pronunciation (McAmhlai) between the two M'Aulay sept names. Irish differentiates thus : (1) M'Auliffe (Anláfr) ; (2) M'Aulay (Amalgaid, Amhalghaidh).

The strong probability that the Middle English *Amlaȝe* is a borrowing from Gaelic makes a reference necessary to the well-known expressive Scotch word *ablach*, or *ablich*, used absolutely as the English word in the passages quoted from "The Wars of Alexander," in the sense of "a dwarf ; an insignificant, contemptible, useless sort of creature" (*cp.* the colloquial Aberdeenshire use in Dr. Alexander's *Johnny Gibb of Gushetneuk*). On the high authority of Mr. MacBain (*cp. Gaelic Dictionary, s.v.*), the word must be resolved into the component parts ad-bal-ac from √*bal*, die ; *cp.* Eng. *quell;* hence *ablach=*"carcase," "object of pity," &c. There can be little doubt that "*aploch*" is merely another spelling of the same word. Mactaggart's *Scottish Gallovidian Encyclopedia* (1823) has an interesting note on "aplochs":—"Some few years ago a field of corn could not be shorn, nor a meadow mowed, without parts of them being left in corners uncut ; these were called *aplochs*: they were left for the benefit of the warlock race, so as to keep their favour, but farmers have long ago defied all beings of the sort to do their worst : *aplochs* now are vanished away."

Dr. Wright, in the first instalment of *The Dialect Dictionary*, places *ablach* among the "words for the present kept back for the want of further information," rightly withdrawing the derivation proposed in the body of the work where reference is made to Gaelic *abhac*, "a dwarf, pigmy, manikin, sprite." *Abhac* and *ablach*, though etymologically distinct, are evidently synonymous ; the former is clearly identical with the word *amhach*, "dwarf, like a fool," given in Armstrong's *Gaelic Dictionary*, and is probably a derivative of *amh*, "a fool, simpleton, dwarf," recorded in the same.

It is impossible to dismiss without comment the remarkable groups of words, ultimately of different etymological origin, used in senses almost synonymous :— (1) Gael. *amh, amhac, abhac ;* (2) Gael. *ablach ;* (3) Gael. *amhlair ;* (4) Gael. *amadon amaidhe,* &c. ; (5) Gael. *amlaidhe ;* Norse, *amlódi ;* (6) probably various derivatives of Norse, *Áleifr, e.g.* Irish, *Amlaibh ;* Welsh, *abloyc* (Havelok Curan).

The second, third, fourth, fifth, and sixth groups have already been discussed ; as regards the first group, Mr. David MacRitchie, who strongly believes in the existence of dwarfish races in former times, in countries where they no longer exist, has the following interesting remark in an article contributed to *Scots Lore* (p. 390) :—"It has been seen that the Gaelic *Na h-Amhuisgean* is translated *The Dwarfs or Pigmies* by the Minister of Tiree, and that in two Gaelic dictionaries (one Irish, the other Scotch) the corrupt form *Tamhasg* (from an-t-amhasg) has the same meaning. Each of these lexicographers gives the variants *amhach* and *abhac* or *abhag*, all signifying 'dwarf;' and these, again, are extensions of the earlier form *amh* or *abh.*" In a letter, Mr. MacRitchie points out that as the aspirated consonant in Gaelic infers an earlier unaspirated form, we are led to "*ab*, an ape, a spell—*anciently*, any little creature," and, contrary to my own views, he is predisposed to assume that the earliest "havelocks" were, as defined by Armstrong, "pigmies"; but this confuses the voiceless Gael. *ablach* with the voiced Welsh *abloyc.* Anyhow, the proposed connection of *ab*, or *am*, and "*ape*," recalls the line quoted above from "The Wars of Alexander," "*thou ape, thou amlaȝe.*"

IV.

FROM the investigations summarised in an earlier section of the essay, it seems at least probable that the Hamlet story, as known to the Icelander Snæbjörn, was fundamentally identical with the groundwork of the story subsequently elaborated by Saxo Grammaticus. The assumption may perhaps be hazarded that, in some form or other, the legend lived on among the myth-loving Icelanders throughout the Middle Ages independently of the more distinguished literary form impressed upon it by the genius of the Danish historian. A noteworthy passage in a later Danish history, "Series Regum Daniæ," compiled by the learned Icelander Torfæus, who flourished in the seventeenth century, may perhaps have had reference to some such "old wives' tale," containing elements derived from pre-Saxo times. "As regards Saxo's Amlethus," observes Torfæus, "as a boy at home in Iceland I frequently heard the story of *Amlode* told by wretched old crones, but I regarded it as merely an old wives' tale: later on, however, when I came across Saxo's noble account of the hero, I abandoned my boyish notion, and thenceforth left my friends no peace, but worried them to find out for me the old story I had once heard; yet without success. At last, a few years ago, they sent me a story of Amlode, but no sooner had I perused it than I cast it aside, as altogether worthless and quite modern. It actually makes Hamlet not a Dane but a Spaniard! It must have been composed after the time of the Scythian Tamberlaine, for some of the details are certainly derived from his history." *

The book sent to Torfæus was clearly not the story he had heard in his youth; yet the worthless volume may well have merited more serious attention on the part of the historian. In spite of the borrowings from Tamberlaine's history, and the general romanticising of the Northern story, some of the closest elements might still have been preserved therein. The manuscript sent to Torfæus is extant among the MSS. at Copenhagen.† It is substantially identical with the " Ambales Saga " issued in the present volume.

Other antiquaries followed up the efforts of Torfæus to discover an older Icelandic Hamlet Saga. The great name of Arni Magnusson must be mentioned in this connection. He commissioned one Jón Thorlaksson (known as " the Saga spoiler ") to send him any such saga he might come across. Demand called forth supply; and Arni, sometime in 1705, received a copy of a professedly ancient story of Amlode; he was not, however, deceived by Jón's professions. The manuscript in question is preserved among Arni's collections, enriched with the following note: " *Me, nimirum decipere voluit*

---

* "Ad Saxonis Amlethum quod attinet, ego in patria puer a vetulis anibusque et ejusdem furfuris homuncionibus Amlodii historiam narratam audivi, inque tenerrima illa aetate pro fabula tantum aestimavi. Verum postquam adultior, suada Saxonis expositam amplificatamque conspexi, conceptam prius per-suasionem ut puerilem antiquavi. Exinde amicorum quosvis sollicitare non destiti ut illam historiam ubique quaererent, qui se nihil profecisse scriptis ad me literis crebro questi sunt. Tandem ante aliquot annos eam nactus, lectione omnino indignam deprehendi, anilem quippe nec tressis fabulam, nuperque con-fectam; *quae Amlodum istum non Danum sed Hispanum fuisse suggerit.* Fabulam post Tamerlanis seu Tamercutli tempora confectam esse ex eo liquet, quod ex ejus gestis aliquod ibi assutum compareat " (*Series Regum Daniœ*); Torfæus was born in 1636.

† *Cp.* Appendix: Summary of Manuscripts, No. 14.

e

INTRODUCTION

vir bonus, et persuadere se rem vetustatam mihi mittere. Sed non ego credulus illi." *

By this time Arni had got together several manuscripts of the more interesting Saga, a version of which Torfæus had previously received from his friends in Iceland; his collection included, too, a long ballad-cycle on the same theme, a rhyming version of the fictitious saga.

During the last two hundred years the "Ambales Saga" has excited the curiosity of many students of the Hamlet story, and it has seemed desirable that it should at length be rendered accessible.†

There can be no question that in its present form the Saga is a modern production, belonging to the sixteenth or perhaps early seventeenth century. The value of the text depends mainly on the possibility that, more especially in the earlier chapters, there may still be found elements belonging to the pre-Saxo Hamlet legend. That the bulk of the Saga is drawn from the Danish history, remodelled under the influence of popular folk-tales, Charlemagne and Arthurian romances, and the stories of Tamberlaine, cannot for a moment be doubted. The name "Ambales," evidently evolved from

---

* *Cp. ibid.* 16 ; Appendix VI. Vedel's Danish translation of Saxo's History (1575) had clearly been used by the ancient sagaman !

† Dr. Ward (*Cat. MS. Romances*, Brit. Mus. 1883) was, I think, the first of modern scholars to summarise the contents of the Saga. Soon after, the present writer began collecting information on the Saga and Rimur. A short account of his results was read before the New Shakespeare Society in 1889 (*vide Transactions N. Shak. Soc.*). Meanwhile a small printed chap-book, "Sagan af Ambalis Kongi," appeared at Reykjavik ("hjá Einari Þorðarsyni," 1886), evidently a normalised text of a poor modern manuscript. Recently Dr. Detter (*Zeitschrift für Deutsches Alterthum*, 1892) gave an account of the Saga, based on Dr. Otto Jiriczek's researches, which were subsequently (1896) published in the *Weinhold Festschrift* of the *Germanistische Abhandlungen* (Breslau)—a valuable summary of the contents of the Arni-Magnæan MSS., with references to the more important differences. It is strange that both Dr. Detter and Dr. Jiriczek were unaware of the published articles of English scholars on the subject.

INTRODUCTION

" Amblethus," a late variant of " Amlethus," points to some such epitome of Saxo as that attributed to the monk Gheysmer. This epitome, probably composed about the middle of the fourteenth century,* was soon translated into Low German, and in this form appeared in print as early as 1485, a quarter of a century before the same honour was accorded to Saxo's Latin original. This Low German version may well have been in the hands of the Icelandic writer of " Ambales." The book is now so scarce that probably no copy is to be found in England ; and Schmeller, the bibliographer of Low German literature, makes the same statement with reference to the libraries of Germany. A careful transcript of the illustrative chapters, from one of the Copenhagen copies of the book, will be found among the Appendices, accompanied by the Latin of Gheysmer's epitome.

Of the "Ambales Saga " there are many manuscripts, though the oldest cannot be assigned to an earlier date than the seventeenth century. In all probability none of the extant copies represent the original form of the Saga. The versions may be broadly divided into two classes, according to their nearness to the Arni-Magnæan MSS. 521a and 521c respectively. There are minute and unimportant differences in style, vocabulary, names, incidents, divisions of the chapters. The second of the two classes seems to preserve the better version. The Saga in this volume, printed without normalisation from a more modern manuscript, belongs substantially to this class.†

---

* Cp. Velschow's Saxo Grammaticus : notæ uberiores. Gheysmer was the scribe, and not the author, according to this view.

† Cp. Appendices VI. and XV. The specimens in Appendix VI. illustrate the sort of differences to be found in the MSS. I have not deemed it necessary to give lists of various readings. The following may be noted :—Page 1, line 11, " Selina, &c.," so c (i.e. A.M. 521c), not in a (i.e. A.M. 521a) ; Holmsetuland (1, 14),

INTRODUCTION

It is hardly necessary to calculate the many divergences in the "Ambales Saga" as compared with Saxo's Amlethus story. The main question is this: Is there any incident in the Saga which may be referred to the older independent version of the story current in Iceland? One such incident is certainly noteworthy. The most striking divergence from Saxo's account is the statement that Ambales had an elder brother who was killed by the slayer of his father because he showed unfeigned resentment, while Ambales saved his life by concealing his feelings under the guise of heartless folly. Saxo says nothing of an elder brother. Now, this very point differentiates the various versions of the Brutus story. According to some historians, Tarquin had put to death the father of Brutus as well as his elder brother; other historians (notably

a Smaland; Sigurdur (4, 45), *a* Sigvarðr; *a* Artabani (14, 22), *c* Arthibanis; Mordia (18, 40), *a* Mandia, *c* Mondia; Victor (22, 24), *c* Vygþor; Roso (26, 54), *a c* Rasi; Anga (54, 2), *a* Angany; Dyla (56, 5), *c* Tyla; Vallanus (56, 9), *a c* Valianus; Fyris (64, 7), *a c* Tyrus; [(?) *read* Leta] Ceta (72, 3), *a c* Leta; Batellus (84, 68), *a* Batthas, *c* Batar; Karon (86, 86), *a c* Garon; Actamund (86, 87), *a c* Artamund; Silla (102, 2), *a c* Salla; Barastatis edur Bastianus (148, 8), *a* Bastianus, *c* Bajasetes eður Bastianus; Tambis (158, 3), *c* Cambis, Cambris.

Perhaps the most important difference between the two recensions is the verse p. 110, 38–40, which is not found in *a ; c* reads as follows :—

> "mann sá-eg stunginn mitt undir kerru
> mann eg það ekki,
> sá hjelt svinum við sælkjöri
> sá-eg þa hrekki."

i.e., "I saw a man stuck under a car; I remember it not. Swine did he tend with dainty morsels; I saw the trick." This is a better version than the corrupt text of the lines in my own MS.; "hét" is evidently an error for "hé[l]t."

As regards Ambales' nickname of "Amloði," there is, I think, good reason for inferring that this passage was not in the earliest form of the Saga, but was added later to account for the likeness of "Ambales" to the proverbial "Amloði": *a*, while substantially agreeing with the statement on p. 12, ll. 98–103, adds the following words: "lá jafnan í eldaskála við öskudyngju ok kom sier allilla, var hans nafni umbreytt ok var Amloði kallaðr," *i.e.*, "he always kept in the firestead among the ash-heaps, and was surly; so they changed his name from Ambales to Amloði."

Livy) refer only to the brother's murder. "Amlethus" has but
to avenge his father's death; the early history of "Ambales"
more closely resembles that of Brutus, in that he narrowly
escapes an elder brother's fate. The resemblance can hardly
be accidental; furthermore, this detail must needs be independent of Saxo's version. It does not, however, necessarily
follow that we have here an element derived from a version of
the Hamlet story earlier than Saxo's. Comparative mytholo-
gists existed before the nineteenth century, and it would not
be surprising to find that scholars of the sixteenth century
had recognised the debt Saxo's Danish Amlethus owed to the
Roman Brutus. Indeed, I have recently found proof of this in
certain pseudo-annals of Iceland preserved in manuscripts at
the British Museum and in Denmark. The annalist gives,
under "anno mundi 3430," a somewhat full account of Tarquinius Superbus, together with the story of Lucrece. The
next entry is a brief reference to Odin's reign in Denmark;
a short note on Cincinnatus follows; then it is stated that
Orvendil was king of Denmark; Plato's fame is recorded in a
couple of lines; and then follows an epitome of the story of
Hamlet, unmistakably drawn from Saxo. One can see at a
glance that the four brief entries dividing the paragraphs dealing with Tarquinius Superbus and Hamlet are but annalistic
padding, and that Hamlet has stepped into the place of Brutus;
the Icelandic annalist recognised the identity of the two stories,
and naturally preferred the Northern to the Roman hero.*

---

* *Cp.* App. XII. and XXV*d*. Finn Magnusson must have known the fictitious
character of these Annals. The Odda Annals are older than 1580, but yet of the
sixteenth century. Torfæus (*Series*, p. 121) quotes Björn of Skarðsa about these
Annals, but he never saw them. All the Icelandic Annals seem to go back to a
common source, perhaps Annals of the thirteenth century. Sœmund the Wise
may have written or copied annals. See *Annales regii*, A.D. 1042 : "Na segir
Sœmundr presti inn fródi." (*Cp.* Gustav Storm, *Islandske Annaler.*)

INTRODUCTION

This evidence that scholars two or three hundred years ago definitely regarded Hamlet and Brutus as twin-brothers, does not absolutely negative the possibility that the author of the "Ambales Saga" engrafted upon his romanticising of Saxo certain elements of a current folk-tale of Amlode derived in far-off pre-Saxo days from Roman legend. The Icelandic form of Hamlet's name, "Amloði," is perhaps the best evidence we possess that some story of the hero was once on the lips of the people, though by the sixteenth century, if not sooner, the name had degenerated into a mere nickname for "an imbecile weak person, one of weak bodily frame, wanting in strength or briskness, unable to do his work, not up to the mark." * According to the Saga, Ambales is called "Amlode," because of his strange unlikeness to ordinary beings. One wonders whether many of the old hearers or readers of his story recognised the identity of the two names, and understood the evolution of the name of Amlode's mother, "Amba." "Call him after thy name, for he shall resemble thee and his mother's kin," bade the Norn before she departed; and the queen names him "Ambales." "But the king and the courtiers call him 'Amlode.'" It would indeed be remarkable if, together with the nickname, the traditional associations of the word, handed down from distant ages, did not find a place in the "Ambales Saga," and so, in spite of its fictitious character, the Saga may well preserve some noteworthy traits of the ancient story, lost in Saxo's more stately history.

The Icelandic folk-tale of "Brjám," though first written down from oral tradition in 1705, is certainly nothing but a

---

* *Cp.* Cleasby-Vigfusson, *sub voce;* amlóðaligr, *imbecile;* amlóða-skapr, *imbecility;* amlóðast, *to behave as an amloði.* Torfæus (*Series Reg. Dan.* p. 302) quotes from an old Swedish rhyme "*rett some han vore en Amblode,*" *i.e.,* "he behaved as if he were a Hamlet." *Cp.* Norwegian *amlod,* subs.; *amloda, amloa,* verb.

levelling down of the story of "Hamlet," cleverly blended with another folk-tale of the "Clever Hans" type. The interest attaching to "Brjám" is mainly due to the fact that it substantially agrees with the "Ambales Saga" where the Saga diverges from Saxo. So clearly is this the case, that one must conclude that the folk-tale has been evolved from the Saga, or it must be taken as evidence that the Sagaman availed himself of some popular tale of Amlode for certain striking elements of his romantic transformation of Saxo's story, and furthermore, that this popular tale is preserved in the story of "Brjám." There are no definite criteria to determine the point, but the impression given by the romance of "Ambales," and general considerations of literary methods, tend to support the view that the old heroic myth of "Amloδi" had been reduced to the humbler condition of a folk-tale before the composition of the Ambales Saga. It is easy, moreover, to understand why the hero of the folk-tale, as we have it, is not named "Amlode," but "Brjám." "Amlode" had already ceased to be used as a mere personal name; the story is therefore told of an "amlode" whose name was Brjám.* Possibly the latter name is not without significance in connection with previous observations tending to associate the development of the Hamlet story with the critical period of the Norsemen's occupation of Ireland. "Brjám" is the Icelandic form of the Irish "Brian;" and the very occurrence of the name in Iceland is evidence of the close relationship of Norsemen and Irish in early times. In view of what has been said concerning "Hamlet" and "The Wars of the Gaedhill with the Gaill," it is at least a strange chance (if

---

* Maurer and Detter call attention to the modern Icelandic "brjáni," an idiot; Detter, ingeniously but not convincingly, suggests that perhaps this was the original name of the hero of the tale, and that only later was the Irish name assigned to him. *Cp.* Cleasby, subs. *brjá*, &c.

not something more) that the name of the hero in the folk-tale should be identical with that of the mighty hero of the decisive battle of Clontarf (1014), the closing scene in the long struggle between the Irish and Norsemen. The noble history of Ireland's King Alfred, the famous Brian Borumha,* inspired alike Irish chronicler and Icelandic sagaman. In dealing with the events of his reign, it must be borne in mind that the hostile Norsemen were intimately connected with their Irish foes; the wife of Sitric, Anlaf Curan's son, was Brian's daughter; Brian's wife was Sitric's mother, the notorious Queen "Gorm-flaith of the Three Leaps." Oral tradition certainly confused at times the achievements of the two sides. An interesting instance has already been referred to; in the story of Havelok Curan, as well as in that portion of Saxo's account of "Hamlet" seemingly derived from the legendary history of Curan, it is told how the wounded men tied to stakes retrieved the fortunes of their party. This device, according to Irish annals, was the crowning act of heroism on the part of Brian's brave Dalcassian soldiers. Of this deed sang Moore in his famous war-song :—

> " Remember the glories of Brian the brave,
>   Though the days of the hero are o'er ;
> .   .   .   .   .   .
> Forget not our wounded companions, who stood
>   In the day of distress by our side ;
> While the moss of the valley grew red with their blood,
>   They stirr'd not, but conquer'd and died."

It is indeed a noteworthy coincidence that the name of "Brjám" should take the place of "Amlode" in the Icelandic folk-tale, which without further comment herewith follows :—

---

* Cp. Joyce, *History of Ireland;* Todd, *The Wars of the Gaedhill;* &c.

INTRODUCTION

THE STORY OF BRJÁM*

I

ONCE upon a time there lived a king and queen who ruled their realm. They were rich and wealthy, and scarcely knew the number of their precious possessions. They had one daughter; she was brought up as most other story-children. For a time nothing befell there, in the way of tales or tidings, noisings or news, unless one were to tell a lying tale.

Now in Wall-nook dwelt an old man and his wife. They had three sons.† One cow supported the whole family. This cow was so good that she gave milk three times a day, and at noon she came by herself home from the pasture.

Once the king went a-hunting with his men, and passed by the herds belonging to him; the old man's cow was there near the herds. The king said: "What a fine cow have I there!"

"Nay, sir," said his men, "that cow is not yours; it belongs to the old man in the cottage yonder."

The king answered: "It shall be mine."

And so the king rode home; and when he had sat down to drink, he recalled the cow, and resolved to send his men to the carl asking him to exchange it for another. The queen prayed him not to do

---

* There are two variant versions of the story, one found in Arnason's collection (cp. Appendix VIII.), the other in Maurer's *Isl. Volkss. der Gegenwart*. The latter is the better version in certain important respects; it gives "three sons" instead of "seven," and makes Brjám the youngest and not the eldest son. The translation is based on Arnason's text (cp. Magnusson and Powell's *Icelandic Legends*), modified where necessary by Maurer's epitomised version; the chief changes are noted. I have divided the story into three divisions: the first and third show clearly their derivation from the Hamlet-tale; the second, while it contains the riddling element suggested in the original tale, was evidently derived from a folk-tale of the "Clever Hans" type. A noteworthy feature of this section is the potency of the fool's words; they are not only oracular but also magical.

† Arnason, "seven sons."

this, as the poor folks had nothing but the cow for their support. The king, however, would not listen, and sent three men to bargain with the carl. He and his children were out in the fields when the messengers came. They told him the king's message, that he wished to take his cow in exchange for another.

The carl answered: "The king's cow is not dearer to me than mine is."

They pressed him, but he would not give way, and at last the king's men killed him. Then the children set up a wail, all but the youngest,* whose name was Brjám. The messengers asked the children where they felt the greatest pain. They struck their breasts, but Brjám slapped his buttocks and grinned.† Then the king's men killed the two children who had slapped their breasts, but said there was nothing lost by letting Brjám live, for he was a witless fool. The king's men then went home, and took with them the cow. But Brjám went in to his mother, and told her all that had befallen, and her grief and sorrow were great. He bade her not weep, for they gained little thereby; he would do what he could.

II

Once it so happened that the king was having a bower made for his daughter, and had given to the builder enough gold to gild it both within and without. Brjám came to the place, behaving like a fool, as was his wont.

The king's men said to him: "What good word have you for this, Brjám?"

He answered: "Lessen measure much, my men!" and went away.

But the gold that had been given them wherewith to gild the bower shrunk so much that it was only enough for half the building. They went and told the king; he thought they had stolen the gold, and had them all hanged.

Brjám went home and told his mother. She answered: "You should not have said it, my son."

He asked: "What should I have said, mother?"

She replied: "You should have said, 'Grow three-thirds!'

---

* Arnason, "the eldest son." † *Cp.* pp. 80–81.

"I shall say it to-morrow, mother," quoth Brjám.

Next morning he met some people carrying a body to the grave. They asked him: "What good word have you for this, Brjám?"

"Grow three-thirds, my men!" he said. Then the corpse grew so heavy that the carriers let it fall to the ground. Brjám went home and told his mother.

She said: "You should not have said that, my son."

He asked: "What should I then have said, mother?"

"'God grant peace to thy soul, thou dead!' you should have said," replied his mother.

"I shall say it to-morrow, mother," answered he.

Next morning he went to the palace of the king and saw a barber strangling a dog.* He went up to him, and the barber said: "What good word have you for this, Brjám?"

He answered: "God grant peace to thy soul, thou dead!"

At this the barber laughed, but Brjám ran off to his mother and told her what had happened.

She said: "You should not have said that."

"What should I then have said?" he asked her.

She answered: "You should have said, 'Why! is it the king's thievish cur you are handling there?'"

"I will say it to-morrow, mother," quoth he.

He went to the palace next morning, and it so happened that the king's men were driving the queen round the city. Brjám stepped up to them. "What good word have you for this, Brjám?" said they.

"Why! is it the king's thievish cur you are handling there, my men?" said he.

They cursed him. The queen bade them desist, nor do the boy any harm. He ran home to his mother and told her.

She said: "You should not have said it, my son."

"What should I then have said?" asked he.

She answered: "You should have said, 'Is it the glorious life most precious to the king which you have charge of now, my men?'"

"I shall say it to-morrow, my mother," answered the son.

Next morning he went toward the palace and found two of the king's men flaying a mare. He walked to them and said: "Why! is

* Maurer, "hangman hanging a thief."

lxxiii

INTRODUCTION

it the glorious life most precious to the king which you have charge of now, my men?"

They hooted at him, and he ran off to his mother and told her all. She said : "Do not go thither any more; some day or other they will kill you."

"Nay, my mother, they will not kill me," said he.

III

Once the king had ordered his men to go out a-fishing. They were getting ready to go in two large boats. Brjám came to them and asked them to let him go with them; but they drove him away and mocked at him. They asked him, however, "What will the weather be like to-day?" He looked now up at the sky, and now down to the ground, and said : "Wind and not windy, wind and not windy, wind and not windy!" * They laughed at him. They rowed out to the fishing-bank, and loaded both boats with fish; but when they turned to row ashore a storm arose, and both boats were lost.

Now nothing of note happened, till once on a time the king bade all his friends and favoured comrades to a grand banquet. Brjám asked his mother to give him leave to go to the palace that he might see how the banquet went off. When all had taken their places at the richly furnished tables, Brjám went to the smithy, and began shaping small pieces of wood with his knife. Those who saw him at work asked him what he meant thereby. He answered : "Avenge father, not avenge father." † They said : "You don't look unlike it," and so went away. He drove sharp spits of steel into the ends of his pieces of wood, and then stole into the guest-room, and nailed quietly to the floor the clothes of all who sat at table, and then walked off.

---

* Maurer, "vindi og ei vindi," i.e., "windy and not windy," with perhaps a play on "ei," not, and "æ," aye.

† Maurer's version, "Hefna papa, hefna papa," i.e., "To avenge father, to avenge father." The various versions of the Ambales Saga give the ambiguous version with the negative (cp. p. 82); A.M. 521 a, b, "hann kvaðst til föðurhefnda ætla og ekki hafa"; A.M. 521 c, "en hann kvað til föðurhefnda, að hefna þá og ekki hefna þá." The printed text reads "pa" for "þa," which corroborates a suggestion already made by Dr. Jiriczek (Germanistische Abhandlungen, 1896, xii. Heft).

INTRODUCTION

When the guests attempted to get up from their seats in the evening, they found themselves fixed to the benches; and they charged each other with having done this; and at last it came to blows, and one killed the other, till none were left alive.

When the queen heard this she was sorely grieved, and she bade them bury the dead. That morning Brjám came back to the palace, and offered himself as the queen's servant. She was glad to get him, for she had but few servants left. Brjám discharged his duty well, and at last married the king's daughter, and became king in that realm, and laid aside all his hare-brained folly. Thus ends this story." *

* While Brjám represents a levelling down of the Hamlet-tale, a brief reference must be made to *Hrolfssaga Kraka* (Fornaldar Sögur, ed. Rafn, 1829, vol. i.) for parallels to the main elements of Saxo's Amlethus story. Helgi and Hroar, the heroes of the saga, have many points in common with Hamlet, so far as motive for vengeance and method of vengeance. Dr. Detter, in the article already referred to, attempts to work out the direct influence of the Hamlet sage on the saga as represented by the late version preserved in *Fornaldar Sögur*, and by the fragmentary verses of the *Helgakorða*. Mr. Elton seems to me to have summed up the case excellently (cp. Appendix to *Saxo Grammaticus*):—"The comparison only establishes that Saxo's tale of Amleth is parallel in its three chief elements to an Icelandic saga, which concerns a historical king, Hrolf Kraki, included by Saxo in his Danish list, but represented by him as living at a period long before Amleth."

Mr. Vigfusson's note on *Hrolf Kraki's Saga* (v. *Prolegomena to Sturlunga Saga*), runs as follows:—"Only seventeenth-century paper copies of one vellum. Whether corruption is due to transcribers or is earlier we know not. There is a part of Biarkamal paraphrased in it (with a little better treatment than Helgi's Lays received from the Volsung composer); and it contains traditions such as must have existed in the lost part of Skiöldunga, whence indeed it may have been taken. False stuffings and fictitious episodes."

As regards the ground elements of the saga, attested by the Helgi Lay, Dr. Detter ingeniously points out that Hamal's words, "you thought you had harboured a sheep (einen Hammel), but it was a grey wolf," recall Cicero's (*De Divinatione*, i. 22) citation of a fragment of Accius to the effect that Tarquin dreamed he led two rams to the altar, and while he slew one, the other struck him down from behind. The augur warned him to beware of him who pretended to be as simple as a sheep (*hebetem æque ac pecus*), but who had a wise heart in his breast. The parallel is striking in view of the undoubted influence of Roman legend on the Hamlet story.

V.

"Margr prísar sumariỗ fyrir fagran fugla-söng ;
En eg hæli vetrinum því nóttin er löng."

*"Many love the summer, for the fair birds' song,
But I like the winter best, for the nights are long."* *

AS early as the thirteenth century the great Sagas of Iceland
were already becoming "unread classics," and were giving
place in popular estimation to "Spurious Sagas" (*Skrök Sögur*)
and "Fictitious Sagas" (*Riddara Sögur*); the former based,
however slightly, on Icelandic tradition, the latter founded
directly on the Romances of Chivalry, or, at all events, indebted
for much of their machinery to the Mediæval Romance Cycles.
From the French Metrical Romances the idea was probably
taken of casting the Sagas, the Old Sagas as well as the later
Spurious and Fictitious Sagas, into metrical form—*rímur*, as
they were called, or "Ballad-cycles," though the varied forms of
versification employed in these rhyming romances were derived
from mediæval Latin verse of the "Golias" type, and not from
Romance metres.† A "Ballad-cycle" (*rímur*) represents the
versifying of the successive chapters of a Saga, each ballad
of the cycle corresponding roughly to a chapter of the prose

---

* *Prolegomena* to "*Sturlunga Saga*," p. clix.

† On the metres of the *rímur*, *cp.* Wisén's "*Riddara Rímur*"; "*Brœgfraỗi*,"
by Helgi Sigurdson, &c. The oldest *rímur* date probably from about the middle
of the fourteenth century, *Olafs Ríma* in the Flatey-Book being the earliest
specimen preserved.

original, and giving an opportunity for pause to minstrel and to audience, much like a scene in a drama. Any number of ballads (*ríma*) go to the making of one cycle, and the whole work may extend to almost any length. The number of sections more commonly found is some five-and-twenty, and the average length about seven thousand lines. The long winter nights were passed in listening to the story unravelled in the successive ballads, the wandering *rímur*-chanter meanwhile being the welcome guest of the household, more especially of the women-folk, whose praise was sure to find some place in many a prelude of the *rímur*.

The diction of these romances exhibits the influence of Mediæval Court Poetry at its worst. Conventional periphrases, too often beyond the comprehension of the simple hearers, and therefore perhaps all the more welcome, constitute the chief apparelling of the verse. Yet despite these "shreds and patches," the *rímur* are of interest to the student from many standpoints. The very shreds and patches recall regal splendour long gone by. Even the most modern of *rímur* link themselves, by their phraseology, to the elaborate mythology of Northern paganism; by their mastery of alliterative effect, to the characteristic system of Teutonic versification; by many of their quaint devices, to the oldest extant remains of Northern poetry. The *rímur*-writers of the nineteenth century play with runes much in the same way as the eighth century Anglo-Saxon poet, Cynewulf: by runic signatures, acrostic-wise, they attest their authorship; by means of the same archaic symbols they tell us many autobiographical facts—the name of their patrons, their homesteads, and important dates in their life-history.

This personal note is often the main, if not the only charm of these special versified Sagas; it is to be heard for the most part in that portion of the ballads which gives the poet the chance of indulging his fancy, to wit, in the lyrical prologue at the beginning of each *ríma*.* To judge from its name, *man-söngr*, this prelude was originally a love-song, addressed to the poet's lady-love; but although, according to the practice of the *rímur*-poets, the *mansöngr* often deals with the writer's love troubles, its scope is by no means limited thereto. The theme may be as varied as the poet's own life, or the troubles which beset the poetic career, or the vicissitudes of life in general. The prevailing tone is elegiac. The poet is young and crossed in love; or, ageing, harks back to the distant days when he knew himself the cynosure of maidens' eyes. "The Ageing Poet" might be the title of many of the preludes. Again, the poet of the *mansöngr* often replies to the "aspersions" of carping critics, to his own foes, or to those who hate all poets; he gives utterance to a long-drawn wail on the low estate of poetry contrasted with its former glory. The "Tears of the Muses" might be a fitting title for a collection of these preludes. "Poetic Art" might summarise another division, where the writer tells the difficulties of his task, dwells upon the failure of poetic aspiration, and describes the toilsome ordeal of becoming a poet; he invokes to his aid all the benign powers of Eddaic song-craft. The "Biographical *Mansöngr*" gives a summary of the poet's life-song; epitomises his literary achievements; links itself more particularly to the circumstances of the special work in hand; or deals with some fateful event in the poet's career— some weird episode calculated to call forth new interest in the personality of the writer.

There can be little doubt that these "autobiographical

---

* *Cp.* Dr. Kölbing's *Beiträge zur Vergleichenden Geschichte der Romantischen Poesie u. Prosa des Mittelalters;* Möbius, Vom *isländischen Mansöngr,*" *Ztschr. für d. phil. Ergänzungsbd.,* p. 42 ff., &c.

notes" must too often be regarded as mere conventions—the necessary items in a properly composed *rímur*; yet occasionally, though rarely, we have evidence to show that some of the most remarkable personal allusions, though seemingly conventional adjuncts, were based on actual fact, or well-authenticated family history.*

These general considerations of the characteristic features of *rímur* will prepare the reader for the statement that the *Ambales Saga* went through the process of being be-rhymed; indeed, it has already been said that Arni Magnusson obtained a MS. of *Ambales Rímur* about the same time as the *Ambales Saga*. The MS. (A.M. 521e) came from that Jon Thorlaksson who had attempted to palm off on the suspecting Arni the pseudo-Hamlet Saga. This copy of *Ambales Rímur* is written in a hand of the seventeenth century; the general appearance of the manuscript is against the chance of its being the author's autograph, though the handwriting seems to be that of Páll Bjarnarson of Unnarholt, in South-West of Iceland, who is said to have "composed" *Ambales Rímur*.† Unfortunately the MS. is defective at the end; the missing half-*ríma* may have contained some reference to the authorship of the work. The seven thousand and nine lines of the *rímur* give us no definite clue, though the *mansöngr* of the twenty-first *ríma* tells the following remarkable story :—

---

* The student of Anglo-Saxon literature, brought face to face with this aspect of the *mansöngr*, will perhaps be inclined to apply the observation to the problem of Cynewulf. Do the autobiographical notes in the Cynewulfian epic bear the same relation to the rest of the poem as the *mansöngr* to the rest of the *ríma*? and if so, may not these passages be similar Anglo-Saxon conventions? Perhaps their value as authentic contributions towards the poet's life-history has been altogether overrated. Anyhow, it is perhaps worth while calling attention to this point, suggested by a study of the *rímur*-poetry.

† *Cp.* Summary of MSS. c. 18, and Appendix II.; Páll lived from *c.* 1600–*c.* 1670. A short riddle by Páll is printed in Arnason, *Islenzkar Gátur*, Copenhagen, 1887, No. 1194 (*q. v.*).

f

INTRODUCTION

"Oft by change of metre have I tried myself: uncunning this metre shall be called. Not mine the power to rival mighty scalds. Yea, too long is the Saga to tell it all in song. . . . *I never saw the story set in my mother-tongue.* 'Tis true that this same Saga I oft was wont to see; *in German speech I owned it once in days gone by.* Though the strength of my memory fail to smithy the goodly tale, yet I have done my best to translate from it aright. Those who are cunning in theft often play folks tricks: into their bag my Saga has fallen: hence I know it not."*

This passage, interpreted literally, must mean that the author used a German original for his *rímur*, and that the *Ambales Saga* was evolved from the *rímur*, and not *vice versâ*. This seems hardly likely, and we have probably to deal here with one of those conventional half-truths often found in the *mansöngr*; unless, indeed, we are indebted to this same author for *Saga* as well as *Rímur*, both based on the Low German version of Saxo's Danish History.

In the Library of the Icelandic Literary Society at Copenhagen there is an entirely different be-rhyming of the *Ambales*

* "Oft við skifti á breyttum brag
búinn er eg mig þreyta
óvandað skal ljóða lag
láta þetta heita

Mig því bresta mærðar faung
að mæta skáldum góðum
þessi er sagan þrauta laung
að þylja hana alla í ljóðum

.   .   .   .   .

Sögunnar ekki sá eg letur
sett í móður málið

Að sönnu tjeðan sagna þátt
sa eg titt að vana
í þýsku máli eg hef átt
áður fordum hana."

A.M. 521e, xxi.

Saga. Throughout the *rímur* the hero's name is always "Ambales," never "Amloðe"; the possible identification is not even referred to. This noteworthy characteristic seems to point to an underlying recension of the *Ambales Saga* older than any we now possess, and confirms one's doubt as to the truthfulness of the statement made by the author of the previous *rímur.* The MS. is imperfect at the beginning, but the end is intact, and has preserved in mystic runes the name of the poet as well as his patron's :—

"Now five-and-twenty ships of Tyr
Are stilled on the sea of Song—
The words of my verse grow sluggish and dim,
And dwindle away, and fail.

Two R's, and add the same of L's	R R L L	
Annual, Hail, and Man,	A H M	= HALLGRÍMUR
Greedy-of-wounds, VVet, and Ice,	G U I	
Have made this Rimur sad.		

Heart-good, generous, and kind,
May his glory never cease !
Rich in fame, of noble race,
The best-beloved of God :

Tears of Hlyrnir two, + D ;	U U D	
(= the sky = úr, *i.e.* rain = u)		
Tamed horse to Ride ;	R	= SIGURÐUR
(*i.e.* reið = riding = r)		
Thunder's Roaring, Ice, + G ;	R I G	
(duna = rushing thunder = Reiðar = r)		
The daughter of Mundil-föri		
(*i.e.* Sól = the sun = the S-rune ; Mundil-föri, the father of the sun and moon.)	S	

lxxxi

INTRODUCTION

Now is come into one verse
The name of my goodly friend :
Lo, now, ye can read the name,
If any here will try.*

Hallgrim Haldorsson, the author of the *rímur*, died in 1769.
He was then an old man. His home was at Steinn, in Reykja-
strönd, in the north of Iceland.† The history of the family is
known; but internal evidence would place the *Ambales Rímur*
after 1700, for the poet alludes to the Saga of "*Balant*":—

"Of Balant's life and deeds
No more here is told ;
More of Balant's life
Doth Balant's Tale unfold."

---

* Tyrs hef eg sneckiur tuttugu og fim
tamið á sónar vyder,
mærðar ordiñ daufleg dim,
· dvyna lox um syder.

Reiden tven og eins mórg L,	r r l l	
Ar Hagall og Madur,	a H m	= Hallgrimur
adgiörð særa úde svell,	g u í	
ort hefur mærð ey gladur.		

xxv. 106.

13 Taaren Hlyrners tvö sem D	u u d	
Tamen joor að giera	r	= Sigurður
Duna svell og dreyst að G	r i g	
Dootter Mundil Fera.	S	

14 Nú es komid niótar brands,
nafn í vysu Eina,
þar má Ráða heitï hans,
hvör sem vilde Reina.

xxv. 13.

Cp. "Her mæg findan fore þances gleaw
Se ðe hine lysteð leoðgiddunga
Hwa þas fitte fegde."
        —*Fata Apostolorum ; Cynewulf's Crist, ed.*
        Gollancz (vide pp. 173–184).

† Some verses of his are to be found in a rare volume printed at Hólar, 1756,
"*Agiætar Fornmannasögur*," a copy of which is in the British Museum.

INTRODUCTION

No prose "Saga of Balant" is known, and the reference must be to the very popular *rímur* on the subject of Balant or Feracut by the cripple poet Gudmundr Bergthorsson, finished in the year 1701.*

Another poet, a contemporary of Hallgrim, belonging to the West Midland district of Iceland, Thorvaldur Sigmundarson,† turned the *Ambales Saga* into rhyming verse. A fragmentary copy of his *rímur* is in the Public Library of Iceland. The *mansöngr* of the second *ríma* is among the best of its kind. It is to be regretted that so far a perfect MS. has not been discoverable.‡

The *rímur* of Thorvaldur Sigmundarson could not have enjoyed any very great popularity; even local fame must have been denied to his efforts. In the next generation a poet belonging to the same district, Thorður Einarsson, a professional *rímur*-writer, turned his attention to *Ambales*, and added *Ambales Rímur* to his growing list of similar productions. His autograph manuscript has come to light while this work is passing through the press.§ The prelude gives us a full biography of the author. He belonged to the district of Eyrarsveit, where he was born in 1786. His various flittings are fully described, until at last he settled at Lagafell, and devoted all his energies to the writing of *rímur*. Some of his works are included in the volume containing the *Ambales Rímur*. Thorður seems to have been the most self-conscious of these rhymesters. Not content with the many personal references to himself inserted in the preludes, he

---

* *Cp.* Summary of MSS. E.

† *Cp.* Summary of MSS. C. 21; Appendix IV.

‡ Thorvaldur's father dwelt at Hjarðarbol, in Eyrarsveit, and was the son of Helgi Olafsson, priest at Stað, in Hrútafirth (North-West Iceland). Helgi died an old man in 1706. His son was a grown-up man in 1689. Thorvaldur was probably born *circa* 1700, and lived till 1760-1770.

§ *Cp.* Summary of MSS. 22; Appendix V.

actually composed a sort of autobiographical epilogue to his works—a self-portraiture in verse.*

While Thorður was at work on the *rímur* in his West Midland home, a North-Eastern poet had probably already issued yet another version of *Ambales* be-rhymed. The poet seems to have been famous in his district, but so far no manuscript of his *rímur* has been discovered, and we only know the fact of his authorship from a note in Einar Bjarnason's literary history, *Fræðimannatal*, the manuscript of which is at Copenhagen. It enumerates, among a list of *rímur*, "*Rímur* of Ambales," by Guðbrandur Einarsson, "with the assistance of his daughter Ingebjörg." Guðbrandur lived at Fljótsbakki and Narfastaðir, in Thingeyjarsysla. He had various suggestive nicknames—"Drauga-Brandur," or "Ghost-Brandur"; "Galdra-Brandur," or "Spell-Brandur"; sometimes he is referred to as "Guðbrandur Norðursýslu skald," "Guðbrandur, the poet of the North." He "flourished" about 1800.†

The stories at the back of "Ghost-Brandur's" nicknames have not come down to us. They were perhaps as attractive as those of another poet, concerning whose ghost-ridden life some weird traditions survive in the North-East of Iceland. Two or three of these ghost-stories find a place in Arnason's great collection of legends. An English rendering will be welcome to the folklorist. They are inserted here as illustrative of the personality of an Icelandic *rímur*-writer, more especially of yet another be-rhymer of "the Saga of Ambales":—

---

* "*Sjálfslýsing Þorðar*," at the end of Dr. Thorkelsson's MS.

† *Cp.* Summary of MSS. No. 22. Nothing more is known about this poet than is found in Einar's book. It is to be hoped a manuscript of the *rímur* will now be searched for throughout Iceland.

INTRODUCTION

I

MYVATNS-SKOTTA;*

THE GHOST "SKOTTA" OF MYVATN

(*From North-Icelandic Tradition, preserved in the MSS. of Benedict Thorðarson, priest at Brjanslæk.*)

"MYVATNS-SKOTTA" was one of the most famous ghosts in North Iceland. The men of Myvatn tell many stories of her marvellous doings: one of their stories is the following :—There dwelt a wizard at Grimstead by Myvatn : he had had a quarrel with a man who lived at Köldukin. Now on the Saturday before Easter, or Whitsuntide, a begging-girl came to Grimstead. The master of the house received her kindly, and brought her to the kitchen, where his wife was just then taking the mutton from the cauldron and placing it on the trencher. Her husband took a leg of mutton from the trencher and gave it the girl, telling her to eat it. The poor girl thanked him, and hungrily devoured the meat. When she had eaten enough to satisfy her, he offered to put her on her way to the next farm. But when they came to the river which ran between the two farms, he caught hold of her, threw her into the water, and held her feet while she was a-drowning. The girl was wearing, as was then the fashion, the high head-dress called "skautskupla," and it was pulled back over her head, while he held her under the water. When he was quite sure that she was dead, he dragged her from the water on to the bank : he then inspirited her with his magic spells, and bade her go kill a certain man he wished to wreak vengeance on. Whenever the ghost was seen abroad, her head-dress was dangling at the back of her head ; where-

---

* Ghosts in Iceland have special names : "Scotta" is a popular name for a female ghost. It is said to be derived from her head-gear ; as she roams about it streams behind her like a fox's tail (*skott*—a fox's tail). *Cp.* Cleasby, *sub voce.*

fore men called her "Skotta." She went on her errand, and did as she was bidden. She then came again to the Master, and told him that she had killed his man, and asked what she was to do next. He told her to go and harass the family of the murdered man. She did so; many an injury she caused them, abiding near Myvatn for the purpose: the kinsmen of the murdered man lived there. It was said that she was the author of all the troubles that befell Illugi Helgason, who composed *Ambales Rímur*. At times he could not compose so much as a verse for hours together, owing to her visitation. He lost wife after wife—they died quite suddenly; his intellect became impaired, and he lost all spirit during the last years of his life: all this was put down to "Skotta." In the Proem at the beginning of the *Ambales Rímur*, the poet refers to his troubles; one of the verses is as follows:—

> "'Neath baleful stars my life is worn;
> 'Neath luckless planet was I born;
> No fate can change my plight forlorn."

The ghost journeyed hither and thither, and it is told that she became the wraith of many a dweller at Myvatn, and many a man blest with second sight saw her apparition before an expected guest arrived from Myvatn. To some she appeared in dreams. It is told how one night an old woman, a nurse, was sitting up in her bed; the child she nursed would not stop crying; the nurse thought there was something uncanny in its cries, and it seemed to her that the child saw something eerie. So she looked about, and lo, she actually saw Skotta sitting there on an empty bed at the other end of the room; there she was swaying her body backwards and forwards, and making wry faces at the child; the old woman could see it quite clearly, for the moon shone brightly into the room. Without waiting a moment she laid the child down on the bed, and seized what was nearest at hand to frighten away the ghost. When Skotta saw this, she hurried off, but the nurse flung the pitcher after her, full as it was, and she heard Skotta a-muttering: "Too bad: this is too bad." *

* Another version is given by Arnason in a footnote at the end of the story. *Op.* Appendix XI.

INTRODUCTION

II

THE ILLUGI GHOST: "ILLUGA-SKOTTA"

(From a MS. in the possession of Gisli Konradson.)

IN the North of Iceland at Arnarvatn, near Myvatn, dwelt Farmer Illugi; he was reputed a great clerk. At Gautlönd dwelt Farmer Magnus Hallson; he was a poet, and withal had the reputation of being a master of nigromansy. Now he was wont to lampoon Illugi, and Illugi vowed vengeance. One day he came to Gautlönd, while Magnus was in the fields with his sheep. The women-folk were in the parlour seated at their spinning-wheels. The room was so arranged that the benches were lengthways. Illugi came into the room, and chatted with the women for a while, standing all the time close by Magnus's bed. In the evening Magnus came home, and soon went to his bed; he asked them if any one had called during the day. The women said no one had called: they had forgotten Illugi's visit. Somehow their answer did not altogether convince him, and he asked them again. Then one of the girls answered that Illugi of Arnarvatn had been there. He had suspected it, said Magnus, and caught up his dog and threw it on the bed: forthwith the dog expired, and Magnus escaped without hurt. As Magnus was going to bed that night, he saw before him something in the shape of a woman, wearing a high head-dress. He was terrified, and feared that Illugi had with evil intent sent the ghost thither to kill him. He determined to inspirit the ghost, and send it back again to Illugi. Its potency was thus redoubled, and Illugi had a mighty task to grapple with, yet it is told that he broke both its arms (so vigorous was the ghost that it was actually corporeal). Long thereafter the ghost proved to be the wraith of Magnus and his family, and was called "Illugi's Skotta." Ari, the wizard, the son of Priest John the Fidgetty, inspirited the ghost yet a third time, and

sent it to Illugi Helgason, the poet, the grandson of Illugi of Arnarvatn. Skotta cruelly afflicted him and many other folks; he is said to
have protected himself from her power mainly by his verse. It is told
that thus it came about that Ari sent Skotta to Illugi. Once on a
time Illugi came to Ari's farm; there was ill-will between them. Ari
was sitting in the kitchen; Illugi knew it; he stood outside at the
window, and sung a lampoon on Ari. Nothing else befell on that
occasion, but later on Ari sent Skotta to Illugi, and she so worried him
night by night that he could get no sleep, or but very little. This
Illugi lived at South Neslönd, near Myvatn; he had married Ingebjörg.
With them dwelt Ingebjörg's brother, John by name; he was much
older than she. For a long time John was able to ward off the ghost
from Illugi, until at last he became enfeebled by old age. It is told
that he resisted the ghost by sheer force, he was so big and strong.
About this time, Haldor, the elder son of John of Reykjahlithe, lived
at Vogar. He often watched over Illugi at night, when the onset
of Skotta was fiercest. One night Illugi woke up in a wild state of
terror; Haldor rushed out; he thought the ghost was at the window
overlooking Illugi's bed. When Haldor came outside, he saw Skotta
wrestling with a youth who had died at Neslönd during the previous
autumn; Illugi had often reproved the youth for his pranks. Haldor
was not scared, and uttered some verses against the ghost, and bade
her be off. She at once vanished, but reappeared the same night at
Vogar. She went to the bedroom, and spoke loudly, so that folk heard
it; the words were these: "Haldor is but a gabbler." She then went
and tickled one of the girls there, and the girl sickened thereafter: she
did not grow well again, until Haldor returned. Skotta killed, too, the
best of Haldor's cows and some ewes. Once when she was the wraith
of the elder Illugi she came to Grasitha in Kelduhverfi; the folk were
a-bed at the time. A farm-servant lived there, Asmundur by name; it
was said of him that he was not altogether ignorant of witchcraft.
Skotta threw herself on his bed and muttered, "Asmundur, I'm
tired." "How so?" "From passing over mountains and hills as the
wraith of so many folk." She always appeared as the familiar spirit of
the kinsmen of Illugi of Arnarvatn.*

* *Cp.* Appendix X.

lxxxviii

INTRODUCTION

It need hardly be said that these stories of Illugi whetted one's desire to re-discover the lost *rímur:* all effort seemed unavailing, until some three years back rumour reached me that a manuscript of *rímur* had come into the possession of Dr. Jón Thorkelsson of Copenhagen. It was generously placed at my disposal. Locked in runic verse was the name of its author, Illugi or Illaugi, by way of title to the whole work :—

"RÍMUR OF AMBALES

Lock of the Sea-god
    (*i.e.* ice = I);
Two Limpid Springs
    (*i.e.* **L L**);
Odin's decked wife
    (= Earth = abundance = ÁR = **A**),
And VVet
    (úr = **U**),
And Gash
    (mein = stunginn kaun = K crossed = **G**),
Three mates of yore ;
The Sea-god's robe
    (marar reif = hles lœsing = Ice = I)
Near Mother-Earth
    (= by the woman)."

The manuscript is in a tattered condition, and defective at the end. It belongs to about the middle of the eighteenth century; but the date of composition can be referred back to the end of the previous century. Illugi was, perhaps, the first of the *Ambales* poets: at the end of the first *mansöngr* he states that he never heard that the Saga had been be-rhymed, but we have seen that these statements are not always strictly

* *Cp.* Appendix III.

true. In the seventh *mansöngr* he mentions certain prominent Icelanders whose dates help us to fix the date of the *rímur* at 1690–1700: he was then an old man. Fifteen years, he tells us, had passed since he had last written verse. The Skotta's spell was answerable for the long delay. The passage quoted in Arnason's tale is not found in the manuscript: the *ríma* which must have contained it is deficient at the beginning, and the *mansöngr* is lost.

I have so far illustrated, indirectly, many of the general characteristics of these *Ambales Rímur*. No less than six different poets attempted the task of be-rhyming the Saga. I know no similar case in Icelandic literature. In spite of the crudeness of the Saga, the eternal interest in the Hamlet-story impressed these poets. Parallel passages from the five extant versions will be found in the Appendices at the end of the volume. It remains but to render intelligible some specimens of the preludes—no easy task, and probably now attempted for the first time in English speech:—

I

1. Lo, Utterance through the Hall of Speech
   wrathful hath wandered abroad;
   to the Valley of Hearing I drove it forth
   hence from me far away.

2. In days of yore the cunning was mine
   to move the quern of Song;
   with poetic device and Eddaic skill
   I fain enriched each rime.

3. From all these joys now turneth my mind;
   few words shall tell my grief:
   nor brave of heart, nor bold am I,
   to grapple with rhythmic art.

INTRODUCTION

4. Small chance of gladness is granted me now;
   I grovel in sorrow's seat;
   life's misery, so hard and long,
   checks merriment and cheer.

5. My body's poor hovel is battered and bare;
   all joy hath passed therefrom;
   yet more battered and bare is the heart within;
   sore bale hath wounded its life.

6. He who himself hath tried such trials,
   sure this he knows, and more;
   no longer will I tell in words
   the anguish of the soul.

7. Though wayward Thought had home returned
   to mould the form of verse;
   like the bird that flies against the storm,
   so seemeth its home-return.

8. Lo, the bird in its longing eagerness
   forward urgeth its way;
   the fell winds drive it far from its course,
   and needs must it tarry and rest.

9. Long hath the longing dwelt in my mind,
   when my evil lot was eased,
   to tell this Saga in *rímur* aright,
   that folk might know it in song.

10. Whether good or ill be in story told,
    all men may learn therefrom;
    all men may gather good from ill,
    and strengthen good with good.

11. My prelude I protract too long;
    no longer will I tarry :
    I pour from bowl the bidding cup—
    a loving-cup for all ! *

II

1 I let my vessel, Dwalin's hawk, in fiery wind,
  sail forth from Saga-land.

2. My crew-mates fain would choose the fair breeze of the south :
   a-land I know it well.

3. Lo, much is wanting; Odin's ragged ferry fails;
   it cannot now be rowed.

4. The gear is loos'd; the bands fall broken from the planks;
   the ship of Song scarce floats.

5. A sorer need constrains me; yea, more pressing toil
   than smithying Odin's boat.

6. Frost, snow-drifts, breaking up of floes, and moving storms,
   hinder my vessel's course.†

III

1. Once more the claw of the eagle of Vindulf
   will I urge onward on Bothn's wide sea,
   whatsoe'er, whether weal or woe, may betide me;
   lo, the wood of my vessel is small.

2. Not mine is the skill for the modes of the *rímur* :
   unto me Hjarandi did ne'er pledge a draught,
   when Gunnloth, the beauteous, gave him to drink
   of the mead from the goodly cup.

* *Cp.* Appendix II., p. 202.
† *Cp.* Appendix III., p. 223.

INTRODUCTION

3. O, the mighty poets of ancient day !
   full well they honoured great Odin's mood,
   when the richest draughts of Bothn he pour'd
   for his guests, and least for himself.

4. In this company here there are scoffers enow ;
   they laugh me to scorn ; their praise is their laughter ;
   wiseacres, indeed, I know them of yore ;
   nor dare I upbraid them withal.

5. Another sort know I, and sure they are here ;
   for one short hour they listen perchance,
   nought do they the while but find fault with the song,
   as it pours from the voice's depth.

6. A third sort follows the story alone ;
   content are they if the drift be but clear ;
   they care not at all for poetic phrase,
   howe'er badly the verse be composed.

7. A fourth sort is here, I trow full well :
   how curious are they of my craft !
   how ardent their praise of Eddaic hopes !
   they give not a thought to the tale.

8. A fifth sort have I seen ere now :
   'tis their joy to join the coward crew,
   who freely blame all poetic work,
   all who tend Poetry's lamp.

9. A sixth sort understand not a word
   of Eddaic trope in the land of speech ;
   where never a kenning or trope is found,
   the poem wins all their praise.

INTRODUCTION

10. A seventh sort have I oft beheld;
    their looks are fierce and grim to see,
    if a keen mind turn to the joys of verse
    to solace a lonely hour.

11. All too soon their minds are resolved
    that he sings to them more than enough,
    if they hear in his verse but a word or a phrase,
    they cannot discern at once.

12. How difficult in this world of woe
    is mankind's life in every place :
    some make us dance the dance of grief,
    who feign to be our friends.*

IV

1. Odin's ship may now
   creep from the land of speech,
   to the snowdrifts of Odin's waves,
   blown by Besla's winds.

2. Am I to set afloat
   my bark on Odin's lake,
   I needs must call to aid
   Modsognir's dwarfish brood.

3. North and South, draw forth
   the poor beginner's craft
   from the silent shed
   on the Sibyl's heath !

4. Get ready the rollers, East !
   Leeward, look to the quay !
   push her, Draupnir, onward !
   Dvalin, bind the mast !

* *Cp.* Appendix IV., p. 227.

INTRODUCTION

5. Ho, Yell and Yelp, blow fair !
   with strong gusts fill the sails !
   Enchanter, dip the oars !
   bale out, bright Gloi, yare !

   .   .   .   .   .   .

7. North and the Dwarfish Brood
   my bidding pay no heed ;
   silent are they, and I
   on other aid must call.

8. Bragi, help me sing !
   help me from thy store !
   the blood of Kvasir slain
   steep my lips in song.

9. Elves, stand ye stark blind,
   strengthen ye my lays !
   ye Gods and Goddesses,
   vouchsafe to grant me help !

10. Odin's thralls are still :
    their silence ill meseems :
    my ferry on Odin's sea
    I needs must drive alone.

11. But this boon, Norns, I pray—
    a happy metre send :
    the matter of my rhymes,
    stands ready to my hand.

12. All that thought can wish,
    on sea and land alike,
    make strong this day for me,—
    a true day for my verse.

INTRODUCTION

13. It helps not before men
    the Muses' lot to wail;
    to kindly women-folk
    I give the meed of praise.

14. The Saga in this hall
    sits down in guise of Song.
    May bale my hearers spare,
    all moody grief of soul!

15. Scalds bring here from far
    each draught of Bothn's mead;
    this Saga, as I trow,
    was ne'er berhymed before.

16. Though sorrow's path I tread
    through windy halls of earth,
    yet all my mind now thirsts
    to tell this tale in song.

17. Aright the Saga proves,
    when Sorrow dwells with folk,
    the mighty cord of grief
    is all uncoiled at last.

18. Yet friends I shall ne'er lack,
    whatever ill befall;
    and so my prelude ends;
    O ye fair ladies, list!

19. The Saga now is here!
    Bow down, O listening house!
    O noble dame, bejewell'd,
    my story thus begins!*

* *Cp.* Appendix III., p. 211.

VI

THE last illustrative extract in the Appendices at the end
of the volume is from Matthias Jochumsson's Icelandic
version of Shakespeare's play. Twenty years ago the translator,
an Icelandic parson for some time resident in England, intro-
duced his countrymen to the master-work in Hamlet-literature.
Though the more cultivated Icelanders may perhaps appreciate
the thought and philosophy of the play, it is questionable
whether the folk, unacquainted with the technique of the
drama, regard Jochumsson's work as anything but an academic
exercise. They probably prefer their more homely *Ambales
Saga* and *Ambales Rímur*. The excellent translation is, indeed,
a right welcome addition to the mass of Hamlet-literature represented in this book. Though the Senecan machinery of the
play may be foreign to theatreless Iceland, at least the framework of Shakespeare's *Hamlet* is to be found, however much
distorted, in the *Ambales Saga* and its various Icelandic
analogues and derivative versions, all of them, directly or indirectly, indebted to Saxo's story of Amlethus—a story well
known to Icelanders long before it reached England through
the medium of Belleforest's *Histoires Tragiques*. This is not
the place to discuss at any length the source of the English
play, or its relationship to Saxo's story; but I may be permitted
to quote in conclusion what I have said elsewhere on this
subject: In the story as in the play we have the murder of the
father by a jealous uncle; the mother's incestuous marriage

INTRODUCTION

with the murderer; the son's feigned madness in order to execute revenge: there are the vague originals of Ophelia and Polonius; the meeting of mother and son; the voyage to England: all these familiar elements are found in the old tale. But the ghost, the play-scene, and the culmination of the play in the death of the hero as well as of the objects of his revenge, these are elements which belong essentially to the Elizabethan Drama of vengeance. It is of course unnecessary to dwell on the subtler distinction between the easily understood Amleth and "the eternal problem" of Hamlet. Taine has said that the Elizabethan Renaissance was a Renaissance of the Saxon genius; from this point of view it is significant that its crowning glory should be the presentment of a typical Northern hero,— an embodiment of the Northern character:

"𝔡𝔞𝔯𝔨 𝔞𝔫𝔡 𝔱𝔯𝔲𝔢 𝔞𝔫𝔡 𝔱𝔢𝔫𝔡𝔢𝔯 𝔦𝔰 𝔱𝔥𝔢 𝔑𝔬𝔯𝔱𝔥."

Hamlet the Fool;

The Icelandic Saga of Ambales or "Amlothi Heimski."

1 Capituli.

ONREK hét Kóngur er rédi fyrer Spanja, Hispanja, Cimbrja, Cúmbrja, og mòrgum òdrum Eýum og þjódlòndum; hann var Stóraudugur af Gódsi, megtugur ad
5 Fólki og mòrgum voldugum undirsátum, honum þéntu margir Eidkóngar hertogar og Jarlar sem honum adstod veittu med stórri framqvæmd Lòndiñ ad verja og audæfum safna, var hann og sjálfur hinn mesti kappi, forsjáll, stór óvinum sínum, enn ljúfur
10 og lítilátur vinum og vitur í rádum því honum var stór vitska lánud. Selína hét Drottníng hañs, bædi vóru þaug mjòg gòmul er Saga þessi gjòrdist. Syni átti konúngur þrjá, vid Drottníngu sinni, enn hún var dóttir Hauks kóngs af Hólmsetulandi, og eptir honum hét hinn
15 fyrsti son kóngs, annar hét Bálant eptir Fòdur sínum, þridje hét Salman eptir fóstra Donreks kóngs. Allir vóru þeir brædur bardaga menn miklir, og vóru fullvaxta er kom ad Sògunni.

Enn er Donrek kóngur deidi, skiptust Lònd í Erfdir,
20 og hlotnadist Hauki Spanja; Bálant Hispanja; Salman vard kóngur í Cimbrja; Bálant stírdi Hispanja til dauda og var hinn mesti kappi, eñ Haukur konungr bjó skamma stund ad Fòdurleifd sinni, því eirn heidin kóngur drap hann og tók þad Ríki eptir hã, sá hét
25 Málpríant ættadur úr Schytja, á hvòrn Saga þessi, miñist Sídar. Salman var kóngur i Cimbrja, þetta land liggur á austari Vallands Sýdu og lá undir Róm á þeim tíma; þar gjòrdist Salman bardaga madur brádlindur,

2

Chapter I.

 HERE lived a king hight Donrek, and he was King of Spain, and Hispania, and Cimbria, and Cumbria, and divers other islands and realms: he was passing rich and mighty, what with his folk and a many brave retainers: many a vassal-king and dukes and earls owed him their service and helped him nobly in his land's defence and in achieving treasure. As for him, he was the hardiest fighter, farseeing, fierce to foes, yet kind and gentle unto friends, and wise of counsel,—great wisdom was lent him. His queen hight Selina; they both were very aged when this saga befel. The king gat three sons by his queen; she was daughter of Hawk, King of Holstein, after whom the king's first son was named; the second hight Balant, after the king's father; the third Salman, after King Donrek's foster-father. The brothers were all great warriors, and they were grown up when this saga befel.

Now when King Donrek died, the lands were parted into inheritances, and Spain fell to Hawk, Hispania to Balant, while Salman became King of Cimbria. Balant ruled Hispania till his death. and he was a hardy fighter. King Hawk held his heritage but a short while, for a heathen king slew him and usurped his realm; he hight Malpriant, by birth of Scythia; the saga will tell of him anon. Salman was King of Cimbria, the which lieth to the east of Valland, and was under Rome at the time; and he there became a fierce-tempered warrior,

3

óvinnannlegur í Sinni og Orustu, enn þó blídur vinum

30 sínum hafdi góda Stjórnun so allir unnu honum hugástum frá þeim mesta til hins miñsta, hafdi hann jafnan Sigur í orustum; hann fiekk eirnrar ágjætrar Drottníngar sem Amba hét, hún var Dóttir Greifa þess er stírdi Burgundíen í Frakklandi. Salman kóngur unni Drottníngu sinni

35 mikid, so hann mátti ei hennar mein vita, og eingum leid hañ henni móti ad gjòra; mjòg vóru heidurlegar samfarir þeirra hjóna hún var spòk í gédi og hlídiñ sínum herra, þar med svo skinsòm ad hún þókti stórvitur, allir létu af henni mikid og hennar rádum og unnu henni hugástum,

40 bætti hún í mòrgu rád kóngs. Ei hafdi kóngur leingi verid ásamt henni, ádur enn Drottníng fæddi eitt Sveinbarn frídt og gòfugt, var þad borid firer kóng uppá þad hann skildi þess nafni ráda, eñ kóngur lét barnid vatni ausa med Skírn kristinna maña, og ódladist Sveinniñ

45 nafnid Sigurdur, því kónguriñ hafdi kristinna manna Trú eptir Pávans reglu haldi, og þaug lònd sem um var gétid utan Spán, hvòrja Málpríant kóngur frá kristni kúgadi, sem ádur er sagt.

2 Capítuli.

$\mathfrak{N}$ú lída so stundir til þess Drottníng vard þúngud í annad sinn, enn þar í Landi kóngs var ein Valva eda vísinda kona, kominn af miklum ættum, og sjálf var hún mañleg í sínu háttalagi ; enn so var hún grim í Skapi

5 ad òllum stód ótti af henni, hér med var hún fjòlkunnug og

4

alike indomitable of will as invincible in warfare, yet therewithal gentle unto friends; his was a righteous rule, and he was beloved of all, the greatest and the least; in battle he never failed of victory. He took to wife a noble dame, Amba by name, daughter of the Duke of Burgundy in France. King Salman greatly loved his queen, and suffered her to take no hurt, nor brooked he aught a man might do in her despite: their wedded life was of honourable accord; she was of gentle mood and yielding to her lord, and therewithal of so discerning mind that men deemed her passing wise; all marvelled at her and at her wisdom, and they loved her from their hearts; ofttime she saved the king from error. They had not been together long when the queen bore a man-child, fair and noble, and the child was brought afore the king that he might give it a name; the king let besprinkle it with water in Christian baptism,—for the king kept the faith of Christian men after the papal rite,—and the boy was given the name of Sigurd, and therewith the lands aforenamed, save Spain, the which King Malpriant cowed from Christianity as has been told.

Chapter II.

Now time passed and the queen was with child a second time. But there in the land of the king was a spae-wife or wise woman, come of high descent; she was not of elfin-kind, but so grim withal that folk were adread of her, and she was eke a great clerk of necromancy

5

forn ad mörgu, hún var ættud austañ úr Gardaríki, og hafdi
vída farid um̄ nordurlönd, og í stórum vyrdíngum haldiñ
verid af kóngum og mikilsháttar höfdíngjum, því hún var
jafnañ sókt þá kónga Drottníngar og frægra manna Frúr
10 skildu börn ala, uppá þad hún mælti fyrir um Barnaña
lán og lukku, hvad]optast þókti mikid eptir gánga; vard
hún af þessu stóraudug og mjög ríkilát. Enn er Amba
Drottníng ól sinn Son er firr var gétid, var ei Valvañ
tilqvödd yfir Drottníngu ad sitja, sem þá var plagsidur, af
15 hvörju Nornin fékk reidi mikla í sitt brjóst, og þessa
sína fólsku magnadi hún med Fjölkíngi. Enn er leid ad
Sængurlegu Drottníngar, gjördi Valvañ sér ferd til borgar
konúngs, og sá svo til hún hitti Drottníngu í hennar
Listigardi, þá mælti Valvañ til hennar: Lukka þín og
20 listileg æfi stendur nú í besta blóma; enn þú skalt þar
ad higgja, ad ádur lángt lídur skalt þú missa alt þetta
utan lífid eitt; kóngur þiñ mun í Strídi drepin verda,
því honum skulu eingiñ vopn bíta meiga nær hann berst
vid óvini sína, so skal og líka þinn Son fá Svívyrdilegan
25 dauda, og so mun ad þér þreyngt verda, ad þér mun
daudin lífinu æskilegri þikja, enn sá þinn Sonur sem þú
medgeingur mun þér ad lítillri gledi verda, því hann skal
öllum fífl sínast; hef eg optlega mætt Sæmdum hiá ædri
höfdíngjum enn þid erud, og hafa mig aldrei forsmád
30 enir ædstu menn og höfdíngjar auk heldur mínir líkar,
enn þid mikid; enn ykkar metnadur mun lægdur verda.
Vid þessa Forspá Völvunnar hriggdist Drottníng mjög,
gékk firir kóng og sagdi honum frá öllu þessu. Kóngur
6

and of ancient lore ; she was sprung from the eastern realm of Gardar, and had fared through northern lands, and was held in worship of kings and noble chiefs, for she was sought whenas queens and the wives of famous men were a-nigh child-bearing, that she might bespeak the children's fate and fortune, the which men deemed followed her spells mostwhiles at least; wherethrough she grew mightily rich and very masterful. Now when Queen Amba bore the aforenamed son, the witch was not besought to sit by her as was the wont; whereat the witch waxed very wroth, and she enfierced her wrath by magic spells. And when the time was nigh the queen should be abed, wended the witch to the palace of the king, onward till she met the queen within her pleasaunce, when she greeted her thus :—" Thy fortune and thy life's delight stand now in fairest bloom, but lay this to heart that ere long thou shalt lose all save life alone. Thy king shall be slain in war; of his weapons none shall strike home when he fights against his foes; thy son too shall meet a death of shame, and so hard shall it go with thee that death shall seem thee dearer than life; and that son of thine thou goest with shall be of little joy to thee, for all men shall hold him witless. Ofttimes have I met with honour from princes higher than ye be, and the greatest of men and chieftains have ne'er slighted me in anywise, much less my peers, but ye two have done so exceedingly,—but your pride shall be brought low." At this foreboding of the witch the queen was sorely troubled, and she went afore the king, and told him of all that had passed. The king

7

Ch. II. gjördist miög grimmur í Skapi, kalladi á meñ sína, og
35 baud þeim ad taka Völvuna til fánga, og láta hana deýa
einum skañarlegum dauda, enn Drottníng mælti : Ei er
ból vort bætt ad heldur, og sjái ei valvann rád vid raunum
vorum, þá mun þad ei ódrum takast, sérdeilis ef henni er
nokkur vinskapur gjördur. Kóngur mælti : þeinkir þú
40 af þeim ílla anda muni oss vinskapur veittur so okkar
Sonum gagn ad verdi ? Drottning mælti : til mun eg
freista, og skulum vid Völvunni veitslu gjöra med stóru
yfirlæti og stórum fiegjófum, vil eg nú kóngur ad þú
filgist med mér til hennar þess erindis. Kóngur svaradi :
45 ad sá hinn versti andi skildi til heñar í siñ stad gánga.
Gékk Drottníng þá frá kóngi á fund Völvuñar, enn gjördi
sig þó blída í máli þó dópur væri med sjálfri sér er hún
fañ nornina, var hún þá búin til burtferdar ; þá mælti Dr.
til hennar : Af óvitsku minni hef eg þad gjört ad leggja
50 óvyrding á þig, vil eg þad nú gjarnan bæta, býd eg þér nú
vinsemd vora med veitíngum og veitslugjördum, og öllum
Sóma er vér meigum þér veita, vil eg þú dveljest hér med
oss þar til mitt fóstur er í heimin fædt. Valvan mælti : ei
mun eg þetta þiggja, því seint verdur þér þín Slis ad bæta,
55 enn eg mun aptur koma nær þín Sængurlega hefst, og
muntu þa ei þurfa ad mér ad spyrja, skildu þær ad so
mæltu, og fór Valvan leid sína. Enn er Drottníng
kénndi sér Sóttar, kom Valvan aptur, og var þá ódruvísi
í hátt eñ ádur, uppá sitt Skapfar ; tók Drottn. blídlega
60 vid henni, eñ norniñ síndi á sér mestu mañþídu, og lagdi
Drottníngu í eina ágjæta Sæng. Drottn. hafdi lánga
8

grew very wroth, called his men to him, and bade them
seize the witch and let her die a wretched death, but the
queen spake :—" Our bale is not thus bettered, for an the
witch sees not remedy for our woes none other will avail,
and more belike, if some friendliness be shown her."
The king said : "Dost thou deem that from that evil
sprite aught of friendship will be shown us for our son's
avail?" "I will assay it," said the queen, "and let
us spread a banquet for the witch with great pomp and
largess, and I would now, king, that thou go with me to
her on this errand." The king made answer that the
worst of sprites might to her in his stead. The queen
went then from the king to seek the witch, and made her
blithe of speech, though her heart was sad within. As
she reached her the witch was journey-bound ; the queen
said to her :—" From my want of wisdom have I done
this to put dishonour on thee, and I would fain now
make amends, and I offer thee our friendship and gifts,
and feasts, and all the worship we may show thee, and
I would that thou bide with us here until my child be
born into the world." The witch said :—"This I shall
not grant, for it will be long time ere thy folly may be
mended, but I shall come again when thy child-bed begins,
and thou shalt then not need to seek me out." Thus
they spake and the witch went her way. And when the
queen knew her sickness near, came the witch again,
and she was then otherwise than she was erst, in her
temper to wit. The queen gave her a blithe welcoming, and the witch was wondrous tender with her, and
placed her on a stately bed. The queen had a long

Sótt og harda, enn fæddi þó um sídir eitt Sveinbarn, var
þad mjög stórt og óásjálegt med dökkvum Skinns-lit, og
broddhærdu hári kolsvörtu, enn þó í augunum dægilegt.
65 Drottn. lét bera Sveinin firir kóng, enn hann vard vid
þad mikid stiggur og hriggur og skipadi med hasti barnid
í burtu bera, vildi hañ einga Sæmd Sveininum veita eda
neitt nafn géfa, enn þó allra síst Völvuna augum líta, eda
neinu gódu vid hana skipta, hvad Drottn. stórū hriggdi;
70 eñ Valvañ filltist upp med grimdar reidi vid þetta, þókti
og öllum kóngi þetta ósæmilega fara. Valvan þjónadi
Drottn. med mestu kostgjæfni, og leiddi hana af Sæng
á venjulegum tíma, dvaldist hún þar sídañ í 3. mánudi,
baud Drottníng henni þar vist alt til dauda dags, edur
75 svo leingi sem hún þiggja vildi. Valvan qvad sér annad
lagid verda. Leisti Drottníng hana út med stórum
gjöfuñ, svo Völvuñi fiell hid besta; enn á þeim deigi er
valvañ vildi í burt, gékk hún iñí hús þad sem Drottníng
var í, og barnid fóstrad, hélt Drottn. á sínum únga Syni og
80 lagdi hann á brjóst, gjördist valvā þá döpur því henni var
ordid vel vid Drottníngu vildi hún qvedja hana. þá mælti
Valvañ til Drottníngar: eingum hef eg ofreid vordid nema
þér, og illa hef eg firir þér og þínum Spád, hvad ei má
bætast, valda því forlögin ein, og rædur þeim sá mönnunum
85 er máttkari, enn á þína mañgjædsku er mér skildt ad
mynnast, og skal þessi Sonur þinn þín ad nokkru njóta, hañ
mun verda Sómi allrar ættar sinnar, þú skalt hónum nafn
géfa af nafni þínu, því hañ mun þér og módur frændum
sínuñ líkjast, sídañ kysti hún Drottníngu og Sveinin

sickness and hard, and bore at length a man-child, the which was very big and unsightly, dark-skinned, and with bristle hair, black as coal, yet beautiful by reason of his eyes. The queen had the boy brought afore the king, but he became thereat most cross and heavy, and forthwith bade them take the child away; he would pay the child no heed, nor give it a name, but least would he set eyes upon the witch, or have aught friendly dealing with her; whereat the queen was sore aggrieved, and the witch was filled with grim anger; and all men deemed the king's behaving was unseemly herein. The witch nurtured the queen with greatest care, and brought her from her bed at the wonted time; she tarried there thereafter for three months, and the queen bade her live there to the day of her death, or so long as she would: the witch said something else was toward. The queen sped her with rich farewell-gifts, and the witch was well content; but the day the witch was going thence she entered the chamber where the queen abode and where the child was fostered; the queen was holding her little son in her arms, at the breast; the witch grew sad, for now she felt tenderly towards the queen; fain would she bid her farewell. Said she to the queen:—"To no one have I been angered out of all measure save to thee, and evil have I boded for thee and thine. This may not be bettered, for fate above rules, swayed by Him who is mightier than men, but 'tis meet that I should guerdon thy kindliness, and this son of thine shall profit of thy merit somewhat at least; he shall be the honour of all his race: thou shalt name him after thine own name, for he shall favour thee and his mother's kin." Then she kissed the queen and the boy,

grátandi, og mælti : mín tóm lofan mun hann lítid stidja ;
gékk sídan burtu ; eñ Drottníng sat eptir hiá Barns
vögguñi og hrærdi hana barninu til værdar ; blés Drottn.
þúngum anda af sínu rauna efni, og nefndi Sveinin
Ambales ; ólust þeir kóngs synir nú upp í Ríkinu ad
95 öllum hlutum ólíkir, Sigurdur var mikid frídur álytum
og hardgjedjadur, so hann lét sinn hluta firir aungvum
mañi, var hann ad mentum og íþróttum hinn frægasti
og framasti.   Ambales var ósélegur ad öllu og miklu
stærri bródur sínum, hañ vildi aungvuñ mañi hlída né
100 neitt gott nema, heldur var hann hinn þrjótskasti vid alla,
hann var útlima stærri ódrum mónnum, honum sáu meñ
fæsta jafna ad öllu háttalagi, var hann af hyrdinni og
jafnvel kóngi sjálfum kalladur Amlóde.   Lidu so fram
Stundir til þess Synir kóngs vóru añar 10 annar 8 vetra,
105 og á þeim árum bar ei annad til tídinda enn seigir.

3 Capituli.

ÞAD seigir í sögu þessari, ad á þeim tíma hafdi sá
kóngur rádid fyrir Skytja er Soldan hét, argur heidíngi
og mjög griñur í skapi, sá ad margar orustur hád hafdi
med Stórum Sigri, hañ átti þrjá Sonu vid Drottníngu
5 sinni, hét hinn fyrsti Tamerlaus, annar Málpríant sá er
drepid hafdi Hauk kóng og iñtekid Spán sem firr seigir.
þridje hét Fástínus, allir vóru þeir hinir griñustu víkíngar,
so hvar þeir herjudu, komst einginn heill undan þeim ;
enn eptir dauda Soldáns kóngs, vard Tamerlaus kóngur
10 í hañs Stad, var Fástínus med bródur sínum, og bar hañs
Sigurmerki í orustum, þókti flestum þeir brædur vera
12

weeping the while, and said :—"My mere promise will stand him in little stead." She then went her way, but the queen sat still beside the cradle of the child, rocking it to soothe the child; heaved the queen a deep sigh from her troubled breast and called the boy Ambales. Now the king's sons grew up in the realm each unlike the other in all things. Sigurd was passing fair to look on, and hard-tempered so that he yielded no whit to any man, and in all skill and cunning he was most famed and foremost. Ambales was all unsightly, much bigger than his brother, would hearken unto none, nor learn aught good; but was most stubborn with all men; he was larger-limbed than other folk; in all his ways he seemed to have but few his like, and the courtiers and the king called him Amlode. So time passed till the king's sons were ten and eight years old, and in these years nought befel but what is told.

Chapter III.

THE saga tells that at this time a king ruled Scythia, and his name was Soldan, a vile paynim, exceeding grim of temper; he had waged a many wars with mighty triumph; he had three sons by his queen, the first hight Tamerlaus, the second Malpriant, he who had slain King Hawk, and had won Spain as has been told, and the third Faustinus. They were all the fiercest vikings, and whereso they harried no man escaped them whole. After King Soldan's death, Tamerlaus reigned in his stead, and Faustinus stayed with him and bore his standard in the fight, and most men deemed that these two brothers were

13

óyfirvinnanlegir. Tamerlaus kóngur var brædrum sínuñ mjòg ólíkur bædi ad ásínd og Skaplindi, hann var spakur í gédsmunum, eñ þó gédstrángur; þar med rádgjætiñ og
15 hinn mesti kappi. Allir vóru þeir brædur bardaga meñ miklir þeir herjudu vída og hòfdu jafnan Sigur. Tamerlaus kóngur gjòrdi herfòr til Fenedí borgar og brædur hañs med hònum, þar gjòrdu þeir mikinn Skada bædi med manndrápum og ráni, so borgar menn sigrudust enn
20 sumir flýdu, og í herfòr þeirri nádi hañ eirnri ágjætri Jómfrú, hvòr ed þar í landi var hin dæilegasta, hún var Dóttir kóngs Artabani er þar hafdi ádur kóngur verid, og nú var andadur, enn ad henni feinginni, létti hann orustum og hjelt heim aptur í Schytja, og sem hann var
25 heim komiñ, gjòrdi hā brúdkaup sitt, og baud þángad vinum sínum og hòfdíngjum; vard þessi ágjæta Jómfrú frá sínum vilja ad gánga og hañs Drottníng ad heita; kóngur gjòrdi vel til hennar og unni henni allmikid, lét hana halda sínum Sidum og Trú alt til dauda, því hún
30 var vel kristiñ og dírkadi sannan Gud, enn kóngur dírkadi Skúrgod, fiell þeim þó allvel hvòrju vid annad; kóngur lét alt eptir henni sem hún óska vildi. Dóttur áttu þaug eina barna, hún líktist módur sinni til ályta og atgjòrfis, og verdur heñar gétid sídar í þessari Sògu.

4 Capítuli.

FÁSTÍNUS var nú í Schytja med bródur sínum og var hañs landsvarnar madur sem firr er sagt, enn er hann hafdi verid med kóngi 5 vetur, mælti hann eitt sinn vid bródur sinn Tamerlaus: Nú beidist eg af þér svo
5 margra Skipa og manna sem mér sjálfum líkar; því eg vil fara hédan burt og abla mér Ríkis, vildi eg einhvòr rýmdi fyrir mér Sæti sem máttugur væri. Tamerlaus

14

invincible. King Tamerlaus was all unlike his brothers in his looks as in his temper; he was of gentle mood, yet firm, and wary in counsel, and the greatest warrior. All these brothers were mighty fighters, and harried far and wide, and ever achieved victory. King Tamerlaus made a raid on the city of Venice, his brothers with him; they wrought great havoc there by pillage and by slaughter, so that the folk was overborne and some fled, and in that raid he took a goodly maiden, the comeliest in the land, daughter of King Arbatan, aforetime king there, but then dead, and having won her, he left off warring, and betook himself to Scythia, and when he was come unto his home, he made his wedding, and bade thereto friends and chieftains, and this fair damsel had, maugré her will, to be his queen. The king bore him well toward her, and loved her much; he let her keep her ways and faith even unto her death, for she was true Christian and worshipped the true God,—but the king was a worshipper of carven images,—and they were well accorded, and the king yielded to her in all she wished. Their one child was a daughter; she favoured her mother both in looks and graces, and she will be spoken of later in the saga.

Chapter IV.

FAUSTINUS was now in Scythia with his brother, and was the seneschal of all his land, as has been said afore; he had been with him five years, when on a time he spake thus with his brother:—"Now ask I of thee ships and men as many as I deem fit, for I would hence abroad and get me sovereignty, and make some man of might void me his seat." King Tamerlaus

kóngur mælti : Eg vil fá þér 80. Skip, velbúiñ ad Fólki
og fararkosti og óllum útbúnadi. þetta líkadi Fástínus
10 og bjóst snarlega til Ferdar, þakkandi bródur sínum
tillógurnar, og ad Skilnadi qvóddust þeir blídt. Tók nú
Fástínus ad sér Skipiñ med Fólkinu, leýstu upp atkéri
og Sigldu sídann Skipunum nordvestur í heim, seigist
ei af hañs ferdum firr enn hann tók hófn vid Spaníen,
15 gékk þar á Land med lid sitt, og lét setja Tjóld á frídri
Foldu, og sem Málpríant kóngur Spyr þessar nýlundir,
bióst hañ med hyrd sína á fund vid komumenn, og hittust
þeir brædur med miklum kjærleika, geingu svo heim
ad hóllinni til gódrar veitslu, Sagdi Fástínus þá kóngi
20 áform sitt, og bad hann á eitthvórt þad kóngs ríki
ad vísa sér sem hónum mætti vel sóma, því hañ
sagdist eigi vantreysta sínum frægduñ þad undir sig
ad leggja.

Málpríant kóngur mælti : hér allnærri liggur eitt
25 ágjætt land er Cimbría heitir, hvórt ad heldur Salman
kóngur hann á hina ágjætustu Drottníngu, þángad skaltu snúa lidi þínu, og þad mun þér til Sóma og Sigurs
verda. þá mælti Fástínus : hjá ydur þarf eg lid ad fá
og hesta til bardaga í þá herfór. Kóngur mælti : þér
30 skal til reidu er kjósa vilt, því mér er áhiggjusamt um
þá brædur ad þeir muni hefnda leita á mína hónd þar
þetta ríki er þeirra Fódurleifd. Fékk kóngur honum þá
alt er hann til kalladi bædi menn og hesta og annad
fleira, þar med gaf hann honum eirn ágjætann hest er
35 Stýrus hét, hann hafdi kosti so góda ad í Landinu var
ekki annar slíkur; hér med tvo mikla kappa Cimbal og
Carvel ad nafni, þakkadi hann kóngi rád sín og tillógur
16

replied:—"I will give thee eighty well-rigged ships, with men and gear and all appurtenance." This pleased Faustinus well, and he got him ready to depart; he thanked his brother for his help, and their farewell was joyous. Faustinus took now in command the ships and crew, weighed anchor, and sailed north-west out into the world. There is nought to be told of his journey till he took to harbour in Spain; he landed his force there and let his tents be pitched in a fair field; and when King Malpriant heard the news, he made him ready with his court to meet the comers; and the brothers met with great love, and they went home to the hall unto a goodly feast. Faustinus told then the king his quest, and bade him tell him of some realm befitting his degree, for he mistrusted not his power to conquer it.

King Malpriant replied:—"There lies quite near a goodly land, Cimbria by name; King Salman holds it; he has the goodliest queen; thither shalt thou turn thy way, and it shall bring thee worship and triumph." Then spake Faustinus:—"From thee needs must I have men and horses for battle in this war-raid." The king said: "All shall be in readiness whenever thou wouldst have it, seeing I am troubled lest the brothers should avenge them on me, for this realm is their inheritance." The king thereupon granted him all he required, both men and horses, and much beside; he gave him too a noble horse hight Styrus, so choice that in all the land there was not such another, and eke two mighty warriors, Cimbal and Carvel by name. And he thanked the king for his rede and his aid.

B

hieldt so lidi sínu med miklu dramblæti í Simbríam, hafdi
hañ 20,000 manna, lét hañ ei firri af enn hañ kom til
40 borgar Salmans kóngs er Mordia hét, hún var sterklega
biggd med miklum Turnum og glæsilegum múrum af
Gulli Silfri og gimsteinum forkostulega prídt; þar lét
Fástinus reisa Tjöld sín med harki og stóru rembilæti, og
firr enn hann gékk til vista sendi hann 12 menn til
45 Salmans kóngs med sín erindi, hét sá Metílus sem oddviti
þeirra var, og er Salman kóngur sat yfir bordum, geingu
þeir í höll hans, tók sá til máls sem firir þeim var og
sagdi: Höfdíngi þessa lands má láta af kosti sínum og
veraldar glaum, því hann mun verda þó hañ vilje ei, hér
50 er komin stórmegtugur kóngssonur af Schytía, hañ býdur
þér, kóngur! ad þú fáir mér í hendur Córónu þína og
Drottníngu ad eg honum þad hvörttveggja færi nú þegar
med mér, añars muntu innan annarar Sólar hljóta ad láta
líf þitt og þína manna, sem og eirnin land og allar eigur,
55 skal þig med Smán og hádúng á gálga heingja, enn láta
þig þó sjá ádur ófagnad mesta á medferd þinna kristinna
manna. Kóngur vard mjög reidur vid ord hañs og mælti:
Ad ödru skal þér og þessum hundi verda, enn ei hyrdi eg
minni frægd né framgaungu firir þér ad hrósa, og skal sá
60 þjófur er þig híngad sendi þetta ad fullu kaupa, og far þú
med þad frá mínum augum, añars mun eg þiñ bölvadan
kjapt med daudanum aptur binda. þá vard Methúlus
grimur mjög, greip eitt Spjót og vildi hæfa kóng, og lagdi
til hañs, enn kóngur tók Spjótid med hendiñi á lopti, og
65 Skaut því aptur til Methúlusar, kom þad firir brjóst hönum,
18

So he went with all his host in great array toward Cimbria; he had twenty thousand men; he stayed not till he reached a certain city of King Salman called Mordia; it was strongly built with huge towers and shining walls, wondrously adorned with gold and silver, and with precious stones. Faustinus let pitch his tents there with great tumult and overweening noise, and before he betook himself to food, he sent twelve men to King Salman with his message. Methulus was the name of their leader. Now as King Salman sat at the board, they went into his hall, and their leader spake as follows :— "The lord of this land must yield up his state and worldly pride and glory; needs must he do so, though he wish it not; there is come a mighty prince of Scythia; he bids thee, king, deliver up into my hands thy crown and queen, so that I take them both along to him forthwith, else shalt thou be doomed within another sun to lose thy life, and thy men's lives, and thy land too, and all thou possesseth, and thou shalt be hanged with shame and infamy upon a gallows; but first shalt thou witness to thy greatest dole the torture of thy Christian men." At these words the king was very wroth and said :— "Thou and this dog shall have another tale to tell than this,—but it would not become my fame and feats of war to vaunt them before thee,—and the thief that sent thee hither shall pay for it to the full, and go thou with this from my sight, else must I bind back thy accursed jaws in death." Then Methulus grew very fierce; he grasped a spear to strike the king, and thrust at him, but the king caught the spear aloft, and shot it back at Methulus; it struck his breast and

og í gégnum hann so hann fiell daudur nidur. Filgjarar
hañs tóku til vopna, og urdu nokkrum ad bana, lét
kóngur drepa þá alla nema eirn, hann komst undan til
síns herra, og sagdi honum erindis lokinn og lát sinna
70 manna. Og er Fástínus heirdi þetta, æpti hann grimilega
med háum hliódum, og uppfylltist med ofurstórum heiptar
hug, sem og allir hañs menn, geingu þá inní Tjöld sín til
náda og vista og sváfu af um nóttina.

5 Capituli.

OG er Salman Kóngur var nú þessara tídinda vís ordiñ,
brá hañs Skapi mjög, lét hann um nóttina lid sitt
búast til bardaga; ei hafdi hann innan borgar fleira vígra
manna eñ 7000, alt var þad valid lid. þrjá kappa hafdi
5 hañ sem lángt báru af öllum ódrum, hét eirn þeirra Hlés,
annar Victor, þridje hét Gamalíel, hann var leindar rád
kóngs, og var þeirra mestur ad vitsku, abli og frægdum, er
nú vopnabrak í höllinni um nóttina. Ekki kunni kóngur
lidi ad safna vegna ofnaums tíma og óvina nálægdar. Ad
10 morgni var Salman kóngur albúiñ med þad lid sem innan
borgar var, baud hann mönnum sínum ad vera vel
hugudum og vígmañlega ad berjast og sagdi: Ei skulum
vér hræddir vera, heldur qvídalaust mæta óvinum vorum,
og úthella blódi þeirra heidnu hunda, og þá meñ sem hér
15 vóru drepnir af þeirra lidi skulud þér á gálga heingja
gagnvart hertjöldum heidíngjanna þeim til ofraunar,
og þótt eg láti líf og land í Strídi þessu, þá skal
mig þó eingin hræddan sjá, látum góda fregn af oss
fara. Svo var gjört vid þá daudu sem kóngur baud,
20

pierced him through, that he fell dead to earth. His
fellows seized their weapons and caused the death of
some, but the king had them put to death all save one,
who got safe to his lord and told him the issue of the
errand, and his loss of men. And when Faustinus
heard it he groaned aloud fiercely, and was fulfilled with
rancour, as were his men; they went then to their tents
to rest and to refresh them, and slept the night through.

Chapter V.

Now when King Salman was ware of all this, he was
passing wroth. He bade his host garnish itself at
night. Within the city he had but 7000 men of arms;
they were all picked men. Three of his warriors were far
above the rest; one of them hight Hles, another Victor,
the third Gamaliel; he was the counsellor of the king, and
was the greatest of them in wisdom, strength, and fame.
There was now a great clattering of weapons in the hall
during night-time. The king might not muster an army,
for the time was short and the enemy was at hand. On
the morrow King Salman was ready with all the troops
which were within the city; he bade his men be spirited
and to fight like warriors, and said:—"Let us not be
afeard, but meet our foes right dauntlessly, and pour
out the blood of the heathen dogs, and hang ye on
a gallows even in sight of the heathen's tents the
men of their host that were slain here, so as to tare
them on, and though I lose life and land in the strife,
yet none shall see me cowed. Let a good report of us
go forth." So was done with the dead as the king bade.

Reid hann nú med öllu lidi sínu á Slietta völlu gégnt
herbúdū heidíngja, var þad mjög snema, Skikkadi hann
lidi sínu ad hentugleikum, og skipar þar hvörjum manni
er honum best þókti. Bar nú Hlés merki kóngs hægra,
enn Victor vinstra handar, enn Gamaliel bar höfudmerki
25 kóngs í briósti Filkíngar, enn kóngur sjálfur var laus
med því valdasta lidi ad stirkja Filkíngar huar vid þurfti.
Var nú Salman kóngur albúin til bardaga med sínu lidi.

6 Capituli.

Nú sem heidíngjar vakna í sínum herbúdum, sjá þeir
herlid kóngs og æstust af mikillri grimd ; Fástínus
æpti nú heróp mikid, og skikkadi lidi sínu til bardaga ;
var þá adgángur mikill sem hann hafdi menn sína ad
5 eggja og framgaungu ad skikka. Sjálfur stód hann í briósti
Filkíngar, en Címbal til hægri og Carvel til vinstri Sídu,
og sem han var albúiñ, gullu lúdrarnir alla vega, og
slóst sídann í harda orustu, Skutu menn first handbogum,
vard örva hríd so mikil og Svört ad ei naut Sólar á medañ,
10 so var Skotid Spíótum og létu-margir líf sitt firer þeim,
þá þessari Skothríd liñti, tóku menn Sverd og drápu nidur
á tvær hendur, var þar öllum Frid lokid á bádar Sídur.
Fástínus og hañs menn sóktu bardagan ákaflega, enn
kóngur og lid hañs vardist vel ok frækilega og stód
15 fyrir so all lítid gékk á hañs lid enn heidíngjar drápust
hrönnum. Enn er Fástínus sá ad sínum her gékk ad
óförum, brautst hann fram og vard margs mañs bani.
þetta fær ad líta Hlés hinn Sterki, og setti hestinn á
rás, enn sökum þess ad ofurebli var vid ad eiga vegna

22

He rode forth now with all his company to a certain plain over against the war-booths of the heathens. It was yet very early. He dressed his host and set each in his proper place as time would best allow. Hles bore the king's standard on the right, Victor on the left, while Gamaliel bore the king's chief standard in the van of the troops; the king kept himself free, and went with his best chivalry, so as to aid his men wherever there was need. King Salman was now ready with his army for the fight.

Chapter VI.

Now as the heathens woke in their war-booths, they saw the army of the king, and were filled with great fury: Faustinus raised a loud war-whoop, and dressed his men for battle. There was much ado, what with egging on his men and ordering their advance. He stood himself in the van of the troops, Cimbal being on the right, and Carvel on the left; and when he was arrayed, trumpets were sounded on all sides, and thereafter there was hard fighting. First they shot with hand-bows, and the storm of arrows was so thick and black that during that while the sun was darkened; then they shot with spears, and many lost their lives by them; and when the shower of darts had ceased they seized their swords and struck men down on right and left; all chance of peace was ended then on either side. Faustinus and his folk sought battle keenly; the king and his men warded themselves right well and valiantly, and stood so firmly that they were but little worsted, while the heathens were slain in heaps. Now when Faustinus saw his army in discomfiture, he darted forward and was the death of many a man. Hles the strong was ware of this, and spurred his horse, but overwhelming hosts opposed him, for the

Ch. VI. lids munar, kunni hann ei til Fástínusar ad ná, því
20 herlidid vafdist firir honum og filkti sér í kríngum hann
med ofsa miklum, enn Hlés setti endilángt Skeid gégnum
Filkíngarnar og hrakti Fólkid alla vega, fiellu firir honum
ædi margir, jafnan hafdi hann 6 í höggi hvörju, og
25 hieldust nú ei heidingjarnir vid, so allur sá Filkíngar
armur ridladist. þetta sér merkis madur Fástínusar er
Daríus hét ættadur utañaf Blálandi, keirdi hann hest
sinn á móti Hlés, og er þeir fundust, vard hardur
adgángur, áttu þeir lánga sókn og harda, so hvörugur
30 vañ annan, enn Hlés neitti alldjarflega vopna sinna,
reiddi Sverd sitt og hjó til Darjusar, kom þad í midjan
Hjálmin, og klauf Darjus ad endilaungu og Essid med,
og nam stadar í jórdu; féll nú merki Fástínusar, enn
Filkíngiñ var rofin. þetta fær ad líta Cimbal, og reid
35 þegar frañ ad Hles, og hjó til hañs med mikilli grimd,
enn Hlés bar Skjöldiñ firir sig, tók nú Sverdid Skjöldin
í Sundur um þveran mundridan, og fékk kappin Sár á
Lærid. Hlés reiddi nú aptur Sverdid sem hardast hann
kunni, kom höggid á Hjálmin þveran; so aftók bardid
40 og brinjuna á brjóstinu og höfudid af hestinum firir
framan bógana, fiell nú Cimbal med Hestinum daudum;
í því bili kom Fástínus ad sem örskot á sínum góda
hesti, og setti Sverdid á háls Hlés so aftók höfudid, og
hraut þad lángt útá völlinn, og fiell hann so vid gódan
45 ordstír, vóru þad 300 manna sem hañ hafdi drepid;
Cimbal tók hest hañs og reid í bardagan. Sem Victor
sá nú bródur sinn fallin, blés hann af mikilli reidi, og
24

numbers were unequal, and so he might not reach Faustinus, the army trammelling his way and arraying itself around him most furiously. But Hles went at headlong gallop through the lines of battle, and scattered folk on every side, and many fell before him. He slew six at every stroke, and the heathens could not now maintain their stand, and the whole of this wing of the army was broken up. This was seen by one of Faustinus's men, hight Darius, sprung from Blue-land ; he spurred his horse at Hles, and when they met there was a mighty tussle. They had a long fight and hard, and neither overcame the other, but Hles made bold use of his weapon ; he raised his sword and struck at Darius, and the blow struck the helm right in the middle, and cleft Darius downward from the head, even through his horse, till the sword stuck in the earth ; the standard of Faustinus now fell, and the battle-line was riven. Cimbal espied this, and rode forthwith 'gainst Hles, and struck at him in great wrath; Hles warded himself with his shield, but the sword cut the shield atwain athwart the handle, and the knight was wounded in the thigh. Hles then raised his sword again as swiftly as he might, and the blow struck Cimbal's helm athwart, so that the helm was cut through, and the burnie at the breast, and the head of the horse, right at the withers, and Cimbal fell with the dead horse. In that same moment came up Faustinus, like an arrow from the bow, upon his goodly horse, and set his sword at the neck of Hles, so that the head was smitten off, and it rolled far out into the field, and he fell with fair fame, having slain 300 men. Cimbal mounted the horse of Hles and rode into the battle. Now when Victor saw his brother fallen, he roared in his fury, and

25

beitti Sverdi sínu alldjarflega, var hann ordin mjóg
módur af ákófum bardaga, enn ei ad sídur herdti hann
50 framgaunguna til hefnda, so hvar sem hann fór, héldust
aungvir vid, drap hann á tvær hendur og hlód mjóg háa
valkésti, og felldi 8 menn í hvórju hóggi, komu þeir
færstir flótta vid sem fyrir honum stódu ; honū mætti
Risi eirn mikill vexti og herdabreidur, sá hét Rosó,
55 Strids-eggsi bar hann þúnga í hendi, reiddi Risin hana
sem hardast hann kunni, stefndi hóggid á kappan, stókk
nu Victor undan úr Sódlinum, so hesturin dó af því
þúnga hóggi, Victor hlióp á Risan og hjó af honum
hendurnar í olbogabótū vard þá óxiñ laus, greip Victor
60 hana í loptinu og setti í hófud Risans, vard þad hañs
bani, því óxin hljóp óll á hol í búkiñ, var nú dúnkur
mikill þá Risin fiell.   Victor sest á hest hans og bardist
alldjarflega.   heidíngjar gjórdu ákafa hríd ad Victor í
risans hefnd, enn hann reid sem hardast í gégnum lidid.
65 Carvel sér nú hvar Victor rídur, og felldi ótal manna,
hleýpir hann Essinu eptir honum og kom á bak til vid
hann og lagdi Spjótinu í herdar honum so út um brjóstid
gékk, fékk nú Victor dauda lag, hañ fañ þad á sjálfum
sér, snéri vid hestinum og bar sig enn merkilega,
70 haldandi merki kóngs uppi med karlmennsku, og reiddi
Sverdid sem hardast til hóggs, kom hóggid á hjalm
Carvels, enn hañ var so traustur ad ekki biladi, enn
so var hóggid þúngt, ad Carvel fiell af hestinum í
óvit.   I sama bili kom Fástínus ad því hann sá þeirra
75 vidskipti ; neitti Victor enn nú vopna sinna, og vardi sig

plied his sword right dauntlessly. He was much awearied by the hand-fight, but none the less he fared forth hardily for vengeance, so that where he came none might withstand him, and he slew men on either side, and heaped huge piles of slain: he laid low eight men at every stroke; but few had chance of flight of those who stood before him. He was met by a certain giant, mighty in stature, and broad of shoulder, who was called Rosó; he bore a heavy battle-axe in his hand. The giant hove it up with all his might, and aimed the stroke at the warrior, but Victor leapt from out his saddle to escape the stroke, and his horse died from the heavy blow. Victor now sprang upon the giant and smote off his arms at the bight of the elbows. The axe was then set free, and Victor caught it aloft and drove it into the giant's head, and that was his death, for the axe went down even to the hollow of the trunk; and there was a great thud as the giant fell. Victor now mounted his horse and fought boldly on. The heathens made fierce onslaught on him to wreak their vengeance for the giant, but he rode his hardest through the lines. Carvel was ware how Victor rode, and laid men low without number; he spurred his horse toward him, and came upon him from behind and thrust his spear into his back, so that it came out through the breast, and thus Victor got his death-thrust, as he felt full well; yet withal he turned his horse about and bore himself still bravely, holding up the standard of the king full valiantly, and he raised his sword at his hardest for a blow, and it lighted on Carvel's helm, but the helm was strong and gave way in no wise, though the blow was so heavy that he fell from off his horse aswooning. At that moment Faustinus came up, having seen their dealings together. Victor still plied his weapons and warded himself right

alldreingilega; enn so kom um sídir ad hann mæddist af blódrás svo hann þraut burdi, hjó Fástínus þá um þverar herdar hanns svo hann féll daudur til jardar; Lofudu menn frægd hañs og framgaungu, vóru þad 1000 manna 80 sem hann hafdi ad velli lagt, og endar hér ad seigja af hañs Frægdar verkum.

7 Capítuli.

ENN sem Gamalíel sá fall þeirra brædra, féll honum ædra í brjóst, því honum þókti vísari daudi enn líf, magnadi hann þá adfòr vid heidíngja og neitti vopna sinna sem hardast, því hann þeinkti sitt líf dírt ad selja og í þeirri 5 framgaungu mætir hann Salman kóngi. Kóngur mælti þá til hañs: módur ertu nú Félagi! enn Gamalíel svaradi aptur: ílla hefur þitt audnuleýsi bruggad oss bòl þetta, því þitt stórlindi þreýtti hugmód vid galdra nornina, og mun ei þar á eptir ad bótum ad bída. Kóngur mælti: Ei 10 kunni eg òllum mínum sem verid hafa vísari og frægri ad verda í því ad umflýa dauda miñ þar eingin hefur hann umflúid gétad nær ad hefur kallad; því þad var so af Gudi áliktad sá sem rád hefur yfir lífi og dauda, og mína lífdaga taldi þá eg var einginn; skildu þeir so talid. 15 Sókti nú ótólulegur lídur ad Gamalíel, enn hann vardist so vel ad einginn kom sári á hann, heldur felldi hann þá hrònnum so ei vard tòlu ákomid; setti hann Essid gégnum endilángar filkíngar, og vo jafnan 10 í hòggi hvòrju þá best hòggfæri gafst, svo eingin komst undan 20 sá er hann adreid, og eingin fékk þar neitt ad verkum gjòrt er hann var firir, og mikill ótti stód heidíngjum af honum. Valkòstur sem hann hafdi hladid af daudum búkum, nam vid axlir honum; hrakti hann sundur allar

28

manfully, but it came to this at last, that he grew aweary from loss of blood, and his strength ebbed away. Then Faustinus smote him across the shoulders, and he fell dead to earth, and men praised his glory and his prowess; and it was a thousand men he had laid low on the field, and herewith ends the story of his famous deeds.

Chapter VII.

Now when Gamaliel saw the brothers fallen, anguish filled his breast, for he knew himself more certain now of death than life. He renewed his onset on the heathens, and used his weapons with all his might, for he thought to yield his life full dearly. In the onset he met King Salman. Then said the king to him:—"Thou art aweary now, fellow." But Gamaliel replied:—"Ill has thy luckless fate brewed us this bale, for in thy pride thou didst slight the witch's spells, and it is too late now to get us remedy." The king said:—"I cannot be wiser or more renowned than all my kin in escaping death, seeing no one has escaped it when the call has come, for so was it fixed by God, who hath power over life and death, and who told my life-days when I was nought!" So their talk ended. A great host now rushed upon Gamaliel, but he fended him well, and no man dealt him a wound, nay he felled them in heaps so that the number could not be told: he set his steed at gallop-pace right through the lines and struck ten men at every stroke, when the chance of striking was best, so that no one against whom he rode fared unscathed, and no man could do aught where he was present, and there was great fear to the heathens because of him. The pile of dead which he had heaped reached to his shoulders; he scattered all the lines asunder

29

filkíngar so þær tóku stórum ad ridlast og undanflía.
25 þetta fær ad líta Fástínus, keirdi Essid sporum, þeisti ad
Gamalíeli, og reiddi Sverdid af Stórri brædi til Greifans,
enn hann skaut firir sig Skildinum so höggid sakadi hann
ei, og reiddi nú aptur Sverd sitt, og setti í midjan hjálm
Fástínusar, enn Adamus Steirn var settur í midjañ
30 hjálmiñ, og brotnadi Sverdid í honum, sér nú Greifin
ad ei muni meiga svo standa, Stökk hann af baki og
svipti Fástínusi úr Södlinum, tókust þeir nú fángbrögdum,
var þeirra glíma en hardasta; víkíngurin bar Greifan og
hrakti, enn fékk honum ei af fótum komid, urdu dínkir
35 miklir af harki þeirra og adgángi so jördinn Skalf. Fiell
nú Fástínus um sídir, vard hönum þad til falls, ad hann
datt um eirn daudañ búk, vard Gamalíel nú ofañ á honū,
enn hafdi eingin vopn hjá sér, greip því firir háls
Fástínusi og vildi kyrkja hann, var honum þá fiörtjón
40 búid, eñ nær heidíngjar litu herra sinn svo staddan,
þusti þángad meigin fjöldi lidsins, handtóku Gamalíel
og vildu drepa hann; enn Fástínus bannadi þeim svo
ad gjöra, var Gamalíel fjötradur mjög hardlega, og færdur
í herbúdir heidíngja, og feingin þrælum til geimslu, átti
45 hann stóra ofraun í fjötrunuñ, því ílla var vid hañ gjört.
Fástínus komst nú enn á Essid sitt, og var styrdur miög
af Greifans miklu átökum, enn þó sókti hann hardan
bardaga vid kóng; kóngur vardist mjög leingi vel, og
var ordin nærsta lidfár, naut hann ílla vopna sinna því
50 þaug dugdu ekki ad bíta.

8 Capítuli.

Nú var fátt eptir lid kóngs, vóru þad alls 11 manna er vígir
vóru, þeir filgdu kóngi þad besta þeir kunnu. Fástínus

30

that they broke up and fled. Faustinus seeing this, struck his spurs into his horse, and rushed upon Gamaliel, and in fierce rage raised his sword against the earl, but he shot his shield before him so that the blow did not harm him, and in his turn he raised his sword and struck the helm of Faustinus in the middle, but an "Adam-stone" was set there in the middle of the helm, and the sword broke against it. The earl wist now that things could not bide long thus, and he leapt from his horse, and swept Faustinus from out the saddle; they took now to wrestling, and their play was the fiercest. The viking bore the earl to and fro, and drove him on before him, yet might not get him off his feet, and great thuds resounded from their hard play and onset, so that the very earth shook. But Faustinus fell at last, and this was the cause of his fall, namely, that he tripped over a dead trunk. Gamaliel was at once atop of him, but he had no weapon beside him, and he caught at Faustinus' throat, meaning to throttle him, and then death was ready for him. Now when the heathens saw their lord in this sorry plight, the main throng of the force rushed thither, seized Gamaliel and would have slain him, but Faustinus forbade them, and he was cruelly put in fetters, and brought into the heathen camp, and given in charge of thralls, and he suffered great trials in the fetters, for he was right hardly used. Faustinus then mounted his horse again; he was very stiff after the earl's fierce handling, yet he kept up a hard fight with the king. The king guarded himself well for a long space: he had now a scanty host about him, but his weapons stood him ill in stead for they would not bite.

Chapter VIII.

Now there were few left of the host of the king; in all there were eleven who could still fight, and they followed the king as best they might. Faustinus

æpti nú á Fólk sitt til ad veita kóngi adför, jókst þar
þúng orusta, kóngur og menn hanns drápu fjölda af
5 heidíngjum og hróktu þá. Kóngi bitu ei vopn sín eptir
því sem norniñ hafdi mælt, hafdi hañ lánga staung í
hendi og digra, og lagdi hann fólk med henni til dauds,
vard fyrir þad margur haus og útlimur brotinn, mættust
þeir nú Salman kóngur og Fástínus í bardaganum, enn
10 Fástínus feilar sér ad mæta kóngi, kóngur mælti : til
einvígs bíd eg þér þú hid arga fól ! og held eg þig grei
hundum ragari ef þú þorir ei ad berjast vid mig. Fástínus
seigir : þess skal nú vid neita sem hamíngjan mér ad
gagni gjörir þad eg er þér fjölmeñari. Baud hann enn
15 adför eina ad auka ; æstust nú heidíngjarnir og sóktu
hardlega ad kóngi, hafdi kóngur nú í hendi öxina Risanaut, og gjördi mönnum hardkeypt so eíngin komst lífs
undan sem öxiñ snerti ; eins var hann tídur í bardaga
sem hvirfilvindur og svo grímur sem lión ; kappar hañs
20 filgdu honum vel og drápu ótal manna, þó fiellu þeir
flestir um sídir. 2 menn lifdu leingst eptir med kóngi,
hét annar Faber enn annar Tellus ; Faber mætti Cimbal í
bardaganum, og áttust þeir Sóknir vid, var þeirra adgangur
mikill, hjó Faber til Cimbals ad liktum med Sverdinu, so
25 höggid nam hægri öxlina og alla brinjuna á hlidinni,
hnéskélina af Fætinum og jarkañ med hálfri Ristinni,
þókti þetta frægdarlega höggvid, enn Cimbal brá Sverdi og
hió höfud af Faber med vinstri hendi ; lét so þessi kappi
líf sitt vid gódan ordstír. Nú sér kóngur meñ sína fallna,
30 fiell honum mikil grimd í hjarta, og bardist med mesta
ákafa, láu daudir manna búkar sem hrís í Skógje fallid
32

shouted now to his folk to make an onslaught on the king, and there fell a heavy fight; the king and his men slew a many heathens, and drove them all about, but the king's weapons would not bite, even as the witch had said. He had in his hand a long and stout pole, and therewith he thrust men through to death, and by it many a skull and limb was maimed. And now they met in the fray, King Salman and Faustinus, but Faustinus fought shy of the king. The king said :—"To a single combat do I charge thee, thou craven fool. I hold thee more cowardly than a cur if thou darest not fight with me." Faustinus said :—"That shall avail me now which fortune places to my profit, to wit, that I am more numerous than thou." And he bade them make another onset. The heathens then raged and made hard for the king. The king had now in his hand the axe, the giant's treasure, and made men abuy it dearly, so that no one whom the axe met might escape with life : he fared in the fight swift as a whirlwind, grim as a lion : his warriors stood by him nobly and slew men numberless, but in the end most of them fell. Two men lived longest beside the king, Faber and Tellus. Faber met Cimbal in the fight and they had fight together. Their combat was fierce : at last Faber hewed at Cimbal with his sword so that the stroke cut through the right shoulder and all the hauberk on that side, and took the knee-cap off the leg, and the outer part of the foot to half the instep; and this was deemed a famous blow; but Cimbal drew his sword, and cut off Faber's head with his left hand. And so this champion lost his life with great renown. The king saw now how his men were fallen, and great madness seized his heart and he fought most fiercely; and the trunks of the dead lay now like faggots of wood strewn all about,

CH. VIII. allavega, so eingin sá sér óhætt, mætti hann nú Fástínus
í bardaganum, lagdi kóngur Staunginni firir brjóst honum,
so hañ hraut lángt útá vøllinn, og kom nidur á herdarnar
35 og Lamadist mjóg, því svo ílla var Fástínus fær, ad ei
komst hann hjálparlaust í Søðulinn. Kóngur fékk nú ei
meir adgjórt vegna fjølmeñis nálægdar; Fástínus gretti
sig ílla, því hann hafdi feingid hálsríg mikinn, og úr því
var hann ei í bardaganum, og áttust þeir ei Sóknir vid
40 fremur, enn Fástínus eggjadi menn sína til framgaungu
og baud Fólkinu med grimd ad sækja ad kóngi, þusti nú
allur herinn ad kóngi, vóru þad 6000 manna sem þá lifdu
af heidíngjum, kóngur og Tellus mætti øllum þessum her
med stórum frægdum og geingu merkilega fram, so nú
45 var heidíngjum ósjen Sigurinn, því þeim baud mjóg vid
ótta; Fástínus sá þetta og mælti : vondum Skræmum hefi
eg ad stíra, sem láta fámenni þetta Sigra sig med hrædslu
og dauda. Sækid þid betur fram og høggvid fól þessi.
Sóktu nú heidíngjar grimilega ad kóngi enn han tók enn
50 hraustlega á móti þeim, kongur drap fjølda manna af
þeim med Spióti sínu Carvel sá nú framgaungu kóngs,
keirdi essid sporum, mætir hañ kóngi og hió til hañs,
nam Sverdid vinstri fótinn so hann fiell af kóngi firir
nedann knéd, kóngur reiddi óxina ad Carvel med miklu
55 kappi, kom høggid á hestinn og lamdi hañ til dauds, því
Carvel var stokkiñ úr Søðlinum. Carvel hlióp ad kóngi í
34

and no one saw safety for himself. Then the king met
Faustinus in the fight and thrust his pole at his breast,
so that he fell far out into the field and came down upon
his back and was mightily lamed, and was in such sore
plight that he might not unaided gain his saddle. The
king could now do nothing more for the host closed
round him. Faustinus made wry looks, for his neck
was very stiffened, and henceforth he was not in the
fight, and he and the king met not again. But withal
he egged his men to make an onset, and fiercely urged
them to set upon the king; and the whole host rushed
upon him, 6000 heathens being still alive. The king
and Tellus met all this host with great glory, and went
forward wondrously, so that now the victory grew doubtful
for the heathens, smitten, as they were, with mighty
fear. Faustinus perceived this and he said :—"Wretched
cowards have I to command, who suffer this handful of
men to cow them with fear and death : set on more bravely
and cut down these fools." Then the heathens made
fiercely for the king, but still he met them bravely, and
slew with his spear a many of their men. Carvel seeing
the king's advance spurred his horse, and met the king,
and dealt him a stroke, and the sword smote his left leg
below the knee, so that it fell from him : the king hove
his axe at Carvel with great hardihood, and the blow
lighted on the horse, and lamed it to death, for Carvel had
leapt from out the saddle. Carvel sprang at the king

annad sinn og hjó höfud af hesti hans; kóngur stökk af baki og sveifladi sér á einum fæti ad .Carvel, enn hann flúdi; komu þá svo margir heidingjar og sóktu ad kóngi,
60 kóngur drap 4 men af þeim, med sínu Spjóti. J því bili brautst Tellus fram ad kóngi, stökk af baki sínum hesti og setti kóng uppá hann, reid kóngur nú allfrækilega fram, bardist hann med sinni hægri hendi og felldi margan mann. Tellus hlióp ad einum digrum heidíngja
65 er sat á einu gódu Essi, lagdi hann í gégn med Spjóti sínu og fleigdi honum til jardar, stökk sídan á Essid og reid til kóngs því hann vildi honum sem nærst vera. Aldrei hafdi kóngur hardari framgauṅgu haft enn nú, ad hann sem mestar hefndir ynni fyrir líf Sitt, drap hann
70 á lítilli svipan 100 manna. Fástínus baud ad bera Skjöldu ad kóngi, og so var gjört ad þeir fjórsettu Skjöldu úr hverri átt ad kóngi, kóngur og Tellus vördust vel og urdu margra manna bani, lét kóngur óxina Risanaut gánga af ákafa, og lemstradi med henni menn
75 og hesta til dauds, og í þeirri framgaungu mætir honum eirn grimmur heidíngi Addómólus ad nafni, og var leindar rád Fástínusar; þessi bar þúngan Stríds hamar í hendi, og laust honum í hægra armlegg konúngs so hann brotnadi, var nú konúngur mjög ílla staddur enn þó vardi hann sig
80 med vinstri hendi. Tellus bar Skjöld sin yfir kóng, og vardi hann alla vega so hann særdist ei meira, og drap margan mann, tók nú mikid ad draga af kóngi, þó vard hann enn nú 30 manna bani, í þessari sinni framgaungu, Sté hann nú af baki, því kraptar hans tóku ad mínka af blódrás

36

a second time and struck off the horse's head, while the
king leapt down and on his one foot swung himself at
Carvel, but he fled. Then there came a multitude of
heathens and sought the king, but the king with his spear
slew four of them. At that same moment Tellus hurried
to the king, leapt from his horse, and set the king upon
it, and the king went buoyantly forward, and fought with
his right hand and felled a many men. Tellus rushed at
a certain stout heathen mounted on a goodly horse and
broached him through and through with his spear, and
flung him to the earth; then he sprang upon the horse
and rode to the king, for he wished to be as nigh to him
as might be. Never had the king made a harder onset
than now, for he would wreak the greatest vengeance for
his life, and in short space he slew a hundred men.
Faustinus bade men bring shields about the king, and so
was done: they placed shields fourfold round the king
on every side. The king and Tellus warded themselves
well and were the death of many men, and the king let the
axe, the giant's treasure, go wildly about, and with it he
lamed men and horses to the death. Now in this onset
there met him a certain grim heathen, Addomolus by
name, who was the counsellor of Faustinus: he bore in
his hand a heavy war-hammer, and smote therewith the
king on the right arm so that it broke; and now the king
was in a passing grievous plight, but yet he shielded himself with his left hand. Tellus brought his shield before the
king and fended him all about, so that he took not fresh
wound, and himself slew many a man. The king now
grew very weak, and yet withal he was the death of
thirty men in this advance. He then dismounted from
his horse, for his strength 'gan wane from loss of blood

37

og mædi, so hann fiell um sídir í ómeigin til jardar, hugdu
86 menn þad hañs dauda. Og sem Tellus sá kóng falla,
þeinkti hā ad forda lífi sínu, brast í gégnum Filkínguna
mikid sár og módur, enn komst þó lífs af og hleýpti útá
eidiskóga, vard nú endir á bardaganum, hafdi hann 3
90 Daga yfir stadid. Fástínus hrósar nú stórum Sigri og
vard allgladur, baud hann ad taka Líkama kóngs og
færa til borgar og so var gjórt, 4 adrir lifdu eptir af óllu
hañs lidi, og sem þrælar báru kóng inn um Borgarhlidid,
raknadi hann vid úr ómeiginu, slóg hann þann med
95 hnefanum hógg vid vánga er nærstur honum stód, so
hann hraut útaf, og kom hófudid nidur vid múrinn so
þad brotnadi og missti sá lífid. Fástínus var nærstaddur,
og bannadi kóng til dauds ad særa, því þér skulud hann
á gálga heingja, þañ sama sem Metúlus í hángir, skipadi
100 hann þá ad sækja Syni kóngs, og so var gjórt, lét hann
sídan kóng uppheingja á Gálgañ. þá mælti Fástínus til
kóngs sona : nú skulud þid sjá þar uppá hvórsu listilega
kónginum Fódur ykkar geingur daudiñ, lét hañ þá leida
þá ad gálganum, enn er Sigurdur sá Fódur sinn so
105 hórmulega deýa, grét hann sárlega og vafdi Skikkjulafi
um hófud sér, enn Ambales gékk all djarflega nær, og
setti Sión á Líkama Fódur síns er hann var í Fjórbrotunum,
Ambales hló mjóg dátt vid hvórn kipp sem Líkamin tók,
og altjafnt vóx hónum meiri kjætiñ sem meir dró af. þetta
110 furdar heidíngja so mjóg ad þá setti hlióda. þá Spurdi
Fástínus þann eldra Son kóngs : hvad sárt hañ tæki ad
horfa á þetta? enn hann mælti : mikid hjartans ángur eikur
þú mér med griñd þinni, og mætti eg nokkra dvól eiga til
38

and very weariness, and at last he fell to earth in a
swoon and men deemed that was his death. Now whenas
Tellus saw the king fall he thought to save his own life,
and he broke through the ranks, mightily wounded and
aweary as he was; and he got off with his life and
galloped to the wild woods, and there was an end to the
fight which had lasted three days. Faustinus triumphed
now in a great victory and was passing glad. He bade
men take up the body of the king and bring it to the
city; and so it was done. Of all his host but four
were left alive besides the king, who came out of his
swoon as thralls were carrying him in through the city-
gates, and he smote with his fist a blow on the cheek
of him who stood anigh, so that the man reeled and
his head struck against a wall and broke, and he lost
his life. Faustinus was standing near, and forbade them
to give the king a death-wound, for " Ye shall hang him
on a gallows, the very same on which Methulus is hanging." He bade them fetch the sons of the king, and so
it was done. Then he had the king hanged on the
gallows. Faustinus said to the sons of the king :—
" Now ye shall have a sight of how lustily the king
your father meets death." He had them led up to the
gallows. And when Sigurd saw his father die so grievously, he wept sorely, and wrapped the skirt of his cloak
around his head, but Ambales went boldly near, and
stared at the body of his father while he was in his
death-throes. Ambales laughed most gleefully at every
pang that stirred his father's body, and he became
the gayer the more life waned. At this the heathens
wondered so much that they were struck silent. Then
Faustinus asked the king's elder son how sorely
he took it to look thereon; but he said :—" Great
grief of heart dost thou cause me with thy cruelty,
and if I might have some respite before death, and

CH. VIII. daudans, og dygdi mér lukkan,—sem eg óska vildi—þá
115 skyldir þú fá þrefaldt verri dauda enn þennan. þá lét
Fástínus heingja hann hjá Fódur sínum. Alt jók þetta
gaman ok kjæti Ambal. svo hann hló hástöfum, tók hann
þá þad er finna kunni og grítti sinn bródur med í
andarslitrunum. Sögdu þá allir ad slíkt grei væri ekki
120 ad hitta eda uppleita sem hann væri; Spurdi þá hyrdinn
Fástínus ad hvört deida skildi Fól þetta? enn hañ qvad
þar eingañ mun til draga, og sagdi hann til Skémtunar
lifa mætti sér og höfdíngjunum.

9 Capítuli.

FÁSTÍNUS gékk med öllu lidi sínu í Stórri hugarkjæti í höll
Salmans kóngs, og settist í hásæti hañs; hann baud
ad Sækja hertjöldin og herfángid, líka hreinsa vigvölluna,
var þetta svo gjört. Var Gamalíel nú fluttur heim til
5 borgarinnar, og tekiñ Skíla frá augum hañs. Fástínus
mælti: hvörjum kostum viltú sæta? Gamaljel mælti:
Daudin þikir mér nú lífinu betri, því íllt er heidnum
hundum ad þjóna og hlídni játa, enn þó mun ekki í
ydar valdi tala minna lífdaga. Med því móti kýs eg líf,
10 ad eg haldi Trú minni, audæfum og nafnbótum öllum og
umdæmum, so og líka allar þjódir þessa lands haldi trú
sinni, enn gjaldi þér Skatt og hlídni alla eptir Sidvana
og Lands Lögmáli; enn vilje nokkur ei gánga ad
þessum kostum, þá skal hann án dvalar strax fánga.
15 Fástínus mælti: mañskadi er mikill ad þér, eñ þúngir
eru kostir þeir þú setur, enn þó skalt þú Sverja mér
eid hér uppá þín og alls landsins vegna, ad þessi þín

40

should fortune help me, as I fain would wish, then shouldst thou have a death threefold worse than this." Thereat Faustinus had him hanged beside his father. All this but added to the sport and jollity of Ambales, so that he laughed loudly. He seized whatever he might lay hands on, and pelted his brother therewith while the life was passing from him. All said that such a dog as he was could not be found. Then the court asked Faustinus whether this fool should be killed, but he said it mattered little; he might as well live and be sport for him and for his lords.

Chapter IX.

FAUSTINUS went now with all his host amid great rejoicing to the hall of King Salman and sat him down in the king's seat. He bade his men fetch the war-booths and the booty, and clear the battle-field, and so it was done. They then brought Gamaliel to the castle, and the bands were taken from off his eyes. Faustinus said:—"What terms will reconcile thee to life?" Gamaliel said:— "Death seems to me better than life, for it is an ill thing to serve heathen dogs and yield them homage, yet methinks the tale of my life-days is not in thy power. On these terms choose I life that I keep my faith, my wealth, my rank, and my dominion, and I would too that all the people of this land keep their faith, and they shall pay thee tribute and yield thee fit obedience after the law and custom of the land: and if any man be unwilling to yield to these conditions, he shall be placed in durance without delay." Faustinus said:—"Thy death would be a great loss: yet the terms thou puttest are heavy; yet thou shalt swear to me here an oath on thine own behalf and of all the land that this thy

heit skuli standa fyrir alna og óborna. Gamalíel gjördi
svo, og Sór kóngi trúnadar eida á þennan hátt. Fástínus
20 mælti : Rád skaltu leggja á med oss, og vil eg þér hlída,
því skulu og mínir menn hlída. Gamalíel mælti : þad
skal vera medañ trigd ei tæmist af þinni hendi. Sídann
lét Fástínus taka kórónu Salmans kóngs og öll konúngleg
þíng og setti á sitt höfud þá kostulegu kórónu, og tók
25 Ríkis sprota í sína hönd, gjördist hann so kóngur yfir
því landi og ríki Salmans kóngs ; hann bad ad sækja
Drottnínguna, og sem hún kom, var hún mjög ángursöm,
og so grét hún mikid, ad ei gat hún borid sig. Fástínus
k. bad hana glada vera, og sagdi : vel vil eg vid þig gjöra,
30 og þann kost máttu af mér þiggja sem kiósa vilt ef þú vilt
mín Drottníng heita, enn þetta fékk henni enn meira
ángur ; sá nú kóngur ad viljug mundi hún ekki ad þessu
gánga, leid svo dagurin til þess til hvílu skildi gánga.
Lagdist Fástínus í Sæng þá er konúngur hafdi átt, og
35 skipadi med valdi ad Drottníng skildi þángad færa.
Þjónar kóngs gjördu sem hann firirsagdi, sá nú Drottníng
ad sinn vilje mundi síst standa meiga, var hún naudug
þángad boriñ og af klædd sídann í Sængina hiá þessum
köngi nidurlögd ; grét hún þá hástöfum ; enn er kóngur
40 ætlar ad sína henni ástar hót med fadmlögum og fiölþreifni
allri, sókti hann mikill kránkleiki so han rédi sér varla
sjálfur, kvaldi hann pína þessi heldst uñ þíng sín og
þarma, so ad tók frá honum alla edlis krapta, þoldi
hann ílla qvöl þessa, vildi hann sér bata leita, og sté af

42

promise shall hold for born and unborn." Gamaliel did so, and thus swore he to the king oaths of allegiance. Faustinus said:—"Thou shalt give us rede, and I shall hearken to thee, as shall my men." Gamaliel said:— "It shall be so as long as faith does not fail on thy side." Thereafter Faustinus bade men take the crown of King Salman and all the kingly gear, and he set on his head the precious crown, and placed the sceptre in his hand, and so made himself king of King Salman's land and empire. He bade them fetch the queen, and when she came she was in sorry plight, and wept so grievously as her heart would all to-break. King Faustinus bade her be of goodly cheer, and said:—"I would act kindly toward thee, and thou shalt have from me all that thou wouldst, if thou wilt be called my queen." But this made her grief the greater, and the king saw she would not yield thereto. So the day passed till the time when folk betake themselves to rest. Faustinus lay upon the bed which had been the king's, and he bade the men bring the queen thither by force. His servants did as he bade them. The queen now saw that her will was of no avail: she was carried thither by force and unclad, and thereafter laid down beside the king, weeping aloud. But when the king was wishful to come anigh her with his wooing, a great sickness fell upon him so that he might scarcely hold himself; all strength of being passed away from him. He bore the pain ill, and arose

43

Sænginni; og sem hann var úr Sængur herberginu
46 geinginn fékk hann albata; enn nær hann hugdi til
Sængur Drottníngar ad gánga, jókst honum þad sama
mein, og því meir qvelst hann sem hann kom nær henni.
Ad morgni gékk hann til hallar og settist í hásæti, sagdi
50 hann þá frá þrautum sínum sem hann átti ad reina um
nóttina, og hvörnin honum vóru hvíluvistirnar bannadar;
hlóu margir ad því í hljódi, sögdu þetta af brögdum
völvunnar. Kóngur spurdi Gamál. hvörju hann þeinkti
þetta mundi gégna? enn hann qvad hónum annars eiga
55 audid verda, því máttu kóngur af huga verda ad fadma
Drottníngu, gjör þú henni heldur allann Sóma og lát
hana naudúngar lausa lifa, og hlíd henni því hún er vitur
og vel ad sér, og viljer þú í nádum lifa, so máttu líka
mínum rádum hlída eins í þessu sem ódru. Kóngur vildi
60 ei ad heldur afláta, og reindi til í 3 nætur, því honum
þótti sneipa ad þetta spirjast skildi, og fór alt á sömu leid
sem ádur, og nær hann vildi í Sængina stíga, qvelst hañ
meir og meir, so hann um sídir hlaut af ad láta; fékk
hónum þetta stórrar hugarsorgar, og af rádum Greifans
65 lét hann Drottníngu vegleg herbergi fá og þernur hennar,
og hielt hana í besta haldi til alls kostar. hennar þjónusta
lindti kóngi vel, Saumadi hún honum kónúnglegan
Skrúda med miklum kostamentum. ei mátti kóngur
hana augum líta, því svo opt sem honum fiell géd í
70 hug til hennar, listi sótt um hans líf, settist hann þá
ad Stiórnan Fólks og landa.
44

from the bed in hope of remedy, and as he was come
from out the room he was restored; but when he was
minded to return to the bed whereon the queen still lay,
the torture grew the more the nearer he approached the
queen. In the morning he went to the hall and sat
adown in the high seat: he told of the pangs he had
endured at night. Many laughed thereat within themselves; "it was the witch's tricks," they said. The king
asked Gamaliel whence he thought it came. He said it
was fated otherwise for him, and the king must therefore
give up all thought of holding the queen in his embrace;
"show her rather all honour and let her live untroubled,
and listen to her, for she is wise and gifted; and if thou
wouldst live in peace, thou must needs hearken to my
rede in this as in all else." The king was nowise ready
to desist, and he tried three nights, for he thought it a
shame that the story should get bruited about, but things
went the same way as erewhile, and when he would
ascend the bed, his pains grew more and more; at last
he was forced to yield, though the matter vexed him
greatly, and following the counsels of the earl, he let the
queen and her maidens, too, have noble dwelling, and kept
her in the best in all she needed. Her service pleased the
king well; she stitched for him a kingly robe of great
price. But he might not look into her eyes, for as often
as it befell him to think of her, he was smitten with sickness throughout his frame. He betook himself then to
rule his folk and his land.

10 Capítuli.

CH. X. **A**FYRSTA ári ríkisstjórnar Fástínusar kóngs, fékk kóngur mikils háttar áhiggju, so hann vard þrátt þögull og fálátur. Greifi Gamaljel spurdi hvad honum bæri til áhiggju? enn hañ qvadst þeinkja til hefnda af Bálant
5 kóngi í Hispanja eptir brædur sína, vil eg því fara á fund Málpríants bródur míns, og med mér taka her mikiñ úr þessu landi, og vid brædur bádir sófnum lidi til bardaga, því vid munum bádir jafnsekir haldnir, og skulum vid ad firra bragdi til verda vid Bálant kóng.
10 Cimbal og Carvel skulu mér filgja, enn þú skalt firir ríki voru sjá á medan. Enn er Greifinn heirdi þetta, þagdi hann nokkra stund, sídan svarar hañ hér til á þessa leid : vel er þó kóngur rádi, enn óvíst er um Sigur ykkar brædra nema ofmikil Svik eda audnuleýsi adsæki
15 Bálant kóng; bjóst kóngur nú á stad med lid sitt til þessa bardaga, urdu þeir kristnu eirnig med ad fara í herfór þessa þó naudugier væru, hafdi hann nú allmikid lid, og létti ei ferd sinni firri enn hañ-kom vid Spaníen á fund Málpríants kóngs bródur síns, seigir Fástínus
20 hónum ad hann vill þeir færi ad Bálant kóngi med allañ siñ her, enn Málpríant kóngur seigir sér þetta leingi í hug verid hafa, og qvadst til reidu vera, og gjórdi hann herbod óllum lídkóngum̄ er honum þjentu ad safna sem mestu lidi þeir kynnu ; dreif því ad kóngi mikill her, so
25 þeir brædur hófdu alls 80,000 vígra maña, og þar ad auki sína þénara, drógu so af Stad med allan þennan her alt til borgar Bálants kóngs, og gjórdu honum tveñ kosta bod med miklu drambi, ad hann skildi annadhvórt verja land sitt eda uppgéfa, og þeim Skatt afgjalda. Bálant kóngur

46

Chapter X.

URING the first years of the rule of King Faustinus, there fell on the king some great trouble, so that he was ofttimes silent and sullen. Gamaliel asked whence this trouble came? He said he feared that Balant, King of Spain, would take vengeance for his brothers :—"Wherefore I would go and meet Malpriant my brother and take with me a great army from this land, and we two brothers shall both muster a host for battle, for we are both alike held guilty, and we two must anticipate King Balant. Cimbal and Carvel shall follow me, but thou shalt meanwhile rule our kingdom." When the earl heard this he was silent for a time ; thereafter he answered thus:—"The king may well have his will, yet it is not sure that thou and thy brother will have victory unless some great treachery or ill-fate beset King Balant." The king now gets ready with his army for the raid. The Christians were also forced to go on this war-raid, though unwilling. He had then a great host of men, and he stayed not till he reached Spain and met King Malpriant his brother. Faustinus tells him that he would they should go to King Balant with all their host; Malpriant says this has long been in his mind, and declared himself ready, and he sent the war-message to all the vassal-kings that served him to gather together the greatest possible force. There drove thus a great army to the king, so that the brothers had in all 80,000 able-bodied men and their servants besides. They set off with all that host to the city of King Balant, and with great disdain gave him a choice of two things, that he should either defend his land or give it up, and pay them tribute. King Balant

47

vard bistur vid þessi tídindi, bædi af falli brædra sinna og
31 því stóra rembilæti og ofsa kónganna, stefndi hann öllum
sínum mönnum til bardaga er hann fá kunni, og fékk
aungvañvegin so miklu lidi safnad sem hann med þurfti
sökum nálægdar óvina sinna og naums tíma, hann hafdi
35 alls 19,000^{um} ad sér safnad vopn færra manna, þar í bland
þess lids vóru 12 kappar Bálants kóngs, og þar med
margir adrir vaskir Riddarar er ad vistum sátu med kóngi,
þó 4 þeirra heldst afbæri til frægdar og framgaungu er svo
hietu: Vilhjálmur, Didrik, Dixin og Karl; þessir máttu
40 vel kallast Skjöldur Landsins, og þókti flestum óárennilegt
Ríki kóngs þar med óvinnandi medann þeir vóru í Lidi
hañs. Lét nú kóngur blása í sína herlúdra med hvellum
hliódum, og stefna öllu sínu lidi útaf borginni á sliettar
grundir er þar lágu nærri. Nú sem kóngarnir urdu þessa
45 vísir, ad Bálant kóngur var til Bardaga kominn, létu þeir
æpa hróp med miklum adgángi, voru þeir nú búnir ad
skipta lidi sínu í tvær Filkíngar, var sídan í herlúdra blásid,
og tókst þar straung orusta med skeitum og handbogū,
Skotspjótum og allskyns vopnum, gékk sú hríd lángan
50 tíma med mesta ákafa, so allir höfdu nógu ad gégna lífid
ad verja, vóru þeir brædur kóngarnir hinir áköfustu og
menn þeirra, því þeir þeinktu sér Sigurinn vísan, og af því so
mikill lidsmunur var sem ádur er gétid, enn Bálant kóngur
baud mönnum sínum kyrrum fyrir ad standa og verjast svo,
55 þess neittu þeir og vid, enn drápu þó ótal manna af her
þeirra brædra, so heldur halladist bardginn á þá heidnu,
flódu þá blódlækirnir allvída er menn beittu Sverdum,
Spjótum, Stríds hömrum og allskyns vopnum, var þessi
48

was wroth at the message, both because of his brother's death, and of the king's great haughtiness and pride. He arrayed all those he could get together for battle; he might in nowise muster as great a host as he needed, for the enemy was at hand and the time was short. He had in all 19,000 weapon-bearing men gathered around him: amongst that host there were twelve champions of King Balant, and therewithal many other valiant knights who eat the king's bread, amongst whom four were the most renowned for bravery and dauntlessness; their names were :—Vilhjalmur, Didrik, Dixin, and Karl : these might well be called the shield of the land, and most men thought the realm of the king unassailable and un-conquerable while they were in the king's army. The king then ordered the shrill war-blasts to be sounded on the trumpets, and all his army to be led out of the city to level plains which were near. And when the kings became aware of this, that King Balant was come dight for battle, they had the war-whoop raised with much ado, and they had now divided their army in two divisions. Thereupon the war-trumpets were blown and a mighty fight befell with shots from hand-bows and spears and every kind of weapons, and that brunt raged for a long time with the greatest fury, so that each man had work enough in guarding his life. The brother-kings and their men wrought great havoc, they thought that the victory was sure, because of great disparity in the numbers, as has been said before. King Balant bade his men stand quiet and keep on the defensive, and this they did; yet they slew an untold number of men of the army of the brothers, so that the chances of the fight were rather against the heathens, and the blood-brooks flowed far and wide where the men were plying swords and spears, war-hammers and every sort of weapon,

D

bardagi hinn adgángs mesti. Kóngarnir sóktu hardt frañ
60 í ákafa, og vóru bádir hinir adgjördamestu. Málpriant
kóngr var í brjósti sinnar Filkíngar, og gjördi Bálant
kóngi hinn mesta Skada á mönnum sínum bædi á lífi og
heilsu. þetta fær séd Karl, og reid á móti Malpríant,
reiddi kóngur þá upp Sverd, og hugdi kappañ sundur ad
65 snída, enn Karl hafdi Spjótskapts brot í hendi, og sló því
á móti höggi kóngs, svo þad kom á midt Sverdid í loptinu
med svo miklum hasti, ad Sverdid hraut úr hendi honum
lángt burt á völlinn, tók þá Karl sverd sitt og reiddi til
höggs mjög röskmannlega, so þad kom á midjann hjálm
70 kóngs, so þad tók í sundur hjálminn allan er þó var mjög
traustur, hvad mönnum þókti stærsti vodi, enn kóngur
særdist lítid ad eins sár og fékk óvit, enn af þeim
mikla brest sem vard af þessu þúnga höggi, brá Essid
kóngsins so vid mjög, og tók ákaflega rás med kónginn
75 burt úr bardaganum, svo Karl gat hér ei meira adgjört.
Enn er Fástínus sér þetta, þeinkti hann bródur sinn til
dauda særdann, því honum vóru fallinn öll vopn, fylltist
hann þá grimdar og jók bardagan med ædis framgaungu,
setjandi essid endilángar filkíngar í gégnum og drap
80 fiölda maña, svo daudir menn lágu alla vega. þetta sér
Dixin, og reid honum á móti, lagdi hann Spjóti sínu til
kóngs, so í gégnum skjöldin gékk, renndi Spjótid med
vinstri Sídu, svo kóngur fékk Sár mikid, reiddi þá kóngur
Sverdid med mikillri reidi, kom höggid á kappan so
85 aftók bardid af hjálminum, og skar brinjuna á brjóstinu
og kom í Skjöldinn, því kappin bar hañ undir, og
hlífdi sér so sárum og lífi hestsins. Dixin hjó þá aptur
50

for the battle was fought with great vigour. The kings pressed on hard and eagerly, and both of them were men of mighty doing. Malpriant was in the van of his army, and did scathe to Balant's men in life and limb. Seeing this, Karl made for Malpriant, who raised his sword, wishful to cut the warrior asunder, but Karl had a broken spear-handle in his hand, and met therewith the blow, so that it suddenly caught the sword aloft, and the sword leapt from the king's hand far out into the field; then Karl took his own sword, and therewith aimed so stout a blow, that it struck even in the middle of the trusty casque, and cleft it all asunder, strong though it was, and men now deemed the peril very great; yet the king was merely slightly wounded, though he fell into a swoon. The mighty crash of the heavy blow startled the king's horse, so it rushed off with the king away out of the battle, and Karl might do no more this while. Now Faustinus saw this and thought his brother wounded unto death, for he had lost all his weapons; and he was filled with wrath, and stirred the fight anew with mad onward rush, spurring his horse right along the battle-lines and slaying a host of men, so that dead men lay all about. Dixin seeing this rode against the king, and thrust his spear at him, so that it went right through his shield; the spear flew along his left side, and he got a great wound; the king raised his sword then with great fury and the blow struck the warrior so that it cut off the rim of the casque, and cut the burnie at the breast, and struck the shield, for the warrior raised his shield to parry the blow, and this saved him from wounds, and saved too the life of his horse. Dixin then dealt

til kóngs, so tók í sundur Skjóldinn allan, og djúpt í Lær
kóngs kóngur greip þá krókaspjót og lagdi því so sterklega
90 til kappans ad festi í brinjunni á vinstri öxlinni; kippti
hann þá kappanū úr Södlinum og fékk varla haldid
hönum, kom hönum þó uppá Södulbriggjuna firir framan
sig, reid so med hann til sinna landtjalda, og fékk hann
þrælum til vöktunar, enn er Bálant kóngur og kappar
95 hañs sáu þetta, urdu þeir mjög ódir og ákafir í bardaganum,
bad kóngur þá vel duga, eñ þeir gjördu svo og juku
stránga hríd, med miklum framgángi, var kóngr sjálfur
hinn adgjörda mesti, hafdi hann Spjót og Sverd sitt í
hvörri hendi, svo hann gat í senn bædi lagt og höggvid,
100 hlaut þá margur skjótann og skadlegan dauda, valkéstir
daudra búka vóru margir og háir so þeir numdu vid axlir
manna. Vilhjálmur komst nærst kóngi í frægd og
framgaungu sinni, allir bördust þeir med ákéfd sem med
kóngi vóru, svo heidíngjar tóku ad flía, þvíad þeir vóru
105 hrönnum drepnir bædi á vígvöllunum og í flóttarekstrinum, so landid vard hulid í daudra manna búkum.
Kóngarnir kalla nú herin á flótta, og hlutu þeir landtjöld
sín naudugir eptir láta med filgjandi audæfum því þeir vóru
lángt á leid frá hraktir. Bálant kóngur rak flóttann
110 medan dagur vannst til, enn sem Sól var undirgeinginn,
snéri hann aptur og bad menn sína hætta flóttarekstrinum,
ridu þeir nú heim til Borgarinnar, enn vegna mirkurs og
vaktarinnar, reid hann ekki í herbúdirnar, tók hann nú
hvíld um næturtímann í sínu konúnglegu herbergi. Ad
115 morgni baud kóngur mönnum sínum ad sækja herfáng og
52

a back blow at the king, and cleft his shield atwain, and wounded him deep in his thigh, whereupon the king seized a barbed spear and thrust it so hardly at the champion that it fastened on the burnie at the left shoulder; he then pulled the champion from off his saddle, and though scarce able to hold him, he brought him on to his saddle in front of him and so rode with him to his war-tent, and delivered him into the charge of thralls. Now when King Balant and his warriors saw this they became exceedingly mad and raged in the fight. The king bade them be right doughty, and they were so, and eked out a mighty war-brunt with vigorous onset, wherein the king himself was the keenest, with a spear and sword in either hand, so that he might cut and thrust at the same time. There many a man gat him a swift and direful death. The piles of dead trunks were many and high and reached up to the shoulders of men. Vilhjalmur came nearest the king in renown and valour. All the men who were with the king fought keenly, so that the heathens began to flee, for they were slain in heaps both on the battle-field and on the route, so that the country-side was covered with the trunks of the dead. The kings had now perforce to call upon their men to flee, and they had unwillingly to leave their camp behind with all the wealth thereto belonging, for they had been chased far from it. King Balant drove the rout while day lasted, and when the sun had set he turned and bade his men desist. And they rode home to the city, and by reason of the darkness and of the watch, he did not ride into the camp, but rested the night in his palace chamber. In the morning the king bade his men fetch the booty herbúdir, var so gjórt og bjuggust þeir ad drepa vaktina. Tóku þeir nú allt herfángid, med Tjöldum beggja kónganna, var Dixín og úr fjötrum færdur og heimfluttur, 120 fundust þeir kóngur og hann med hinni mestu blídu og stórri sigurhrósan, vard mönnum kátt af Flótta kónganna. Bálant kóngur baud ad hreinsa vígvölluna, og lét kasta kroppum daudra manna í djúp vötn, og Síki, og þvo völlinn med vatni og sá yfir hann Salti. Settist kóngr 125 nú um kyrrt med stórri gledi, og skipti herfánginu med þeim gersemum er þar vóru ad fá medal sinna manna, því hañ þeinkti óttalaust í nádum sínu Ríki ad halda. Nú víkur Söguñi aptur til kónganna, ad þeir höfdu leigid med her sinn allañ undir berum himni, og þóktust Smánarferd 130 farid hafa, þeinktu því um hvórnin þeir skildu sinnar Svívyrdíngar hefna, qvádu þeir Bálant kóng ósigrandi vera, fiell þeim þad í géd samþikkilega, ad gjóra landi hañs enn meiri Skada med eldi og járnum. Málpríant var um landid fródari ad kunnugleika, og seigir bródur 135 sínum ad eitt ágjætt hérad lægi útaf Hispanja til austurs áttar, skulum vér þángad stefna her vorum öllum seigir hann, og leggja þennañ landspart undir oss, mun kóngi þad verda meiga til mesta Skadrædis, því hann hefur verid sem ein hurd firir landi þessu; kann vera ad oss 140 verdi sídar audsóktara ad vinna þetta. Þókti Fástínus og ödrum þetta efnilegt rád, og stefndu nú þángad med allañ sinn her.

11 Capítuli.

FYRIR héradi þessu var jarl ríkur til yfirstjórnar Calítor ad nafni, og sat í ágjætri borg er Anga hét, hún var ramlega biggd med gilltum múruñ og

and the war-booths, and they did so, and prepared to slay
the watch. They took now all the booty, and the tents
of both the kings; Dixin was freed from his fetters and
brought home, and he and the king met with greatest joy
and triumph, and the men made merry at the king's
flight. King Balant bade the battle-fields be cleared, and
had the bodies of the dead thrown into deep waters and
ditches, and the fields washed with water and bestrewn
with salt. The king then settled down to peace in great
delight, and shared the booty and the precious things
found therein among his men, for he deemed that he
could then fearlessly enjoy his realm in quiet. Now the
saga turns to the kings, and tells how they had lain with
their army beneath the open sky, and they judged they
had gone on an errand of shame, and they cast about in
their minds how they could avenge their ignominies.
They said that Balant was invincible, but they both were
at one in this, to wit, that they would do the country still
greater scathe with fire and sword. Malpriant had greater
knowledge of the country, and he told his brother that
out of Hispania to the east there was a choice territory.
"Let us thither with all our host," said he, " and make this
part of the land subject to us; it may prove the greatest
scathe to the king, for it has been to the country even as
a gate; perchance we shall hereafter more easily gain it."
The plan seemed goodly to Faustinus and the rest, and
they now made their way thither with all their host.

Chapter XI.

OVER this land there ruled a certain mighty earl,
Calitor by name, and he dwelt in a noble city
called Anga. It was a stoutly built city with golden walls

55

Turnum. 3 Dætur átti Jarlñ vóru tvær af þeim heiman
5 géfnar, átti Bálant kóngur adra er Dýla hét; þessi Jarl
var gamall madur, enn hafdi verid enn mesti frægdar
madur um daga sína, og þann tíma er Donrek kóngur
hélt Hispaníam, hafdi hann hañs Líd kóngur verid. Med
Jarli var eirn Riddari úngur er Vallanus hét sá hafdi
10 útlægur gjördur verid af Bálant kóngi firir ágirndarsakir
kóngs, því Vallanus hafdi átt kostulegan gard med dírum
Landkostum, hvórn hann hafdi ad erfdum tekid eptir
Fódur sinn, enn kóngur vildi halda þennan gard eign sína
med ódru þar nær er til landsins kom. Vallanus vardi
15 sitt mál med réttindum þad frekasta hann kunni,
gramdist þetta kónginum so mjóg, ad hann gjórdi hann
fridlausan í landinu; komst hann þá til Calitors jarls, því
Fadir hanns hafdi leingi Félagi Jarlsins verid, þeinkti
Jarl med Tídinni ad sætta Vallaníus vid kóng, og ná
20 aptur hañs eignar rétti. Mjóg óvart komu Víkíngar
Borgar líd þessum, var þad firri um morgunin eñ vaktiñ
kalladi; brutu þeir þegar upp borgar hlidinn ad víkínga
vana og drápu vókumennina, enn sumir flúdu undan og
gjórdu jarli kunnugt uñ hernad víkínga. Jarl klæddist
25 skjótlega og qvaddi meñ til lids sér, því hann vildi heldur
med frægd falla enn sitt med ósæmd uppgéfa vóru þad alls
300 vígra manna er med honum til varnar vóru, slæst nú í
bardaga, og verst Jarliñ óvinum sínum med stórum frægdum
og gjórdi þeim allmikid manntjón, so á skómmum tíma
30 fjellu 60 manna firir hanns vopnum, og er Fástínus kóngr
56

and towers. The earl had three daughters, of whom two had been given away in marriage, one being wife of King Balant; she was named Dyla. This earl was now an old man, but in his day he had been most famous, and at the time whenas King Donrek had held Spain, had been his vassal-king. With the earl there was a young knight called Vallanus; he had been outlawed by King Balant through that king's avarice. For Vallanus had had a noble castle with lands exceeding choice which he had got as a heritage from his father. The king desired this castle for his own with all the country sides thereto belonging. Vallanus defended his cause, justly, to the utmost of his power, and thereat the king grew so angry that he made him an outlaw from the land. He got him then to Calitor, for his father had for a long time been a comrade of the earl; and the earl planned to bring about peace between Vallanus and the king as time went on, and to obtain for him the right of his property. Now the vikings came very suddenly upon the men of this city; they reached there in the morning-tide before the watch was called. They forthwith broke up the gates of the city, after the wont of vikings, and slew the watch, though part fled and made known to the earl the raid of the viking army. The earl dressed quickly and called men to his aid, for he chose rather to fall with glory than dishonourably to yield his own. Three hundred doughty men in all gathered round him for defence, and now a battle befell, and the earl defended himself against his foes with great glory, and caused them much loss of life, so that in a short time sixty men fell before his weapons; and when King Faustinus

sá framgaungu Jarls, fór hann til móts vid hann, og hió af hañs vinstri hónd, enn Jarl hafdi Sverdid í hægri hendi og hjó til kóngs so aftók eirad, þar med mikid af hjálminum so kóngur fiekk Sár á óxlina, greiddi nú 35 kóngur aptur hógg, og setti Sverdid á háls Jarli so aftók hófudid, so jarl féll daudur til jardar, enn þeir menn sem eptir lifdu bádust fridar, var þeim þá óllumm líf géfid. Vallanus var nú í bland þessara; leiddi hann kóngana med hernum óllum í hóll og hásæti Jarls, og játadi þeim hlidni 40 ad veita og trúa þjónustu ; tóku þeir þá undir sig alt land Jarls med óllum hans audæfum, og er Vallanus gjórdist þeim handgeingē, sógdu þeir hónum frá sínum óforum og vidureign þeirra vid Bálant kóng. Vallanus mynntist nú á gjórdir kóngs vid sig, og þóktist nú sjá rád til ad launa 45 hónum vondsleg vidskipti, því nærst mælti hann vid kóngana : Bálant kóngur á Skuld í minn gard, og væri gott henni ad lúka, mun eg víst bæta meiga Skada ykkar ef mér hlída viljed. þeir qvádust honum hlída skildu. Vallanus mælti : Eg vil nú þegar rída á fund Bálants 50 kóngs med fjólda manns og marga góda Fjárhluti, og kuñgjóra honum, ad Calítor jarl mágur hañs komi á fund hanns ad þrem dógum lidnum, og því mun kóngur víst trúa ; á þeim deigi máttu, Fástínus kóngur ! taka á þig búníng jarls, og rída med 500 manna til 55 borgarinnar, alla búna ad landsvana, mun þá Bálant kóngur ei annad ætla eñ þad sé jarl med sína menn, uppslá þegar hlidum og brúrnar nidurláta, þú munt þa med miklum fagnadi innrída í Borgina, eñ

saw the earl's advance, he went to meet him and smote off his left hand, but the earl had his sword in his right, and he struck at the king, so that he took off his ear and therewith a good deal of the helmet, and the king got wounded on the shoulder. And now the king dealt another blow, and set his sword at the neck of the earl, and it took off his head, and the earl fell dead to the earth. The men who were still alive asked for quarter, and life was granted to them all. Now among these was Vallanus; he led the kings with all their troops into the hall and to the high-seat of the earl, and he promised to yield them allegiance and faithful service. They then took to themselves all the land of the earl, together with all his wealth. Now when Vallanus had become their right-hand man, they told him of all the disasters in their dealings with King Balant. Vallanus called now to mind the doings of the king towards himself, and thought he saw now a way to pay him for his wrongs. Eftsoon said he to the kings:—"King Balant is in debt for my castle, and it would be well to have it paid, and I may assuredly mend your loss if ye will but obey me." They said they would do so. Vallanus said:—"I shall now forthwith ride to meet King Balant with a host of men and many goodly things, and make known to him that Earl Calitor his father-in-law is coming to meet him within three days, and the king will surely believe it. On that day do thou, King Faustinus, take upon thyself the garb of the earl, and ride with five hundred men to the city, all arrayed after the fashion of the country, whereby King Balant cannot but then believe that it is the earl and his suite: forthwith he'll throw open the gates and let down the drawbridges, and in great glee thou'lt ride into the city, but

59

meigin herin skal filgja Málpríant kóngi, og vera Fjalla
60 á millum í einum þraungum dal sem þar er, og bída þar ;
enn þegar þú ert komin í borgina, skaltu láta blása
þrisvar í þiñ lúdur, þá skal Málpríant k. bregda vid og
stefna sínu lidi heim til borgarinnar. Bálant kóngur
mun vilja ykkur mótstódu veita, enn þú Fástínus skalt
65 því hamla ad hañ kuñi borgina aptur ad láta, edur hlidum
læsa, þar til þinn bródur kémur med sinn her, og munud
þid þá fá hefnt ykkar á þessum kóngi. Kóngarnir sögdu
þetta allgott rád, og sögdu hann skildi þessa sína trigd
med særum festa ; enn hañ sór hér traustan eid uppá.
70 Fóru þeir nú öllum þeim rádum fram er Vallanus hafdi
géfid, og tókst þeim þetta alt med hañs rádum, og sem
Bálant kóngur þeinkti gledilega veitslu ad gjöra jarlinum
mágje sínum, vard úr heñi hinn mesti ófagnadur og
mannfall hid mesta, kom öllum þetta óvart, vard þar
75 mikid mannfall í borginni. Bálant kóngur og kappar
hans vórdust med vopnum sínum þad besta þeir kunnu,
enn af því eingin brinja huldi líkami þeirra, bárust sár
á þá. Vilhjálmur brautst fram hid frækilegasta, og drap
lid sér til beggja handa, so hann hrakti þá ad borgar-
80 hlidunum til baka ; enn er þetta sá Málpríant kóngur, sníst
hann ad Vilhjálmi, hljóp hann þá ad kóngi og greiddi
honum högg mikid med Sverdinu yfir þverar herdarnar so
í sundur tók brinjuna, fjell kóngur af þessu mikla höggi
flatur til jardar, eñ fékk þó ekkert sár, olli því hid

let the main army follow King Malpriant and keep between the mountain-passes in a certain narrow dale
which is there, and abide there. And as soon as thou
art come within the city, thou shalt cause the war-blast
to be blown three times, and then King Malpriant shall
bestir himself at once and march home with his army
to the city. King Balant will make a stand, but thou,
Faustinus, shalt hinder him from shutting the city and
locking the gates till thy brother come with all his
host, and then shall ye be able to wreak vengeance on
the king." The kings said 'twas excellent counsel, and
ordered him to pledge his faith in the matter by oaths;
and he swore a mighty oath thereon. Now they acted
withal on the counsel Vallanus had given, and things
befell even as he had counselled, and when King Balant
weened he was to give a joyful banquet to the earl his
father-in-law, it turned out a sorry welcome, and the loss
of human life was great in the city, since this befell all
men unawares. King Balant and his champions defended
themselves with their weapons as best they might, but as
their bodies were not covered with burnies, many a wound
fell on them thick and fast. Vilhjalmur rushed forward
most dauntlessly, and slew the host on either side, so that
he drove them back to the gates of the city. Now
when King Malpriant saw this, he turned to Vilhjalmur,
who rushed at the king and dealt him a great blow
with his sword athwart the shoulder, so that the burnie
was cut through, and the king fell by the mighty
stroke flat to earth, yet without being wounded, because

þikkva dírsledur sem kóngur bar undir klædunum.
86 Fjöldi af heidíngjum vóru nærstaddir, tóku kóngin ílla
færan og settu hañ uppí sinn Sódul. Enn Wilhjálmur
sá nú menn síns kóngs allfáa, enn Bálant kóng og Dixin
sá hann hvórgi; í því kom Didrik til hañs, spurdi
90 Vilhjálmr hañ ad Bálant kóngi, enn hann sagdi hann
fángin vera. Sagdi Vilhjálmur honum þá, hvórnin hann
hefdi Málpríant k. af hesti komid. Kom þá Karl til
þeirra; kom þeim þá öllum samañ ad flýa og forda lífinu,
og so gjórdu þeir, ad þeir brutust frañ alt ad Borgar
95 hlidum og drápu ótal maña, komust so med stærstu
þrautum í borgina um sídir, þeir áttu ad borgum og lands
bigdum ad gjæta, þar konur þeirra og bórn vóru inni,
fóru þeir þángad, var og Dixin í sína átthaga kominn,
léttu nú kóngarnir orustu, enn Bálant kóngur var fángiñ,
100 og gáfu þeim öllum grid sem eptir lifdu utann Sonum
Bálants kóngs sem á barnsaldri vóru þá drápu þeir, vóru
þeir 3; Drottníng kóngs sprakk af harmi því hún vard ad
sjá uppá dauda barna sinna. Kóngarnir settu Vallanus
yfir Land og borgir, enn fóru sjálfir heim til sinna landa
105 med stórri Sigurhrósan, og fluttu Bálant kóng med sér í
Spanja fángiñ, og þrjátíu af hañs mónnuñ med honum
þeir tóku og dóttir Jarls med sér þá sem ógéfinn var, og
mikid af vóldum Fjárhlutum.

12 Capítuli.

Þ EGAR Kóngarnir komu nú heim i Spanía, þá
bad Fástínus bródur sinn Málpríant kóng ad
þeir mættu drekka þar brúdkaup hañs, því hann
vildi taka sér til Drottníngar dóttur Calítors jarls;

of a thick deerskin which the king wore beneath his kirtle. A multitude of heathens standing near took the disabled king and set him in the saddle. Vilhjalmur saw now right few men of the king's host, and as for King Balant himself and Dixin, he espied them nowhere. But anon Dixin came up to him, and asked him after King Balant; he said the king was now a prisoner, and told him how he had brought King Malpriant from off his horse. Soon after Karl came up to them, and they were all agreed to save their lives by flight, and they did so, by rushing forward all the way to the city-gates, and they slew a countless number of men. At length after greatest perils they got into the city, and they proceeded then to guard the citadels and road-side homesteads wherein their wives and children abode; thither they went and Dixin got back to his home. Now the kings stinted their combat, seeing that King Balant was their prisoner, and they gave quarter to all those left alive, save to the sons of King Balant who were still in childhood; they were three in number, and they slew them all. The queen burst for very grief, having to witness with her own eyes her children's death. The kings made Vilhjalmur their seneschal of the country and cities there, and went home to their own lands in mighty triumph, and they took King Balant with them as their prisoner into Spain, and thirty of his men beside, and the earl's unwedded daughter, and much choice treasure.

Chapter XIII.

Now whenas the kings were come to their home in Spain, Faustinus asked King Malpriant that they might drink his bridal there, for he was minded to take the daughter of Earl Calitor unto himself as his queen.

þessu játar Málpríant kóngur blídlega, og bjó til hina
6 sæmilegustu veitslu, og baud öllum höfdíngjum síns Ríkis
þar til. Málpríant kóngur átti eina ágjæta dóttur er Fýris
hét, hún var ad aldri 15 ára, og nam íþróttir og
qvennlegar listir, var hún fremri öllum meýum í Spanja,
10 eingin fannst henni frídari, sómasamari, sidferdisbetri né
vitrari, kóngur unni dóttur sinni mikid, hún sat ad
veitslunni med sínum þjónustu meýum. Kóng Bálant
höfdu þeir brædur sett í mirkva stofu ásamt hans Sveinum,
er þeir komu í Spanja, sat hann þar í jarnvidjum og
15 fjötrum. Fýris kóngs dóttir spurdi Fódur sinn ad hvar
Bálant kóngur væri? enn hann svaradi henni svo: eingu
skiptir þig þad. þá mælti Jómfrúiñ: þess bid eg þig,
Fadir elskulegur! Lát þú Bálant kóng nióta fagnadardags
med oss so hann sitje hér í höll þinni, og so eg sjái hann.
20 Kóngur mælti: nær veitsla þessi er afstadiñ, dóttir! þá
skal þér þad veitast hún qvad þad ofseint vera og mælti:
higg ad því Fadir miñ! hve völt hamíngjann er, so sem
þú mátt nú sjá og sanna á Bálant kóngi, ad honum þénti
stór lukka fyrir skémstu, þar med mañvirding og mikil
25 frægd, enn nú situr hañ í mirkvastofu hriggur og vesæll,
og kann ykkur sídañ líka hid sama ad henda þótt nú
sé stór ydar gledi og lukka allmikil, þá kann þessi
ydar velgeingni í skjóta Sorg ad uñ snúast; kóngur
bistist vid ord hennar, enn hún lagdi bádar hendur
30 um háls hönuñ og bad hann veita sér þá bæn. þá
dignadi géd kóngs, og baud ad sækja Bálant kóng og
menn hañs, var so gjört. Var þá Bálant kóngur
leiddur í höllina og meñ hañs, og fjötur af þeim
leist. Málpríant kóngur mælti: kosti vil eg géfa þér til

King Malpriant assented blithely, and let purvey for a
great feast, and he bade thereto the chieftains of his
realm. Now King Malpriant had a goodly daughter
hight Fyris; she was at this time fifteen years of age,
apt in all the grace and lore of womankind, and she far
excelled all other maidens in the land of Spain. There
was not to be found a damsel fairer, worshipfuller, more
modest, nor wiser than she, and the king loved his
daughter much. She sat there at the feast, her maidens
with her. But as for King Balant, when King Malpriant
and his brother had come to Spain, they placed him in a
dark dungeon, together with his men, and there he sat
in iron chains and fetters. Fyris asked her father where
King Balant was. He answered, "It concerns thee in
nowise." "Yet," said the maiden, "I beg thee, dear
father, let King Balant share with us this day of joy, and
let him sit here in this hall that I may see him." Said
the king, "When the feast is at an end, my daughter,
thy wish shall be conceded." "'Twill then perchance
be all too late," answered the maiden. "Bethink thee,
father, of the fickleness of fortune which thou mayest
see and learn e'en from King Balant's fate. Fair fortune
was his vassal but awhile agone, and therewithal worship
among men and great renown, but now he sits within a
dungeon, sad and bereft; and a like fate may sithence be
thine; tho' now thy cheer be goodly and thy lot so fair, thy
bliss may quickly turn to grief." The king frowned then
at the maiden's words, but she put her arms around his
neck and begged him to grant her prayer; and the king's
mood softened, and he bade them fetch King Balant and
his men, and so 'twas done. King Balant was then led
into the hall, his men along with him, and their fetters
were loosed. "On these terms," said King Malpriant,

E

lífs og lausnar, og vilier þú lofa því og med eidi stadfesta
þina lofun : ad vera vorri herralegri magt undirgéfin alla
þína lífdaga, og gjalda oss árlega Skatt af þínum londum
og eignum, þá vil eg þér líf og lausn géfa. Kóngur vard
miög hriggur vid þetta, enn lofadi þó þessu ; lét þá Mál-
40 príant mýkja sár hañs med kostulegum Smyrslum, klæda
kónglegum skrúda, og leida í hid óædra öndvegi. Bálant
kóngur var mikid frídari álytuᵯ enn allir hinir.—leid svo
dagurinn—var þá Bálant kóngur leiddur til Sængur og
menn hañs med honum, hófdu þeir allir eitt Herbergi, og
45 sem menn allir vóru í svefni, gékk Fýris kóngs dóttir í þad
herbergi sem Bálant kóngur var, og sem hún kom iñ þángad, gjórdi hún kóng advarañ, og áttu þaug samtal í
miklū kjærleika uᵯ nóttina. Hún mælti til kóngs : þann
kost seigi eg þér vel sóma, ad þú bidjer mín þér til eigiñ
50 ords af Fódr mínum. Kóngur mælti : þad er mikil lífs
hætta firir mig. Jómfrúiñ mælti : Eg mun rád til sjá ad
þér skal þad einginn hætta. Alt tekst sem audid skal
verda, seigir kóngur, og gladdist hér vid stórlega. Bundu
þaug nú þenna sinn trúnad fastmælum, og skildu ad so
55 mæltu med kjærleika. Dagin eptir geingu menn undir
bord, og settust kóngar í Sæti sín ; Fýris kóngs dóttir
kom í Höllina og fögnudu henni allir vel. Bálant kóngur
vard furdu hýrleitur, og hafdi kóngs dóttir jafnan augu sín
á hönum ; þetta sá Fadir hennar og sætti hann þad mjóg
60 lítt, tóku menn ad gjórast gladir af drykkju. Bálant
kóngur drakk miög lítid. Hann mælti þá til Málpríants
kóngs : Hvórsu tekur kóngur ordum mínum þeim eg vil nú
fraᵯbera firir ydur, sem er : Eg vil bidja dóttur ydar mér

"I would grant thee life and liberty, if thou assent thereto and fortify thy promise with an oath, to wit, that thou be subject to our lordship all thy lifedays, and pay us yearly tribute from thy lands and wealth; on these terms I grant thee life and liberty." At this the king grew heavy, but withal he promised. Malpriant bade his men then salve his wounds with choicest unguents, and he had him dight in royal array and led to the seat of lesser dignity, the high seat opposite the king's, and King Balant was by far a goodlier man to look on than all others there, and so the day went by. King Balant was led then to his couch, his men with him, and they were altogether in one chamber. Now when all men were fast in sleep, Fyris the king's daughter fared to the chamber where King Balant lay, and when she was come therein, she made the king ware of her presence, and they conversed in great love through all the livelong night. Said she to the king, "'Twere best, methinks, to ask my father for my hand." "'Twere great peril of my life," said the king. "I shall find rede," said the maiden, "that it shall peril thee nought." "Things fated fare forward," said the king, and he was much gladdened; and they bound their secret troth by mutual pledges, and parted in great love. On the morrow the men ranged themselves about the board, and the kings sat on their seats, and Princess Fyris too came to the hall, and all men gave her goodly greeting. King Balant was wondrous blithe of cheer, and the king's daughter rested her gaze on him throughout; her father espied it; it pleased him little. Men grew merry then with drink, but King Balant drank little, and anon he spake thus to King Malpriant :—"How will the king receive the thing I will now disclose? yea, I ask of thee thy daughter for my wife,

67

til eiginn ords, svo mín Herleidíng fái nokkra bót, máské
65 ekki mínki vid þad fremd ydar og frægd. Málpríant
kóngur brást vid afar reidur, og baud mónnum sínum ad
taka Bálant k. og heingja hann firir ofdyrfd sína. þegar
Fýris kóngs dóttir heirdi þetta, bliknadi hennar yfirlitur,
gékk hún fyrir Fódur sinn og mælti: minnstu, Fadir! á
70 þad sem eg firri sagdi þér um valta Lukku heims þessa,
ei kann þig sídur ógjæfan henda eñ þennan stórfræga kóng,
því þad veitstu sjálfur, ad meiri frægdarmadur er Bálant
kóngur enn þér erud, því med Svikū einum er hann af
ykkur Brædrum yfirunnin, og med þessum hætti neitar
75 þú tign þinni og hamíngju, því ad hañs teingdum er Ríki
þínu mikil upphefd, ef þid med kjærleika haldid ydar ást,
munid þid stóran sigur hafa, og lónd og ríki jafnañ unnid
géta. Allir hófdíngjar er þar sátu, qvádu þetta alt satt
vera, sem Jómfrúinn hafdi sagt. Málpr. kóngur þagdi
80 leingi, eñ um sídir mælti hann: med þeim hætti játa eg
þér Dóttur mína ad þú takir trú hennar, eñ kastir þinni,
og á vora trú leidir þú allt fólk í landi þínu enn þó þeinkti
eg þig til annarar útfarar úr landi þínu enn í fadm dottur
minnar. Bálant kóngur mælti: óvísir eru veigir hins
85 audnusama, enn allskostar mun eg til þess vinna, sem
mér berst í bætur, mína trú skal eg afleggja og mínum
mónnum til þess halda, sór hañ nú sterkañ eid uppá
þetta, þa gladdist Málpríant kóngur, stód upp og lagdi
sína hónd í hónd Bálants kóngs, og festi hónum dóttur
90 sína, og lét nú auka veitsluna med vistum og fjólmeñi,
68

that my captivity may find some recompense, and, per-adventure, thy fame and worship will not thereby be lessened." King Malpriant waxed exceeding wroth, and bade his men seize King Balant and hang him for his overweening pride. The Princess Fyris when she heard all this grew pale of face, and she went to her father, and said to him :—"Remember, father, the words I spake to thee erewhile of the fickleness of this world's fortune; evil may no less cross thy path than that of this most famous king; as thou thyself best knowest, King Balant is a man of greater fame than thou, and by mere treachery has he been vanquished by thee and by thy brother, and by this deed thou must needs lose thy glory and thy fortune; but an he be thy son-in-law, thy power would be mightier, and if thou keepest faithful friendship with him, glorious triumphs will be thine, and thou wilt ever win victory o'er foreign realms." The nobles present said the maiden spake aright. King Malpriant was long time silent, but at last he spake : " On this term will I give to thee my daughter, that thou take her faith, and cast away thine own, and turn too to our faith the folk of all thy land; certes I deemed thy exit from thy realm should bring thee elsewhere than to the bosom of my daughter." King Balant said : " Little he heeds whom fortune speeds," but at all hazards I would gain that which shall better my plight;—I cast away my faith, and shall urge my men to do the like," and he swore a mighty oath thereon. Then King Malpriant was full glad, and he stood up and laid his hand in the hand of King Balant, and plighted him to his daughter, and now he had the feast renewed with goodlier cheer, with rich supplies,

var nú drukkid brúdkaup beggja kónganna med mestu
vid höfn og veraldar prjáli; þar allnær stód goda hof
Málpríants kóngs, þángad geingu kóngarnir daglega med
stórum fórnfæríngum og bænagjördum, Bálant kóngur
95 filgde þeim til goda Hússins ad votta sinn átrúnad, og sem
hann kom firir þaug, fiell hann fram fyrir þaug og sór þeim
átrúnad med þakklætis fórn og bænagjördum, og til sannrar
þakkargjördar kysti hann á þeirra hendur og fætur, en er
Málpríant sá audmýkt Bálants kóngs, gékk hann til hañs
100 og mynntist vid hañ af stórum kjærleika, og sagdi hann
skildi sjálfur Löndum, Skóttum og þegnum sínum ráda,
vóru brudkaupiñ endud med stórum fiegjöfum af kóngun-
um og þeirra rádaneiti; fóru nú allir heimleidis. Fýris
kóngs dóttir fór mz kóngi sínum heim í Hispanja, og filgdu
105 þeim enir tignustu menn úr landinu, sem þeim vóru til þjónustu géfnir med miklum audæfum; enn sem Bálant kémur
heim, verda lands menn gladir, en sem þeir vissu hann
frá kristinni trú geinginn, abladi þeim þad stórrar hriggd-
ar, því hann kúgadi meñ til heidni med píslum og
110 dauda, og létu margir líf sitt firri en kristni, enn fiöldi
manna neitadi kristinni Trú; kóngur lét brenna allar
bækur heilagrar skriftar, og brióta myndir Drottins úr
kyrkjum og helgum húsum, enn setti þar aptur mynder
Mahómets og hañs kénníngu; enn þeir fjórir kappar sem
115 firr umgétur flúdu med öllum sínum þénurum og teingda
mönnum til Frakklands undañ ófridi og íllum átrúnadi
Bálants kóngs, og gjördust þar lendir menn til daudadags

and with multitudes of men, and the bridales of both kings were drank with greatest circumstance and with all pomp. Close anigh stood the temple of King Malpriant, and the kings went thither daily with rich offerings and with prayer. With them went now King Balant to the house of their gods to testify his faith, and when he came afore the gods he fell before them prostrate and avowed his faith, and offered thank-offerings and prayer, and in unfeigned thankfulness he kissed their hands and feet; and when King Malpriant beheld King Balant's humbleness, he came to him and kissed him with great love, and said he should himself rule all his lands, his tribute, and his subjects. And these bridales ended with great gifts from the kings and from their counsellors, and all folk went then to their homes. Fyris, the king's daughter, fared with her king to his home in Hispania, and the highest lords of the land went with them, to wit, those given them for service, and they had, too, much wealth. Now when King Balant reached his home his folk were right glad, but when they learnt that he had turned from Christianity great misery fell on them, for he cowed them into heathendom with torture and with death; and many liefer left their life than cast away their faith, but a many men forsook their Christianity. The king let burn all books of holy writ, and let break the images of the Lord in churches and in holy houses, and placed therein images of Mahomed and books of his teaching. The four warriors afore-named fled with their servants and their kin to Frankland away from King Balant's hate and treachery, and they lived as barons there unto their death-day.

Vallanus og Bálant sættust ad forlagi Málpríants kongs
og þeirra brædra, kóngur fékk honum eignir sínar aptur,
120 Vallanus lét kristni, og stirdi Ríki Calitors jarls, því hañ
átti dóttur Jarls; og var heidni í Hispanja alt til daga
Karls hins mikla er firstur vard keisari fyrir nordañ
Grikklands haf.

13 Capítuli.

$\mathfrak{A}$D endudum þessum brúdkaupum hieldt Fástinus heim
med drottníngu sína í Cimbria og settist ad Ríkinu;
Ceta hét Drottníng hañs og var hún stird í samförum
þeirra um lángā tíma, því hún hafdi naudug verid, kon-
5 gúngur unni henni vel, og lét flest ad vilja hennar, sefadi
þad géd Drottníngar mikid, sem og þad ad hún umgékkst
med kristnum mönnum̄; samfarir þeirra hjóna vóru
adgjördalausar því þaug áttu eingin börn landstjórn gékk
med stórum óhægdum enn aungvum vægdum, Gamalíel
10 stillti þad hann kunni, og mælti mönnum bjargvætti, ei
síst Amba Drottníngu og Syni hennar. Víkur nú þángad
Sögunni sem Ambales ólst upp med hyrd Fástínusar,
öllum mönnum ólíkur ad hegdan, hañ síndist og hinn
liótasti ad limaburdum lit og lundarfari, hañ hafdi jafnan
15 vist og dvöl í eldaskála, og mettadist af réttum þeim er þar
gjördust, og hætti ei firri enn fullur var, þókti þá flestum
í skarda, enn ef þjónustu konur réttaña vildu þar nokkud
mótmæla, jós hann eldi og heitu sodi á þær, og þad lét
hann jafnan fram̄fara þar til hann var mettur ordiñ, andlit
20 hañs var og hófud fullt óþekktar, Saurinda og annara
72

Vallanus and King Balant made peace together at the instance of King Malpriant and of his brother, and the king gave back to him his own, and Vallanus cast away the Christian faith and ruled the realm of Calitor, for he was wedded to the daughter of the earl, and heathendom obtained in Spain all along unto the days of Charles the Great, the first emperor north of the sea of Greece.

Chapter XHH.

WHEN these bridales were over, Faustinus went with his queen to his home in Cimbria, and settled there within his realm. His queen hight Ceta; she was longtime hard in her manner towards him, for she had wedded him maugré her will, but the king loved her well, and did much to please her, and so softened her mood, and moreover, she had converse with Christian men. Their wedded life was fruitless; they had no child. The land was governed with great rigour, and no mercy was shown. Gamaliel sought to quiet things as best he might, and pleaded for the lives of men, but first for the life of Amba and her son. And now the saga turns to Ambales, who grew up in the court of Faustinus unlike to all men in his conduct; he seemed the ugliest in gait and look and temper. He kept mostwhile in the kitchen-stead, and fed on whatsoever was there, and he stayed there till he was glutted, and folk deemed he made a huge hole in the dish he tasted; but when the maids said aught to him, he bespattered them with fire and with hot swill, and stinted not till he was sated. His face and head were most uncanny, what with dirt and filth;

73

óhreininda, eñ ef nokkur vildi hañs rád rækja og þvo hañs andlit og klædi, þá kvoladi hann þad jafnskjótt med Skarni og óþekkt, mælti hónum nokkur gódyrdi, þañ ord-skémdi hañ þar á mót, enn þeim sem honum hatur mælti, 25 síndi hann blidlindi, allfrekt; aldrei fékkst hann vid vinnustórf, nema tálga lángar spítur, og brá oddum þeirra í eldsloga, eingin þóktist kunna í huga sinn ad festa til hvórs þær mundu þéna; barna húsa bigging var þar vid eldaskálan sem borgar manna bórn áttu, þar med var 30 hreisishola afskræmileg sem Ambales átti, í hana lét hann Spítur sínar, og bjarghurdadi fyrir framañ. A vinnumanna í þróttir horfdi hann ákaflega, enn eingu ordi skipti hann ef nokkud tókst illa, meiddi sig nokkur þá hló hañ af ædi, enn færi vel, lét hann sig stiggañ 35 sjá;—J óllum hlutum síndist hann fiflum líkur, enn ad vexti og abli var hann umfram alla sem í borginni vóru, lidu nú tímar þar til hann taldist 12 ára gamall, hann var í bláum kubli daglega, med ledur belti um sig, med hatt eptir Hófdi Skaptan, sem klædasnid var þar í landi. 40 Amba Drottníng þoldi stóra ofraun af syni sínum, og hriggdist miög þar af, enn Greifi Gamaljel fékk henni jafnann fógnud og syni hennar audsýndann,—Eitt sinn var þad ad Fástínus kóngur gjórdi gésta bod mikid med stórum kostnadi, og baud landsins hófdíngium þar til, 45 þókti óllum sá vænsti kostur ad þiggja bod kóngs, og þá veitslañ stód í besta blóma, baud kóngur ad Ambales skildi og þángad koma, og vóru Sveinar kóngs sendir eptir honum

74

and if a man strove to mend his ways and washed his face and clothes, forthwith he befouled them anew with dirt and filth. If one spake kindly to him he spake evil in return, but to a man that showed him hate he was passing kind. He plied no other work than the wittling of long wooden spits, and he stuck them with their points into the glowing fire, and none could tell for what these spits were destined. Anigh to the kitchen-stead there was a children's playhouse for the children of the townsmen, and beside it was a wretched hovel belonging unto Ambales, and therein he kept his sticks, and he closed it with a huge stone. He cared greatly for the servants' sports; he said nought when things went amiss; if one hurt himself he laughed right madly, but when things fared well he showed himself full wroth. He seemed withal most like unto fools, yet as to growth and thews he excelled all others of the town; and so time passed till he was twelve years old. He was wont to dress in a blue cloak, with a leathern girdle round his waist, and a hat fitted to his head, as was the guise then in the land. Queen Amba was greatly troubled for her son, and she grieved mightily for him, but through Gamaliel kindness was always shown to her and to her son. Once on a time King Faustinus made a goodly feast at greatest cost, and bade thereto the chieftains of his realm, and all men deemed it a right welcome thing to be bidden of the king. Now when the feast was at its height, the king bade that Ambales should come thither, and servants of the king were sent for him.

75

þeir sáu hvar þikkur madur og Herdabreidur sat vid
eldinn á Stóli og var ad matast, enn konur vóru hónum
50 mjóg mótsnúnar, og vildu ei láta skéma matgjórdina,
jós hann eldi og sodi á þær, æptu þær þá hástófum og
lómdu hann, mátti þá heira hrinur Skóll og Skræki;
þókti sendimónnum gaman ad vidskiptum þeirra, og
horfdu ákaflega á hann, og þókti þeim hann stórmannlega
55 matast, so ei mundi hañs líka meiga finna. þeir sógdu
hónum med hastyrdum ad hann ætti ad gánga til kóngs
hallar; hann blés vid og setti raudan, stód upp og hljóp
undan þeim og sté fast til jardar so dundi undir, kom hañ
ad hallardyrunum og gékk inn, rauk þá aska og óþefur af
60 honum, og þókti flestum ódaun mikill filgja honum;
eingvum heilsadi hann; hann skimadi vída um bekki,
og sá Greifa Gamaliel sitja í Hásæti, þángad hljóp hann
skindilega og Sló Greifann mikid hógg, og þókti þad
flestum svívyrdilega gjórt sínum velgjórda manni. Am-
65 bales tók ad láta óllum ólátum, og hló fólk ad honum.
Addómólus mælti vid kóng: grei þetta er fullt flærdar og
falskleika, og hylur heipt sína med limskunni, þad færi
betur ad þú kóngur létir sem Skjótast drepa hann, annars
stundar hann þér dauda. Ambales heirdi hvad hann,
70 sagdi, hljóp ad honum med fagnadar látum sem þá barn
fagnar módur sinni, og tók ad leika á als oddi fyrir honum,
hann svipti brókum og brólti berlæradur um gólfid, og
hristi þíng sín med miklum yndis þroska ad konum er þar
sátu veitslu, so þeim þókti mikid um þad gaman. Skémtun

76

They saw where a big and broad-shouldered fellow sat by the fire on a chair and eat, and the kitchen-wenches were at quarrel with him, for they would not have him spoil their dishes, and he was pelting them with fire and swill, and they screamed aloud and made for him, and cries and howls and shrieks might then be heard. To the messengers their dealings seemed good sport, and they watched him closely, and deemed he fed for all the world like to an alderman, so that his like could not be found for gluttony. They told him in commanding voice to make for the king's hall. He growled thereat and his face grew red, and he stood up and sprung before them, and stepped hard upon the earth so that it trembled. He came to the door of the hall and went in, and ashes and filth reeked off him, and men deemed a most foul stench came with him. He greeted no one, but glared about the benches, and when he saw the Count Gamaliel on a high seat there, he sprang thither swiftly and struck him a great blow, and people judged that in this he had ill repaid his kindly friend. Ambales began then to disport himself in foolish fashion, and folk laughed much at him. Addomolus said to the king:—"The cur is full of guile and falsehood, and hides his anger under wiliness; 'twere best for thee to have him slain with all dispatch, ere he compass thy death." Ambales heard what he said, and ran up to him with all blitheness, even as when a child cheers up unto his mother, and he pranked right merrily before him, and he doffed his hose, and barelegged gambolled upon the floor.

gjördist ̄mikil af þessu í kóngs höllinni, margir hlóu ad
hanns látum, enn hann geingdi aungvu ordi nokkurs
mañs. Kóngur talar til hañs og seigir: viltu med
nokkrum Sæmdum vera, né gjæta ad hvad þér sjálfum
sómir? nú mun eg drekka þér til, eñ þú munt ádrykkj-
80 unni halda, og so gjördi kóngur, Skeinkjararnir létu
eirn kosta drikk á eitt mikid Staup, og báru kóngi, hañ
tók vid, og baud Ambales vid ad taka, Ambales tók vid
án allrar vyrdíngar vid kóng, og drakk hálfañ Skérf
Staupsins, gékk so ad Addómólus med stórri kurteýsi
85 og vyrdíng, réttandi Staupid ad hönum. Addómólus
ýgldi brún vid, enn tók þó vid Staupinu, Spurdi kóng
hvört hañ drekka skildi, kóngur qvad svo vera meiga.
Drakk hann af Staupinu og rétti aptur ad Ambales, tók
hann vid því kurteislega, hielt á því og mælti: þess
90 géldur nú kónguriñ ad hér er ekki í mínu valdi þad eg
vildi og vid þarf, því efnalaus orkar ei neins þó vildi,
mje hann nú staupid ad mestu fullt, setti þad so á bord
firer kónginn; þá vard kóngur miög reidur, greip Sverd
sitt, og reiddi þad til Ambalesar, enn hann hopadi úr
95 högg færinu svo Sverdid nam hann ei, eñ odduriñ kom í
gólfid, Ambales sveif jafnskjótt ad kóngi, þreif eptir
Sverdinu med hægri hendi, og greip þad af kóngi, heldt
hann um odd Sverdsins, eñ hafdi Hjöltiñ framá, þá þóktist konúngur í daudans hættu vera, því Ambales snéri
100 Sverdinu í hendi sér. Kóngur heimti vopn og menn
til sín ad drepa Ambales, enn Ambales rétti þá Sverdid
ad kóngi, runnu þá tvær grímur á kóng ad lífláta Ambales eda ei, enn hyrdmenn sögdu kóngi ena mestu smán
78

At this the folk there in the hall had great delight, and
many laughed at his doings, but he paid no heed to the
word of any man. The king spake to him and said :—
" Wilt thou not behave in seemly fashion and remember
what becomes thee ? I will drink to thee now, and thou
shalt drink to me." The king did so : the cup-bearers
poured out a costly drink into a large goblet and bore
it to the king, who took it, and bade Ambales to take
it of him. Ambales did so, but paid no courtesy unto
the king, and drank to half the goblet, and went then to
Addomolus, and with all courtesy and reverence reached
him the cup. Addomolus frowned thereat, but yet he
took the cup and asked the king if he should drink.
The king replied that he might do so. And he drank
of the cup and gave it back to Ambales, who took it
in his hand with all due courtesy, and held it up and
said :—"The king may be thankful that there is not in
my power that which I wish and he doth merit ; without
the means a man can do nought though he would." He
spat then in the cup and placed it on the board afore the
king. The king grew mightily wroth, and seized his
sword, and raised it at Ambales, but he sprang away,
out of the reach of the blow, so that the sword touched
him not, but stuck in the floor. Ambales swung him
anon toward the king, seized the sword with his right
hand, pulled it from the king, and holding it by the
point he reached him the hilt ; but soon enough the
king deemed he was in jeopardy of death, for Ambales
turned the sword. The king called then for weapons,
and bade men come and put Ambales to death, and then
Ambales gave back the sword unto the king, and the
king doubted whether Ambales was to be slain or not ; but
the courtiers said unto the king, 'twere greatest shame

Ambales ad drepa, qvádu í hañs valdi verid hafa, bædi
105 konúnginn og marga adra ad drepa, þar hann nádi svo
hañs nöktu Sverdi, og mætti þad sannlega seigja, ad
Ambales hefdi kóngi og hañs mönnum líf géfid. Kóngur
slidradi þá Sverdid, eñ alt þángad til hafdi Amales stadid
i höggfæri kyrr og mjög blídlegur, enn þegar hañ sá kóng
110 Slidra Sverdid, hliódnadi hann allmikid. Þá Spurdi
konúngur hann : hvar tók þig Sárast er þú sást Fódur
þinn deía? Enn Ambales hló þá mjög dátt og svarar : rétt
í rassinn ; ad þessu hlóu meñ mikid, og var allstór gledi
í Höllinni ; meñ sögdu þvílíkar athafnir og framferdi
115 Ambalesar fíflalegt vera, med ord og verk, enn kristnir menu hriggdust mjög, þeir sátu allir í eirnri röd
samañ, til þeirra færdi Ambales leikiñ og fór á Setur
sínar fyrir fótum þeirra og gjördi þar sín þarfindi. þá
lagdi ólikt mikla um höllina so meñ hieldu firir vit sín,
120 magnadi þetta kjætina í Hyrd kóngs, enn margur bad
honum dauda, sögdu þá sumir hann lifa mætti mönnum
til Skémtunar, og vid þetta gékk Ambales úr Höllinni til
Elda Skála.

14 Capítuli.

Nu sem Amlódi kom í elda-skála, var módir hañs þar
kominn, og Drottníng kóngs, og þernur hennar
sátu vid eldsglædur á Stólum, enn katlar vóru ei ad
seidi, greíp Ambal. upp módur sína med stólnum og
5 setti hana á katla hlódir, so svidna tóku klædi hennar,
hlióp Céta Drottníng þá ad med þernur sínar, þryfu
upp Ambu Drottníngu og báru til dyra, eñ Stólliñ
brann allur, skundudu þær nú med felmtri miklum
80

to put Ambales to death, since he had had it in his power
to slay the king and many others too, for he had had in
his grip the naked sword, and it might be said with
truth that Ambales had spared the king's life and his
men's. The king then sheathed his sword; till then
Ambales had stood in reach of it, quiet and of friendly
aspect, but when he saw Faustinus sheathe his sword, he
grew full sullen. The king said to him :—"Where didst
thou feel sorest when thou sawest thy father die?" Ambales laughed heartily and answered :—"In the buttocks."
At this the folk laughed merrily, and there was great glee
in the hall. Men said that in word and in deed Ambales
was passing droll, but the Christians there were sore
aggrieved; they sat together all in a row, and thither
Ambales now brought his play, and his sport before
them was of the foulest, and thereat the merriment in
the hall waxed mightily, though a many wished him
dead. But men said he might as well live for the sport
of men, and Ambales went from the hall into the kitchen-
stead.

Chapter XIV.

Now when Amlode came in to the kitchen-stead he found
his mother there, and Queen Ceta and her maids
sat beside the gleeds on chairs, but the cauldrons were
not then a-boiling, and Ambales seized aloft his mother
on her chair and placed her on the cauldron-hearth, so
that her clothes began to singe. Then Queen Ceta
together with her maidens rushed thither and caught
up Queen Amba, and bore her to the door, but all the
stool was burnt. And now they rushed in great terror

F

til Hallar kóngs, og sôgdu af verkum Ambalesar alt hvad
10 gjôrst hafdi, enn allar qvádu hann hid argasta Fífl vera,
og alldrei mundi hann mannvitsku ná eda neinum mentuñ,
og ekki þyrfti neirn hann ad óttast ad hefndum, kom þad
þá öllum samañ ad láta hann lifa mónnum til Skamdægris.
Kóngur var strángur mjôg í yfirbodan, ei síst vid lata og
15 íllgjórdasama, setti hañ þá í þrældóm, enn hina er ekke
vildu neita sín, til þjónustu, lét hann drepa. Eitt sinn
mælti hann vid hyrd sína: þad þikir mier ad óskilum
fara, ad Ambles hefur hina bestu kosti og listir sem
honum líkar, enn vinnur þó ekkert gagn þar med, því
20 vil eg láta til reina hvórt hann gétur ei med Fjárhyrdurum
verid, hjardar vorrar ad gjæta. Enn Gamalíel og rádid
seigir þetta reýna mætti, var þá Fjárhyrdurum skipad
hann med sér ad hafa til ferdar, þeir geingu þá ad Eldaskálanum, og var Ambales ad tálga Spítur sínar med
25 sama hætti sem firr, þeir spurdu til hvórs þær duga
skyldu; enn hañ qvad: til Fódur hefnda og ekki til
Fódurhefnda. Þeir kvóddu hann til ferdar med sér, og
sôgdu hónum skipun kóngs og vilja; eñ hann stód upp
skindilega og fór med þeim; so var mikil fôr á gángi
30 hañs ad þeir sáu ei eptir honum, enn í rétta átt stefndi
hann ad einu Fjalli þar ed fjárins var von, var þá lidid hid
hærsta dags er þeir komu í Fjallid, var þá mikid heitt
vedur med hægum vindi, vatn eitt lá annarsvegar med
Fjallinu, grunnlaust og mikid myrkt, þar beid Ambales
35 Fôrunauta sinna, og þar fundu þeir hann, sveif hann
þa ofann ad vatninu og lagdi sig nidr vid þad, setjandi
Hlustir sínar vid þad á bádar hlidar sem til einhvórs
hlustadi, sídann stód hann upp og sagdi til siña

to the king's hall, and told of Ambales' doings, all as it had befallen, and they all said he was the wretchedest fool, and would never come to the wit of man, or to any breeding, and no one need fear vengeance from him. And then all there agreed that he should live to be the sport of men. Now the king was most stern in his rule, and not the least so with lazy folk and evil-doers; he made slaves of them for the most part, but those that would not bestir themselves he had slain. Once he spake with his courtiers and said:—"It seemeth wrong that Ambales with skill and prowess to achieve whatso he lists yet doeth naught of any profit. Wherefore I would try whether he cannot stay with the herdsmen and guard the herds." Gamaliel and the other counsellors said it might well be tried. So the herdsmen were told to take him with them. They went to the kitchen-stead where Ambales was whittling at his spits, as was his wont, and they asked him of what use they were. "For father-revenge and not for father-revenge," he said. They bade him go with them, and told him the king's bidding and his pleasure. He rose swiftly, and went with them; but such was the speed of his walking that they soon lost sight of him; yet he took his course in the right direction toward a certain mountain where the herds were to be sought; when they reached the mountain noonday was passed, and the weather was very hot, with a gentle breeze. There was a water on one side of the mountain, bottomless and very dark. Ambales awaited there his comrades, and there they found him. Swiftly then he went down to the water, and lay flat beside it, turning his ears now here now there, as he listened for something; then he stood up and said to his

83

Fórunauta: vindur er komiñ í vatn, og vindur ætlar úr
40 vatni. Enn þessi ord héldu þeir galinnskap, geingu
sídañ á Fjallid, vóru þeir 6, enn hann sá 7^{undi} enn sem
þeir komu á Fjöllin, tókust upp Sauda-leitirnar, fundu
þeir hnöppum samañ nokkud af Fénu, hlióp þá Ambal.
í gönur med skringilegum hliódum og ólatum, elti hann
45 og Stiggdi féd allavega úr þess atthógum, so ad fjárhyrd-
arar feingu aungvu vid þad rádid, því Ambales hlióp
þeim miklu hardara, so þeir feingu ekki til hañs séd né
Saudanna, gjördist þeim nú íllt í Skapi, er þeir leitudu
lángt yfir vana sinn og sáu þó hvörki fied né sinn
50 Fórunaut, höfdu þeir þá lángt géingid yfir máta til nordur-
áttar, fundu þeir þá Féd alt ad heilli tölu med einni
Fjallshlíd, eñ Fórunaut sinn Ambales sáu þeir ekki
heldur, hamrar vóru þar med hlídum nordur leingra,
þar sáu þeir Hellir vera mundi eigi lítill, þar heirdu
55 þeir Skraf og háreisti, gyrnti þá ekki dvöl ad eiga lánga,
og ráku hjördina heimá vid med kappi miklu, sjá þeir
nú hvar madur geingur á Fjallinu, mikill vexti og hafdi
Svedju mikla í hendi, kienna þeir nú Fórunaut sinn, og
skundar hañ undan þeim heimleidis, litlu sídar sjá þeir
60 18 menn hlaupa uñ sama veg, vóru þeir allir stórir enn
þó tveir af þeim stærstir, stefndu þeir beint ad hyrdurunum, þetta vóru Hellirsbúarnir, eirn af þeim mælti
med allþúngu Skapi: Hvar er nú sá er Sverdi minu
stal? Hyrdarar seigja ad hañs sé leingra ad leita
65 enn þángad. þá mælti Blámadurin: þér skulud allir
hañs gjalda. Hellirsbúarnir höfdu tvenn vopn hvör
um sig, Hyrdararnir höfdu fáir Sverd, enn handboga
höfdu þeir; Foríngi þeirra hét Batellus, hann skaut

comrades :—" Into water wind has come, out of water wind will go ; " but these words they deemed were madness, and they went up to the mountain ; there were six of them, and he was the seventh ; and as they came up on the mountain, the gathering of the sheep began, and they found some of the sheep clustering together here and there. Then Ambales ran heedlessly about with weird screams and with wry looks, and he pursued and drove the sheep in all directions out of their haunts, so that the herdsmen could not muster them, for Ambales ran much faster than they could, and they might not see him or the sheep ; and they grew ill-tempered, being forced to search afar, much farther than was their wont, and yet they saw nor sheep nor their companion. They had gone far to the north, when they found their sheep, the number fully told, along a certain mountain-slope, but of their comrade Ambales they saw nothing. Along those slopes still further to the north there were steep rocks, and they thought they espied there a cave, by no means small. They heard, too, talk and loud bickering, but they had no wish to stay there long, and drove the herd homeward at their quickest. Suddenly they beheld a man walking along the mountain ; he was of large size, with a mighty knife in his hand ; they recognised their comrade ; he stalked along ahead of them homewards. Short while thereafter, they saw eighteen men running in the same direction, all of them huge, yet there were two tallest of all ; they made straight for the herdsmen ; they were the cave-dwellers. One of them asked them in a fierce temper :—" Where is he who stole my sword ? " They told him they would have to go farther than there to find him. " Ye shall all pay for him," said the cave-man. The cave-dwellers had each two sets of weapons, but few of the herdsmen had swords with them though they had their hand-bows : their leader hight Batellus ; of all men he

manna best af boga, neitti hann nú listar sinnar, og
70 skaut ad Hellirsbúunum vel og leingi, og so gjördu þeir
allir hvör sem meira mátti inn til þess 12 létust af
Stigamöñum, var þeim vid hættu búid er eptir lifdu,
og í því kom sá sem Sverdid hafdi tekid, og rétti þad
ad Stigamanninum enn hann brá því ad Ambales, hann
75 brást undan högginu, hlióp sídann aptur ad Stigamanninum greip hann í fáng sitt og bar hann um völlinn,
kisti hañ og klappadi hönum mikillega, hafdi so á
harda Skeidi med hann, og so fast hélt hann hönum ad
hañ kunni ei um ad brjótast, eñ er hañ hafdi leingi med
80 hann um völluna hlaupid, bar hann hann heim ad Hellir-
num aptur; nú sem hinir Hellirsbúarnir sáu þetta, skaut
þeim skélk í bríngu og kom ædra mikil í hug þeirra,
hlupu þeir burtu frá hyrdurunum, sem þá feingu fjör-
lausn med þessu, flýttu nú Ferd sinni og Hjördinni. Enn
85 er Ambales kom ad hellirsdyrunum, lét hann byrdi sína
lausa; dólgur sá sem hañ bar hét Karon, hann var foríngi
Hellirsbúanna, eñ broder hans hét Actamund er nú kom
aptur med þeim er lifdu af Hellirsbúunum. Karon mælti
þa vid Ambales, abl og hreýsti vantar þig ei, so ad eingin
90 trúi eg þinn jafningi se, því er þér þad Skadi enn mér Skömm
þig ad deida, þu hefur nú þrisvar átt rád á lífi mínu, og
má seigjast þú hafir mér líf géfid þar svo hefur sked.
86

shot best with the bow, and now his cunning served him, and he shot at the cave-dwellers well and long, and they all did as best they could until twelve of the robbers had been done to death, and those who were left were in great peril; at the same moment he who had taken the sword came up to them, and he gave the sword to the robber, then he brandished it at Ambales, who turned from under the blow and sprang upon the robber, and caught him up and bore him about the field and fondled and patted him, and ran about with him with all speed, and clutched him so firmly that he might not wrest himself free, and when he had run with him for some time about the fields, he bore him back into the cave. Now when the other cave-dwellers saw this, fear shot through their breasts, and great dismay seized upon their hearts, and they ran from the herdsmen, whose lives were thus saved, and they speedily went on their way together with the herd. When Ambales came to the door of the cave he let down his burden: the fellow he was carrying hight Caron; he was the leader of the cave-dwellers; his brother hight Actamund; he now came back with those of the cave-dwellers who were left alive. Caron said to Ambales:—"Thou wantest neither strength nor prowess; methinks thy equal liveth not; wherefore 'twere pity and shame for me to kill thee; thou hast had my life thrice in thy power, and I grant that thou hast given me my life."

I þessu sama bili kom Actamund þángad og hañs Félagar
hlióp hann þegar ad Ambales med nakid Sverd, og greiddi
95 honum högg um þverar Herdarnar, fékk Ambales þá Sár
mikid, snérist hann vid allreidur, og þreýf hann upp med
miklu abli, fleigdi honum á lopt sem hærst mátti, so hann
kom nidurá Herdarnar þar klettarnir vóru undir, og brotnadi í honum hvórt bein, á sómu leid fóru allir hañs Félag-
100 ar; Hlióp nú Ambales ad Karon, greip hann upp med
sama hætti og vildi hann lifi Svipta, enn Karon badst
fridar og lífs, let Amb. hann þá lausan og gaf honum líf.
Karon bad hann hjá sier dvelja, og baud hónum alla þá
Sæmd ad þiggja er hann kyñi, enn Ambales qvadst ad
105 sinni ei þann kost þiggja mundu, eñ seirna mun eg þig
ad Sáttum sækja. Skundadi nú Ambales heimleidis,
og nádi brádt Fjárhyrdurunum; var Hjórdinn þá bágræk,
því þeir vóru fáir; beindi þá Ambales ad med þeim og
dugdi sem þeir kjósa mundu, alt þar til ad hjórdiñ kom
110 af Fjóllunum, þá aptradi Ambales gaungu Fjárins, og
stód í stígnum sem í Fjallinu var ad gánga, enn þá var
miög dimt ordid, því í loptinu tók ad þikkna og vedur
um ad briótast, þókti hyrdurunum þessi hañs gjórníngur
hinn versti. Lækir fiellu vída af Fjóllunum med straungu
115 hliodi og stórum fossum hlióp Ambales nú úr Fjár-stöð-
dunni ad einum fossi er mestur var, hló mjóg ad gángi
vatnsins, áttu hyrdarar þar leid allnærri, þa kom Ambales til þeirra og mælti: I kvóld renna fossar sem
ádur vóru allir upp aptur enn eingiñ nidur. þetta mælti
120 hann þrisvar og lét hlé á milli. Ráku nú Hyrdararar

In this same nick of time Actamund and his fellows came up to them, and he sprang forthwith at Ambales with a naked sword, and dealt him a blow athwart his back, so that Ambales got a great wound, but he turned in great wrath and caught him up with all his strength and flung him aloft as high as he might, so that he fell upon his back among the rocks, and every bone in him was broken, and thus it fared with all his fellows. And now Ambales rushed at Caron and caught him up in like manner, meaning to kill him too, but Caron prayed for peace and life, and Ambales let him loose and gave him life. Caron begged him to dwell with him, and offered him all homage that he could give, but Ambales said he would not then take what he offered, "but later I shall make my visit of peace to thee." Ambales turned now homeward, and soon he reached the herdsmen; the herd was hard to drive, for the men were few. Ambales lent them his help and served them to the best of their wishes all along till that the herd was come from off the hills; then Ambales hindered the drove of sheep, and blocked the mountain-path they had to pass; and by now it had grown dark, and the sky was overcast and a storm was brewing; the herdsmen deemed that now his conduct was of the worst. Streams ran far and wide adown the mountains with great noise and mighty torrents; and Ambales sprang now from where the herd was standing toward one of the greatest of the torrents, and laughed loudly at the rush of water: the herdsmen had to pass close thereto, and Ambales came up and spake to them :—"To-night the falls that were before all run up and none adown." Thus spake he thrice with a pause between. Now the herdsmen drove

Hjòrd sína ad birgjum sínum, og geingu sídan til biggda
og fundu kóng, spurdi þá kóngur og Hyrdiñ ad fòrum
þeirra sem og Fòrunaut, enn þeir sògdu alt sem farid
hafdi uṁ gjòrdir hañs, þòkti kóngi og mònnum hañs
125 ad þeir hefdu í stóra ofraun komid.

15 Capituli.

AMLODI gékk ad vana til Eldaskála, og settist þar nidur
er hann var ei yanur, heldur innar leingra, konur
þóktust sjá hann dæstari enn hann var vanur, báru þær
honum þá mat, þann þær vissu honum haga, enn hann
5 át sem honum gégndi best Hirdararnir vóru í Hòll kóngs,
og sògdu honum og mònnum hans frá Ambales, hvòrsu
mikla adstod hann hefdi gjòrt þeim í frammgaungunni
med mikillri ablraun. Kóngur Spurdi þá ad ordum
hañs, eda hvòrt hann hefdi ekkert talad, enn þeir sògdu
10 honum allt hid sanna. Kóngur mælti þá : Amlódi mælir
ord af viti og af óviti. Dagurinn var þá runnin, enn storm-
ur var úr òllu hófi, so vída hrundu turnar. Kóngur
mælti : opt géfast Fíblinn gétspòkust, enn af frásògn
Hirdaranna dæmdu fleyrstir þad um Ambales, ad hann
15 mundi aldrei vís madur verda, heldur fífl og afglapi so
leingi lifdi, og eingiñ þyrfti hañ ad óttast. Kóngur
qvadst ei mundi framar þad til óhagnadar gjòra ad láta
hann med þeim fara, qvádu meñ þar stóra naudsýn
til vera. Nú er ad seigja frá Amlóda, ad hann eptir
20 máltíd gékk úr eldaskála, og vildi leita sér ad nádug-
um hvíldarstad um nóttina, hvòrju ad olli Sár hañs,
var þá diṁt ordid miòg, enn óvedur med Stormi og
regni gékk ad, enn sem hañ var Skaṁt frá eldaskála
geinginn, mætir honum madur mikill vexti ; hann bar
25 Sverd í hendi, þad var búid vel og lísti af því í mirkri
90

the herds to the pens, and thereafter they went to their homes, and they saw the king, and the king and the court asked after their journey and of their comrade, and they told everything as it had come to pass concerning his doings there, and the king and his men thought they had been in a most sorry plight.

Chapter XV.

AMLODE went to the kitchen-stead and sat him down in an unwonted spot, somewhat nearer to the upper end of the place, and the women thought him even more dazed than at other times ; they bore to him the meat they knew he best liked, and he fed to his heart's content. The herdsmen were in the king's hall, and told him and his men what great help Ambales had been to them in the fight by reason of his mighty strength. The king asked about his words, or had he said nothing, and they told him all the truth. The king then said :—"Amlode's words are wise and witless." The day was then spent, but the storm raged beyond all measure, so that towers fell far and wide. The king said :—"Oft in sooth, fools guess truth," and from the story of the herdsmen, many deemed this true of Ambales, for he would never grow to the wisdom of man, but remain a fool as long as he lived, and none need fear him. The king said he would not again put them to such trials by sending Ambales along with them ; the men said 'twas to be hoped so. Now it is to be told that Amloth after his meal went from out of the kitchen-stead, and sought a quiet spot to rest in for the night, for he was wounded ; it had then grown dark, and tempest and storm and rain was abroad, and when he had been gone some short way from the kitchen-stead a man of huge size met him ; he bore in his hand a sword of goodly make, and it shone

sem af fögru liósi, hvörju valda máttu gimsteinar og
gullbúníngur Sverdsins, þad var miög stórt, kilfu bar
hann mikla í hendi, í lodnum kubli var hann; hann
hafdi 8 karla abl, íllkéndur var hann mjög af mörgum,
30 sökum þjófnadar og mandrápa, því hann mirdti menn um
nætur, var hans heldst ad vænta þá íllvydri vóru; kóngar
höfdu fé lagt til Höfuds honum, því hann hafdi leingi ad
slíkum íllvyrkjum kéndur verid, þessi madur hét Drafnar; Nú sem hann sér Ambales, hradar hann gaungunni
35 og vildi drepa hann, reíddi kilfuna til höggs, en Ambal.
þóktist vita Skap hans, hlióp hann ad honum og þreif
í vinstri handlegg hans í hvörri hendi Sverdid var, og
kreisti miög fast, og Sveifladi honum so vid falli var
búid, vard honum nú laust Sverdid af Stirdum átökum,
40 þreif nú Drafnar til Ambalesar og urdu Sviptingar miklar,
áttust þeir fáng vid all leingi, var nú ýmsum vid falli
búid; Ambales þóktist finna ad ei mundi þurfa vært
ad bjóda, og gjördi honum hardan adgáng og þreýf hann
upp med hrigg spennu og bar hann ad hallar dyrunum,
45 enn af umbrotum þeirra Skulfu Strætin, enn brestir og
brak urdu so mikid ad flestū baud vid ótta, dyraverdir
Hallarinnar flúdu af hrædslu, þókti Drafnari frama lítid
þó hann nú mætti koma í kóngs höllina, bar nú Ambales
hann inn í Höllina, og lét hann lausann fyrir kóngs
50 bordi, vóru menn þá ad vistum, gékk Ambales sem
snarast úr Höllinni og læsti fliótlega dirunum, var nú
stór stans á kóngi og mönnum hans, kóngur kalladi
á menn og baud þeim ad fánga géstin, því hann var
92

in the dark, perchance by reason of the precious stones and its golden fittings; it was of large size; he bore, too, a mighty club in his hand, and wore a shaggy cowl; he had the strength of eight churls, and was held in great dread by many men, for thefts and manslaying; he murdered men at night, and was mostwhiles to be met with when evil weather was abroad. Kings had put a price upon his head, for he had long been known for his evil deeds; this man hight Drafnar. Now when he caught sight of Ambales, he quickened pace and thought to slay him; he raised his club for the blow, but Ambales guessed his purpose, and leapt at him and clutched him by the left arm, in which hand was his sword, and he grasped him very tightly and swung him that he was nigh a-falling, and his sword was loosened from his strong grip. Drafnar clutched hold of Ambales and great wrestling befell; they grappled each with the other long time, and each was on the point of falling. Ambales felt that no slight clutching of his foe would now avail, and made for him with most fierce onset, and caught him by the back and bore him to the doors of the hall, and the ground shook with their tussle, and the crash and din were so great that folk were afraid, and the warders of the hall fled in dismay. Drafnar deemed it but little honour tho' now it were granted him to enter the king's hall. Ambales bore him therein and freed him before the table of the king; the men were then at food; Ambales went then with all speed from the hall and quickly shut the doors, and great fear fell upon the king and his men, The king called to his men and bade them seize the guest; he was

93

mjóg hræddur.   Þusti nú Fólk ad honum med vopnum.

55 Drafnar sá nú líf sitt í hættu og mundi hann Þad verja
eiga, Skók hann, nú kilfuna, og drap skindlega med henni
12 meñ, tok nú Fólk ad flía og miög hrædt ad verda, og
í sama bili var Hallardyrunum upplokid, kom Ambales
inn og greip Drafnar upp aptur og bar hann Þángad
60 sem Þeir fundust fyrst, og liet hann Þar lausann, tók
Sverd Drafnars sem Þar lá og fékk honum Þad aptur.
Drafnar mælti : Þér má eg framar ódrum hæla, og býd
eg Þér mína vináttu, filgi og Fjáraflát eignar og adtektar.
Ambal. mælti : Ei Þigg eg Þad, enn Þú mátt finna mig
65 adra nótt í Þessum Stad, og Þad ei bregdast láta, annars
er Þrot á vináttu minni og filgi vid Þig, játadi Drafnar
Þessu, og Skildu Þeir med kjærleika.   Amlodi hitti firir
sér kastala, Þar var í Herbergi módur hañs og géstanna
fágad med skrautlegū búníngi, gékk hann í Herbergi
70 módur sinnar ; Þar voru margar Sængur forkostulega
búnar, lagdist Ambales nú í eina og afklæddist Fótum
sem adrir menn og tók fastan svefn.   Kóngi og hans
mönnum fiell allur ótti vid burtför Drafnars, og Þóktust
stóra vansemd hlotid hafa af hañs komu, og hvörsu lítid
75 Þeim vard ad vegi er Þeir urdu af honum sigradir, sögdu
margir sá væri sekur ens versta dauda sem Þeim hafdi
óvörum í Þessa daudans hættu komid, og sögdu hañ hér
med kóngi hafa hugad daudans hefnd.   Þá mælti Gamalíel:
Þótt oss sé mikil ærusmán ordiñ í Þessu, Þá meigum vér
80 vidurkénna, ad Þjófur Þessi hefur um lánga tíma stolid fé,
og myrdt svo marga menn ad ei veit tölu á, hafa konúngar

94

much afeard. The men rushed at him with their weapons, and Drafnar saw that his life was in great peril, and that he must needs guard it well; he brandished his club, and in a trice slew twelve men therewith. The folk took now to flight, for they were greatly adread; but in that same moment the hall doors were thrown open, and Ambales came therein, and caught up Drafnar and bore him thither where they first had met, and let him loose there, and took Drafnar's sword which lay there and gave it him again. Drafnar said:—"I honour thee before all men, and I offer thee friendship and rule over all my wealth and riches." Ambales said:—"Nay, I wish it not, but meet me this next night here on this spot, and fail not therein, else there is end of friendship and of aid." Drafnar assented, and they parted in friendship. Amlothe came now to the castle, where his mother and her guests abode in noble state. He went into his mother's chamber, and there were many couches there all richly dight, and Ambales lay adown in one, undressed withal even as other men, and he slept soundly. The king and his men lost all their fear when Drafnar left, and it seemed to them that they had gotten great shame from his coming thither, seeing they had done but little, while he had triumphed over them. Many said that he should be doomed unto the worst of deaths, who had plunged them unawares into this death-peril, and they deemed he had intended thereby dire vengeance on the king. Then said Gamaliel:—"True we have gotten us great shame in this, yet must we remember that this thief has long time robbed us, and has murdered men, so many that the tale may not be told. Our kings

95

vorir lagt stórar útlógur peninga til hófuds hónum, því
hann var sá versti vidureignar, og hefur ad vitund allra
manna flest og verst nídíngs verk gjórt, og því var hann
85 af óllum Land Herrum útlægur gjórdur, enn nú sem hann
var oss í Hendur feingiñ, vogadi eingin sér vid hann ad
hætta, hvórki kóngur sjálfur ne Hyrdinn sem þó mestar
vidlógur hófdu stadfest um hann, því raunar stódum vér
allir í daudans hættu, hefdi óvinur þessi margra bani
90 vordid firr enn sigrast hefdi, enn þar hann var af einum
manni sigradur er þó var án vopna, má oss mínkun
þikja, því þá Fífl þetta skynjadi vort atburdaleýsi, og sá
dauda vorra manna, hjálpadi hann oss úr þessum daudans
voda, hvórniñ skyldi hann þá hafa daudan forskuldad?
95 Kóngur mælti: þetta er satt talad, og má oss þikja
Skómm ad oss, þar vér létum grei þetta sigra oss. Fjellu
nú þessar rædur nidur, og geingu menn heldur daprir
til Hvíldar. Amba Drottníng gékk hrigg til ad Hátta,
og sem hún kom í sitt Svefnherbergi, litast hún um, og
100 sér hvar madur liggur mikill vexti, þángad gékk hún og sá
þad var Sonur hennar. Kubl láþar, hóggvinn sundur um̃
þverar Herdarnar, hún dró hægt klædi ofann af honum, og
sér hann sárañ mjóg, því hann sneri baki vid henni, hún
bar ágjæt smyrsl á Sárid og mýkti þad, sídañ gékk hún ad
105 sofa, ad morgni klæddist hún árla, og vildi græda Son sinn;
hann var þá vaknadur, og qvadst þad eí þiggja vilja, lá
hann leingi þángad til menn vóru til um̃svifa geingnir,
reis hann þá upp og sá aungvan nema módur sína, hann
mælti: Líf þitt og mitt mun vidliggja ef eg þigg grædslu
110 þína á Sárum mínum, og því vil eg þad ei, klædi vil eg af

placed a great price on his head, for he has always been the most terrible of men to deal with, and as all know has done the worst and wickedest of deeds, and he was made outlaw by all the lords of this land; but now when he was put into our hands not one of us was bold enough to risk encountering him, neither the king, nor the court, tho' they had vowed the direst vows against him; yea, we all stood in very fear of death, and our foe would have been the slayer of many a man before he had been vanquished; but he was overpowered by one single man, and he un-weaponed; verily we must deem it our shame that when this fool beheld our helplessness and the slaughter of our men, he saved us from the jeopardy of death. How then does he merit the punishment of death?" "'Tis rightly spoken," said the king; "we must needs deem it our shame that we suffered this dog to vanquish us." The talk ceased then, and men fared somewhat heavy to their rest. Queen Amba went to her chamber, sad of mood, and when she came there she looked around and saw a man of huge size lying there, and she went up and she saw it was her son. A cloak lay there; it was cut athwart from shoulder to shoulder. Gently she drew the coverlet from him, and saw that he was sorely wounded, and he lay with his back toward her; she salved the wound with goodly ointment and soothed it, and went then to rest. On the morrow she dressed her early, wishful to tend her son, but he was awake then and said he would not have it. He lay there long till the men were gone unto their work; then he rose up, and seeing none there save his mother he spake with her:—"Thy life and mine will be in peril if I take cure for my wounds from thee,

G

Ca. XVI. þér þiggja, og hiá þér mun eg á nætur dvelja medan eg er
í raunum þessum,—ber þú þig vel, þó eg þér ofraun gjóri,
því alt mun um sídir enda taka. Veglegan kubl og kirtil
gaf hún hónum ; mynntist hann nú vid módur sína med
115 ástar atlotum.

16 Capítuli.

A MBALES lá lángt fram á dag í Herbergi módur sinnar, á
móti kvóldi klæddist hann og gékk í eldaskála, tóku
konur honum vel, og hieldu honum máltíd, þókti þeim
hann af vana sínum bregda og þeinktu til batnadar berast
5 mundi um Sidi og Sæmd ; hañ neitti sem vanur var ; enn
ad gjórdri máltíd gékk hann úr eldaskálanum þángad sem
þeir Drafnar hófdu mælt mót, var Drafnar þar komin eptir
sinni lofan, og fundust þeir med kjærleika. þá mælti
Ambal. vid hann, nú skulum vid ferdast á Fjall upp í
10 nótt ; Drafnar játadi því, hann hafdi þá Sverdid Sigur-
lióma, dró þad út og hófdu þeir liós af því á heidunum,
liettu þeir ei firr gaungunni enn þeir komu ad Hellir
Karons, var hann þar fyrir og tók þeim allskostar vel
med miklum kjærleika, leiddi þá í Hellirinn, og hugdi ad
15 sárum Ambales og bar á þaug dírmæt Smyrsl so úr þeim
dróg verk allan, spurdi hann ad hógum Drafnars, enn Ambales sagdi honum hid sanna, ad hann væri sinn Félagi,
og bad hann gjóra vel til hañs sem framast hann kynni.
Karon játadi því, og sagdist mundi reýnast hónum
20 kjærlega eins og hann væri Ambales skyldugur ad
audsýna, þó so ad hann reýnist mér trúr, seigir hann,
í óllum samfórum. Ambales mælti : víst mun hā þér
triggur reýnast og þarfur í óllum vidlógum, og vilie
hann mæta mínum gódvilja, þá þeinki hann so ad gjóra ; á
98

wherefore I will take nought; but I fain would have garments from thee, and I would tarry with thee at nighttime while in this plight: bear thyself well, though I put thee to greatest trials; everything at last has ending." She gave him then a rich cloak and a kirtle, and he kissed his mother with great love.

Chapter XVI.

AMBALES lay long into the day in his mother's chamber; toward evening he dressed him and went unto the kitchen-stead; the women gave him blithe welcome and prepared a meal ready for him; they thought him changed from his wonted way: and deemed that in mien and manner he was turning to the better: he took to his food as he was wont, and when his meal was ended, he went from out the kitchen-stead thither to where he and Drafnar had fixed on as their meeting-place. Drafnar was come there as he had promised, and they met in great friendliness. "We two must journey to the fell to-night," said Ambales to him. Drafnar agreed; he had with him then the sword hight Victor-gleam, and he drew it out, and they had light upon the heaths: they stinted not their journey till that they reached the cave of Caron. Caron was within, and gave them blithe welcoming with great show of friendship, and led them into the cave; he looked at the wounds of Ambales, and bore precious ointment thereto, which drew forth all the pain: he asked then what Drafnar was, and Ambales told him all; how he was become his fellow, and bade him do for him all that he could. Caron assented to his wish, and said he would show himself kindly toward him as behoved him, at least on Ambales' account: "On this condition, iwis, that he be true to me in all our dealings." "Be assured," said Ambales, "he will be true to thee and helpful in all thy straits; an he wishes my goodwill, 'twere best for him to do so."

því liggur okkur bádum seigir Karon. Ambal. mælti ; þid
26 meigid bádir saman halda í þessum Fjallbigdum, og abla
fjár med frelsi eñ ei sem þjófar, því réttfeingid fé lukkast
vel jafnan, enn ódigd og þjófnadur fær og forþénar ætíd
versta last, haldandi þeim í dauda sem þad höndla ; Enn
30 fái eg aptur míns Födurs ríki, og géti eg drepid þann
kóng sem því nú heldur, þá kannské þid meigid meira
frelsi fá í landi þessu. Drafnar baud honum lid sitt til
Hefnda vid kóng, og audæfi sín í uppákostnad. Ambal.
qvadst þad ei ad sinni þiggja mundi, enn kubl þinn máttu
35 mér falañ láta. Drafnar seigir hönum kublin og Sverdid
til reidu, Ambales tók vid kublinum og klæddist hönum,
enn fékk Drafnari sinn kubl, sem módir hañs hafdi géfid
honum, er þó var þíng gott, enn Sverdid vildi hann ei ;
sídañ qvaddi hañ þá med kjærleika, og skundadi heim til
40 borgariñar aptur, var hann nú mjög tröllslegur vordinn,
og sú mesta ósýn, því sá grái kubl gjördi hann mjög
skringilegan, þó ei þækti ádur íllu ad spilla ; veik hann
nú ad eldaskála, og sem konur sáu hann, urdu þær mjög
óttafullar, og fordudu sér, eñ hann tók til sinna firri leika,
45 og át þad eitt af réttunum er hann sjálfur vildi, alla sína
fornu Sidi hafdi hañ, og enn jók hann vid spíturnar, var
þad hans tídarsta ydja ad smída þær ; margir gjördu
gis ad smídi þessu, enn hañ gaf sig fátt ad því ; jafnann héldt hann næturgistíng í Herbergi módur sinnar.
50 Eitt Sinn skédi þad, ad marger af vinum hennar vóru
komnir ad finna hana, þeir ed höfdu kóngs erindi,
og hieldu næturgistíng í þeim Sal er Amba Drottníng
héldt, áttu þeir vingjarnlegt Samtal vid hana ; enn

"Twere best for both of us," said Caron. "Ye two shall dwell together in this fell-land," Ambales said, "and ye may freely gain wealth, but not as thieves; for wealth gained honestly prospereth well, but knavery and thieving bring, and merit too, the worst reproach, and deliver them to death who traffic in them: and when I succeed to my father's kingdom, if I achieve to kill the king who holds it now, know well ye two shall have more freedom in the land." Drafnar proffered him his help for vengeance on the king and his riches too for achieving it. Ambales said he needed nought then, "but thy cloak I would have from thee in purchase." Drafnar said the cloak and sword were at his service. Ambales took the cloak and wrapped himself therein, and gave to Drafnar his own cloak, the which his mother had given him, and it was of great price; but the sword he would not take: sithence he bade them farewell and speeded home unto the city. He was now a weird troll to look on and most ugly, for the grey cloak made him of strange aspect, though at no time had folk ever deemed him a goodly thing to spoil. He fared now to the kitchen-stead, and when the wenches saw him they were adread, and hurried off. He took to his old ways and eat whatsoever he liked best, and kept, too, to his former habit, still increasing the number of his spits, and it was his chiefest work to whittle at them. Many mocked at this craft of his, but he paid no heed. He took his night-abode in his mother's dwelling. Once on a time it befell that many of her friends were come to see her; they were vassals of the king, and they stayed in Queen Amba's hall throughout the night and had friendly converse with her; but when night

er náttadi, kom Ambales þángad, sem hann var vanur, og
55 lét öllum þeim verstu látum er hann kunni, so aldrei hafdi
hann meira vidhafst edur verr látid, öll sín skilningar
vit afmyndadi hann med miklum Skrípagángi; af þessu
kom Stans á alla; enn þá er hönum leiddist, lagdi hann
sig til Svefns, og gjördi sér hrotur miklar og óvenjuleg
60 Svefnlæti, so mönnum stód þar af bædi ótti og ónád, svo
menn gátu eigi Svefn fest firri enn dagadi, og um Ambales var hliódt ordid. Um morgunin geingu men firir
kóng, og vard þeim þá tídast ad seigja frá því er Ambales
hafdi adhafst um nóttina, og höfdu margir men gaman af,
65 er heirdu af hans apaverkum. Kóngur mælti þá: vondur
er hann, allt jafnt hinn sami, og þó enn verri. Hirdin
sagdi öll einum rómi: ad hann væri eitt skamar grei, og
aldrei yrdi hann sér til Sóma.

17 Capítuli.

K ONGUR átti 6000 Svína, og vóru 7 Hyrdarar þeirra,
oddviti þeirra hét Silla, hann dó á 15da ári Ambalesar. Kóngr taladi vid menn sína hvörn mann velja
skildi í hans Stad ad stiórna þeirra vökturum. Gamalíel
5 gaf þad rád, ad Ambales skildi þar til skikkast, og svo
var gjört, tók nú Ambales ad sér þetta Embætti, og
tókst honum þad vel, gékk hann umm daga á Skóga
og merkur, og drap villudír og Hross og bar þeirra
hræ heim, enn er kvöld var komid, tók hann Sod alt

fell, Ambales came thither as was his wont, he was then at his worst, he had never made greater show of folly nor had behaved as badly, and all his visage was distorted and awry, and at his lewdness all men were aghast. Yet withal he grew tired and he went to sleep, but his snoring was so loud and he made such ugly noises in his sleep that men were both afeard and vexed, for they got no sound sleep until it dawned, when Ambales at last was quiet. In the morning the men went before the king, and their main talk was of Ambales and of his conduct in the night, and many men had sport therefrom, when they heard his apish pranks. The king said:— "He is bad as ever, if not worse," and the court with one voice declared he was a shameful cur, and would never come to good.

Chapter XVII.

THE king had 6000 swine, and there were seven swine-herds over them; their chief hight Silla; he died when Ambales was in his fifteenth year. The king spake now to his men as to whom he should choose in Silla's place to watch the swine as chief swineherd. Gamaliel counselled that Ambales be chosen; and so 'twas done. Ambales undertook the charge then, and things went well. During the day he was wont to go to woods and forests, and he slew there wild deer and horses, and bore their corpses home; and when evening came he took all the swill that he could find,

sem til fékkst, hjó Hræiñ í sundur í Stikki, lét í kétil all-
11 stóran, og kyndti Eld þar undir, og sem volgt var ordid,
lét hann hina vaktarana þetta svo tilbúid Svínunum færa ;
ad þessu var hann lángt fram á nætur. Tóku nú Svínin
bradan þroska þóktu og Störf hañs öllum ólíkindum
15 fjærri, enn þess á milli hélt hann vid sína gömlu Sidi,
bædi til matfánga og margbreitni fáheirdrar fíflsku. Eitt
sinn lá kóngur í Hvílu sinni eptir middags máltid, Svaf
og lét allílla í Svefni, vildu meñ vekja hann, enn Drottníng mælti : ad gott væri ad konúngr nyti drauma sinna,
20 um sídir vaknadi kóngur med miklū umbrotum, og qvad
sér heill manna horfna er eingin hefdi aumkad Sorg sína.
Drottníng mælti : Oss þókti mikils umvert, ef þér vitrast
mætti ófarir ókomnar, edur gjæfugeingi ; enn hañ kvadst
fyrir ófórum ílla drauma þolad hafa ; enn Drattníng hló
25 í Huga sínum. Gamaliel mælti : Seigja muntu oss
draum þinn ? Kóngur mælti : " Eg þóktist vera úti
staddur, lángt frá ódrum mönnum, vard mier til Himins
litid, Sá eg Sólina mér allnærri vera, hún þókti mér mjóg
raud ad liti, eg þóktist sjá úr henni Sverd falla er á
30 mitt Höfud stefndi, enn eg brá mér undann, og nam
Sverdid mína Hægri hönd af, eñ eg kéñdi ei eptir
vonum til, og var mér þá horfinn Sólinn, eñ í heñar Stad
komid Stórt og ógnarlegt Sverd, þad sama stefndi á
Höfud mitt og var glóandi sem Eldsofn, undan—því sá
35 eg eingann veg ad komast edur mér neitt til Hjálpar
verda meiga" enn þó vil eg ad vitrir menn rádi draum

and hewed the carcases in pieces, and placed them in a
huge cauldron, and kindled fire thereunder, and when it
was warmed he let the swineherds take it, thus prepared,
unto the swine; he went far into the night at this. The
swine grew quickly fat; this thing seemed to folk by far
the strangest of his doings, but withal he followed his old
ways, both in the matter of his food and all his unheard
of follies. Once the king lay a-bed after the midday
meal; he slept, but his sleep was restless; men wished
to wake him, but the queen said 'twas well that the
king should dream his dreams. Anon the king awoke
in great alarm and said his good luck in faithful folk
had left him, for not one of them had taken pity on him
in his sore plight. "We set great store thereon," said
the queen; "if perchance thou wast to have a vision
of some mishap not yet befallen, or of some good fortune."
But in her heart the queen laughed. Gamaliel said :—
"Wilt thou tell us thy dream?" The king said :—"Methought I stood without, far from other men, and I looked
toward the sky and I saw the sun very near to me, and it
seemed very red in hue, and methought I saw a sword fall
from it, and its point was turned towards my head, and I
drew myself away, but the sword took off my right hand,
yet I felt not such pain as one might ween; the sun had
then vanished from my sight, and in its stead there came
a huge and fearful sword which was also pointed at my
head, and it was glowing like a furnace, and there was no
way whereby I might escape, nor saw I aught that might
then help me : and I would that wise men might interpret

þenna.—Greifi Gamalíel mælti: Sólinn sem þú sást er
Gud sjálfur Skapari allra hluta, enn roda hennar Skaltu
hans reidi þída, og þér allnærri vera, enn Sverd þad er
40 þú sást á þig úr henni falla er þinn líkhamlegur daudi,
sem þér mun ei sárbeittur verda, því þú munt drukkin
déja; enn þad þú leitst upp aptur, og sást ekki Sólina,
skaltu vita, ad eptir þitt líkamlegt andlát, muntu ekki
sjá miskunsemi Guds, heldur finna hañs eýlífa griñdar
45 reidi, sem merkir þad mikla og hrædilega Sverd er úr
henni stód og á þig stefndi, og sú pína mun eýlíflega
ad þér þreyngja; enn svo þú fáir umflúid þá eílífu qvöl
tapadra manna, þá gjör þú yfirbót so þú fáir nád firir
Drottni, því þetta er hañs vitjun til þín, því hann vill
50 þér enn nú miskun sína. Kónguriñ reiddist og mælti:
þú bölvadur íllsku madur skalt deja hid Skjótasta, og
vondskufullum daudans böndum reirdur verda. Enn er
hann taladi þetta fiell óvit á konúng, og sm̄ Hyrdinn sá
hann daudvona, safnadist hún þángad öll, enn gat þó
55 einga lífs björg kóngi feingid; þá kom Gamalíel þar ad,
og lagdi sína hægri Hönd á brjóst kóngs, vaknadi þá
hañs andardráttur, svo hann raknadi vid, furdadi hañ
þá atburdi þessa, fékk hann af þessu stóran kjærleika á
Gamalíeli. Þá mælti Addómólus Dróttseti: Heimskur
60 ertú mjög kóngur! ad þú vyrdir med kjærleika Svikara
þeñañ, því falskleiki hans svíkur af þér lífid um sídir, þar
med mun og Amba Drottníng í slíku rádi filgja, munu þaug
öll ad þér þreýngja med sínum flærdum, og fólk þitt til Hel-
jar heim færa, eda hvar mun Amlódi gista um nætur? þar

this my dream." Gamaliel said :—"The sun which thou didst see is God Himself, the Creator of all things, and the redness thereof must thou interpret as His anger, and know too that it betokens vengeance against thee. The sword which thou sawest fall therefrom on to thy head is thy bodily death, which will not be brought about by a wound, for thou shalt die when thou art drunk with wine; and in that thou lookedst up again, and sawest not the sun, thou must know that after thy body's death thou shalt not see God's mercy, nay, rather His anger fierce and eternal, as is shown by the great and fearful sword which stood from it and was pointed toward thee, and torture shall harass thee for evermore; but an thou wouldst escape the endless torment of the damned, make thou amends that thou mayest gain grace from the Lord, for this is His visitation to thee, and He will yet show mercy unto thee." The king grew wroth and said :—"Accursed man of ill! thou shalt die forthwith and shalt be bound in wretched bonds of death." And as he said this he fell into a swoon, and when the courtiers saw him look like unto death they came thither, but no cure was found. Then came Gamaliel, and he laid his right hand on the bosom of the king, and therewith he again drew breath, and he came to himself again, and he wondered at this mis-chance, and conceived great love toward Gamaliel. Then said Addomolus, the steward of the king :—"Verily, O king, thou art foolish to regard this traitor with thy favour, for his treachery will in the end betray thee of thy life, and Queen Amba will join him in that plan, and with their wiles they will encompass thee and bring thy people to destruction—or where is Amlothe wont to bide at night?

skal eg brádt forvitnast um, so eg viti þeirra öll vond rád·
66 Kóngr þagdi vid, því honum var vel til Greifans ; þó sagdi
hañ : hvörnin kann Gamalíel ad hata mig, þar hann mér
samstundis frá daudanum bjargadi ? og mundi hann ei
so gjört hafa ef hann girntist dauda minn. Addómólus
70 mælti : þar færi ad maklegleikum, enn eg skal vid slíku
gjöra ad þeir fái oss ei audveldlega Svikid.

18 Capítuli.

Eɪᴛᴛ kvöld gékk Addómólus í Herbergi þad er Amba
Drottníng átti, og leindist undír Sænginni, var Drottníng í Svefni og hennar þjónustu meýar, enn er hún vaknadi lét hún qveikja ljós, því hún beid komu Sonar síns,
5 því hann var ad störfum sínum ad matgjöra í eldaskála,
sídann gékk hann ad vita hvörnin skipad var sætum í
Höll kóngs, og sem hann vard þess var, ad Addómólus
sat ei ad máltíd konúngs, gékk hañ í Herbergi módur
sinnar, og þar ad sem vopn láu í kérfi, þreyf mikid Spiót,
10 og æddi med þad ad þernum Drottníngar og lagdi því á
ýmsar Sýdur ad þeim med ófagnadi og óhliódum svo þær
hrukku undan, og þóktust eiga fótum sínum fjör ad launa,
sídann veitti hann módur sinni þúngar árásir, og otadi tídum
ad henni Spjótinu, enn hún héldt samt kyrr vid hvílu sína,
15 lagdi hann þá Spjótinu í ýmsar áttir, og útum gluggana,
enn í þessu umsvifa vastri, þóktist hann var verda ein-
hvörs undir Sænginni uppí þá Sæng hlióp hann, og lagdi
Spjótinu nidur í gégnum hana, og í því heirir Drottníng æ !
vidqvedid, enn Ambales herdti á hliódin so þaug alt
108

I shall soon ferret the matter and learn their wicked plans."
The king was silent, for he was fond of the earl. He said :—
" How can it be that Gamaliel hates me, seeing that he
has saved me from death this very moment? He would
not have done this had he been wishful of my death."
Addomolus said :—" Nay, he merits it, but I shall beware
they do not easily betray us."

Chapter XLIII.

Now one evening Addomolus went to Queen Amba's
chamber, and he hid him 'neath the bed. The
queen was then asleep, as were her serving-maids, but
she awoke anon and bade them kindle light, for she
awaited the coming of her son, who was then a-sodding
meat in the kitchen-stead. When he had done his toil
he entered the king's hall to note what men were seated
there, and when he was aware that Addomolus sat not
at the king's table, he hied to his mother's chamber, to
where his weapons lay heaped all together; and he
clutched a huge spear and raged with it at the queen's
serving-maids, and thrust it at them in all directions,
with hideous jeers and ugly noises, so that they huddled
away, and deemed they owed their life then to their feet.
He then made wild onsets at his mother, and at whiles
pushed at her with the spear, but she kept quiet in her
bed, while he thrust his spear here and there and all
about, and even through the windows, but in the midst
of all his madness suddenly he seemed aware of something 'neath a bed there, and he leapt on the bed
and thrust the spear right through it, and that same
moment the queen heard a cry of " Ah ! " but Ambales
strained his voice louder, so that they drowned the cries,

yfirtóku og lagdist á Spiótskaptid, og lá á því svo leingi
21 sem hañ hélt ad duga mundi, dró þad sídan ad sér og
sier blód á því, þá hló hann mikid, og lét Spjótid aptur
í kérfid í sitt lag, hafdi hañ þá heldur geimsmikid gaman,
so vída heirdust hañs læti um Herberginn, og þusti þáng-
25 ad fjöldi fólks, tók Ambales þeim öllum blídlega, og átti
leikfáng vid þá, og þó þrír mættu í senn, hafdi hañ jafnan
betur, eingiñ vard var hins dauda, gékk þetta svo framm
undir dag, fóru menn þá ad Sofa; enn er Ambales vissi
ad allir vóru í Svefn komnir, fór hann á fætur, tók kropp
30 hins dauda, bar hann ad Svínabælinu, hió hann í Stikki,
lét í heitt Sod med ödrum hræum, og gaf Svínum ad eta,
so þaug átu hañ upp med ögnum öllum, enn klædi hañs
brénndi hann öll, sídan þvodi hann blódid úr bælinu, og
þerradi med eldsglædum, gékk sídann til Sængur; enn
35 um daginn þegar meñ voru til Sætis komnir, saknadi
kóngur Drottsetans, var hañs vída leitad og fañst hann
hvörgi. Ambales gékk í Eldaskála ad matast, hann
mælti þá hann vid glædurnar sat: mann sá eg stúngiñ,
midt undir kérru, man eg þad ei, sá hét svínum vid
40 sælkjórum, sá eg þad hvorki. Sídan fór hann leid sína á
merkur og Skóga eptir vana. Kóngur var íhugasamur
um hvarf Addómólusar, var hañs leitad í mánud og fañst
ei miñsta til hañs; konúngi barst til eirna hvad Ambales
hafdi talad í eldaskála, lét því kalla hann firir sig, og
45 spurdi ad Addóm: enn hann taladi sömu ord og fyrri,
þókti öllum ólíkindi ad Ambales hefdi drepid Addó-
molus, því hann var hinn mesti kappi, vard sú ályktan
um sídir, ad Drafnar mundi hann myrdt hafa, enn

and he laid him then on the shaft of the spear, and lay on it as long as he thought would suffice, and then he drew it out and saw blood thereon, and laughed loudly, and put the spear into the bundle where it was wont to lie, and he made mirth out of all measure, and his glee was heard through all the dwelling. A multitude rushed thither, and Ambales welcomed them with blithe cheer, and sported with them, and even where three were matched with him at once, he came off best; but no one knew of the dead man there, and things were thus until near dawn when men betook themselves to rest. Now when Ambales saw that all men were asleep he got up and took the corpse of the dead man, and bore it to the swine-place, and cut it into bits, and put it into the swill with other carcases, and gave it to the swine to eat, so they eat him up to the last morsel; but his clothes he burnt. Afterwards he washed the blood from the spot where he had killed him, and dried the spot with glowing gleeds, and then he went to bed. During the day, when men had gone to their seats, the king missed the steward, and he was sought for all about, but was nowhere to be found. Ambales went to the kitchen-stead to take his meal. As he sat beside the fire he said :—

> "A man I saw pinned right under a car, I remember it not:
> Swine did he tend with a dainty morsel, nor did I see that."

Then he went into woods and wastes as was his wont. The king was much troubled at the disappearance of Addomolus, and they searched for him a whole month, but no trace of him was found. Word reached the king's ear of what Ambales had spoken in the kitchen-stead, and he had him called to him, and asked him after Addomolus, but he spake the same words as before. Men thought it all unlikely that he had killed Addomolus, for he was the greatest of warriors, and folk were of one mind in deeming that Drafnar must have murdered him,

Ambales mundi hafa géfid kroppin Svínunum og var hér 50 ei fleira tillagt.

19 Capítuli.

FASTINUS Kóngur tídkadi jagtreid á Skóga í sama mund á hverju ári, og dvaldist ad því tvo mánudi. Eitt sinn er Ambal. gékk um Skógjen, sá hann hvar Flagd eitt mikid og ógnarlegt gékk, og bar lítid Sveinbarn á 5 Handlegg sjer, hann heirdi ýlur miklar hjá Bergi einu, þángad gékk hann og sá þar Dverg grátandi, er tjádi honum sitt rauna efni, ad tröllkonañ hefdi frá sér tekid Son sinn, og bad hjálpar og Hefnda. Ambales hlióp eptir Skéssunni, og er hún sá hann, skálmadi hún mjóg, 10 allmikid Hár hafdi hún, svo þad tók ofanná lendar henni. Ambales sigradi Skéssuna á gánginum, og þreýf í Hár heñar og rikkti ad sér, enn hún stód kyrr í sömu Sporum, þá sté hann fæti í knésbót henni, og rikkti enn ad sér so fast ad Skéssañ datt, vard henni þá laust barnid, kom þá 15 Dvergurinn og tók Son sinn allshugar feigiñ; tók nú kérling ad brjótast uñ fast, og komst á Fætur, lagdi hún hreñsur sínar ad Ambales, og vard hann léttur í fángi hennar, áttust þaug leingi vid, mæddist hún þá um sídir, fiellu þaug bædi og bar hún lægri hluta, þá kom Dverg-
20 uriñ, og rétti sverd ad Ambales, enn hann vildi ei vidtaka, greip hann þá fyrir Háls Skéssunni, og hugdi hana svo lífi Svipta, þá bad hún Fridar og baud hönum gjafir og adra gjæfu; þad þág Ambales og lét hana

112

but that Ambales had given his corpse unto the swine, and so the matter rested.

Chapter XIX.

AT the same season each year King Faustinus was wont to go into the woods to hunt, and he spent two months in sport. Once on a time Ambales strolled through the woods and saw where a huge and fearful ogress went along and carried on her arm a small man-child; he heard, too, great shrieks beside a craggy rock; he went thither and saw a weeping dwarf who told him the cause of all his dole, to wit that a troll-woman had taken his son, and he asked him for help and vengeance. And Ambales ran after the troll, and when she saw him she strode on the harder; her hair was so great that it reached down to her loins. Ambales came up to her, seized her by the hair and pulled her toward him, but she stood firm and immovable; he planted then his foot into her knee-bight and pulled her toward him again, so hard that she fell, and the child fell from her in her fall; and the dwarf came up and took his son, right glad of heart. Now the carline began to writhe and she got on her feet, and dug her clutches into Ambales, and he was light in her arms; their tussle was a long one, but at last she grew weary and they both fell, yet she fell undermost. The dwarf came then and reached a sword to Ambales, but he would not take it, and he clutched the troll-woman by the throat to bring her to her death; then she begged for peace, and promised him gifts and good luck ; and Ambales yielded, and let her

uppstanda, leit hún þá blídlega til Ambalesar og mælti :

25 Eingan veit eg fremri ad digdum né frægari eñ þig, vil eg þér alls góds unna, til minna bigda ertu velkomin, enn hér er Sverd og Steirn er eg vil géfa þér, hann hjálpar gjæfu manna og géfur vitund af óvordnum skada, Ambales mælti : Steininn mun eg þiggja og med mér flytja, enn 30 biggdir þínar mun eg seirna heimsækja ; þid skulud sættast Dvergurin og þú, þaug gjórdu sem Ambales beiddi ; hann mælti : haldid nú bædi trausta vináttu, og gjórid aungvum íllt. þau qvádu sér kiært svo ad gjóra qvaddi nú kérlíng Ambales, og fór heim.

20 Capítulí.

A̱MLODI fór nú med Dverginum til hañs biggda, og var hjá honum um nóttina, enn um morgunin bjóst hann til Heimferdar, Dvergurin baud honum gérsemar og vopn gód, eñ Ambales bad hann geima þar til hann sjálfur hafa 5 vildi, enn eina Skikkju vil eg af þér þiggja, sem ad þeim kostum sé gjór, ad sá henni klædist sýnist ódrum frídari, so og vil eg ad þú filgir mér heim til borgar og breitir yfirlitum þínum og sýnist sem adrir menn, smídatól þín máttu og med þér hafa. Dvergurinn gjórdi so, og fékk 10 honum Skikkjuna, enn þeir umbreyttust ad óllum yfirlitum, sídan geingu þeir heim til borgar, og sem þeir þar komu, horfdu menn á þá og heilsudu þeim med knéfóllum vegna tíguglegs ályts sem þeim sýndist, og átti Drottníng tal vid þá, kunnu þeir og margt

114

rise, and she looked blithely at Ambales and said:—
"None know I greater than thee in doughtiness and
fame, and I would fain grant thee all good fortune:
thou art welcome to my dwelling, and this sword and
stone I would give thee now: it furthers the good luck
of men and gives them warning of dangers not yet come
to pass." Ambales said:—"The stone I accept and take
with me, but thy abode I shall visit later on; and thou
and the dwarf shall make peace together." They did as
he bade them. "Keep now a faithful friendship with
each other," said Ambales, "and do evil unto none."
They said that they would do so right gladly, and the
carline bade farewell to Ambales and went unto her
home.

Chapter XX.

Now Amlothe went with the dwarf to his abode, and
stayed there with him for the night: but on the
morrow he got ready to go homeward. The dwarf presented him with costly gems and goodly weapons, but
Ambales bade him keep them till he wished for them.
"But I would fain take of thee a cloak of such virtue as
would make the wearer fairer to look on than all other
men; and I would too that thou go home with me into
the city, and do thou so change thy mien that thou shalt
look like other men, and bring thy smithying tools along
with thee." The dwarf did as he bade him, and he gave
him the cloak, and they were both changed withal. Now
they went to the city, and when they came there men
gazed at them and did obeisance to them at sight of
their majestic mien. And the queen talked with them,

af ódrum lóndum ad seigja, sérdeilis hvórjer Sigur og
16 ósigur hófdu, og hvórjer frægstir kappar væru. Drottníng baud þeim vín og vistir ad þiggja, enn þeir neitudu
því og qvádust ei mettast af mannlegri Fædu, heldur
baud hann þénara sínum ad prída Sæti konúngs, og allra
20 þeirra er þar Sæti áttu, var þó konúngs Sæti eitt þad tignarlegasta, og so hvórs eins eptir hans burdum; enn gót
gjórdi hann á hvórs mans Sæti, prídilega útskorinn,
og er Hófdíngin umlitadist, þókti honum fullnægt vilja
sínum, og ad þessu smídi endudu fóru þeir í burt, og er
25 þeir vóru skaṁt frá borgar hlidinu komnir, klæddist
Amlódi úr Skikkjunni og bad Dverginn ad geima hana,
fór hann so til biggda sinna; Tók Amlódi ad sér aptur
Stórf sín sem ádur so eingin vissi neitt um Ferdir hañs.

21 Capítuli.

Að lidnum tíma kom kóngur heim aptur, og er hann
kom í Hóllina sá hann þá miklu umbreitíng er á
henni var ordiñ, og sætinn oll prídilegri miklu enn ádur,
spurdi hann hvórju þad sætti? enn Drottníng seigir
5 honum alt af komu géstaña og þaug mórgu tídindi er
þeir henni sógdu. Kóngur spurdi þá ad háttum þeirra
og hegdan, hún seigir alt sem var, og seigist ei slíka
Sómamenn séd hafa. Kóngur spurdi: hvórju gégna
mundi? enn hañs Rádgjafar er sómu trúar vóru og
10 hann, sógdu þetta víst þeirra Gud verid hafa, mun hann
hafa vor vitjad sógdu þeir, og vor Sæti med þessum

and they had much to tell her of foreign lands, of con-
querors and of conquered, and of most renowned heroes;
the queen gave them wine and meat, but they refused
and said they might not feed on human food; but he
bade his servant adorn the king's seat and the seats of
all who sat within the hall. The seat of the king was
dight by far the noblest, and the seats of the others
according to their rank, and in each man's seat he made
a hole, carved out with great cunning, and when his lord,
Ambales to wit, looked round he deemed his bidding had
been done. And when the work was ended they went
their way, but when they had gone a little from the city
gate Ambales doffed the cloak and bade the dwarf to
keep it for him, and went then to his abode, and took
to his former ways, and none knew of his journeyings.

Chapter XXX.

Now when the time had passed the king came back,
and as he came into the hall, he saw that a great
change had come over it, for lo! the seats were nobler
far than ever they had been before, and he asked the
cause thereof. The queen told him of the coming of
the guests, and of the many tidings they had told her,
and the king asked her then concerning their bearing
and their mien, and she told him all as had befallen,
adding thereto that she had never set her eyes on
seemlier men. The king questioned as to what this
might mean, and his counsellors who were of his own
faith said this must needs have been their god: "He
must have come to visit us," said they, "and in thus

Сн. XXI. Sóma stadfest, ætti honum hér firir þakkir ad vanda.
Kóngur qvad Satt vera, og baud helgihald sínum afgudi
til lofgjördar, var sú Hátíd afgudanna haldinn 3 Daga
15 samfleýtt med þakklætis fórnum og bænagjördum. Gamalíel gaf sig fátt ad þessu, þó gaf hann af Fé sínu til
Fórnarinnar. Ambal. héldt fram Sidum sínum sem firri,
og enn jók hann vid Spíturnar, var þad hañs tídarsta
ydja ad smída þær, margir gjördu gis ad Smídi þessu,
20 enn hañ gaf sig fátt ad, jafnañ hélt hann næturgistíng
í Herbergi módr sinnar.—þad var Sidur þeirra kónganna
Málpríants og Fástínusar, ad hvór héldt ódrum Jóla-
veitslu, og átti nú Fástínus kóngur ad þiggja í Spanía,
sókti hann þángad med miklu fiólmenni, og sem hann
25 var þadañ heimkomin, gékk hann eitt sinn drukkiñ til
Sængur, lét hann leingi ílla í Svefni þar til Drottning vakti
hann, blés hann þá mædilega, og qvad sig ílla dreýmt
hafa, enn ad morgni er allir vóru til Sætis komnir, og allir
menn í Höll kóngs, bad hann sína vísinda menn ad
30 ráda draumin, og mælti: Eg þóktist hér staddur í Höll-
iñi, og Málpríant kóngur bródir minn med sínum
tveimur Sonum, hieldum vér samvistir med allskonar
Skémtun og eptirlæti, þókti mér andi nokkur innbrjótaz
um Hallar dyrnar, ósýnilegur ad líta, og hafdi bagga
35 mikin á herdum sér, þókti mér reikur gjósa af bádum
endum baggans med miklu eldneista flugje, so þar af urdu
menn blindir og heirnarlausir, líka misstu þeir mál sitt
sem neistarnir snertu og urdu sem daudir; en Gamalíel
þókti mér þetta umflúid géta, og Drottning vor med
40 nokkrum ódrum, enn sídarst urdum vér fyrir áhlaupum

honouring us he has made firm our seats : for this we should give thanks." The king said that belike 'twas true, and he ordained a festival for the glory of his idol, and this heathen feast was kept three days with thanksgivings and prayers. Gamaliel took little part in this, yet he gave his share toward the sacrifice. Ambales went his own ways as before, and still increased the numbers of his spits, and busied himself with whittling at them, and men jested thereat, but he minded not; his abode at night was always in his mother's chamber. 'Twas the custom of the kings Malpriant and Faustinus, that the one made a Yule-feast for the other, and it was now Faustinus' turn to share his brother's feast in Spain. He journeyed thither with a numerous company, but when he came home again, he went drunk to his bed. For a long time he was ill at ease in his sleep till the queen awoke him ; he heaved his breath full wearily and said he had had an evil dream, and in the morning when all men had gone to their seats in the hall, he bade his wise men interpret his dream and spake thus :—"Methought I was in this hall together with my brother and his two sons, and we were feasting together with all glee and merriment, and then methought a certain sprite broke in through the door of the hall, invisible to the eye, and it had a huge bag upon its back ; methought smoke came out from both ends of the bag with flight of fiery sparks, so that men grew blind and deaf thereby, and they lost their speech whom the sparks touched, and they became as dead : but methought Gamaliel was able to escape, and our queen, too, with some other folk, but at last I and the King of Spain

andans, kóngurin af Spanja og eg, og er þetta draumurinn. Allir qvádu mikinn Drauminn og ferlegañ. Kóngur mælti : Frañ mun koma þad mig leingi uggad hefur, ad Ambales mun Andi þessi verda, því skal ei leingur
45 dauda hañs draga, mun falskleiki hans því valda ad svo leingi dregist hefur. Þá mælti Drottníng, meinar þú ad þú gétir þinn dauda umflúid þar fyrir? þótt hann deýi, mun þinn deidandi lifa. Allir qvádu ord Drottníngar sònn vera. Sefadist kóngur þá, og bad Gamalíel ráda.
50 Hann mælti : þaug rád vil eg géfa ydur, ad þér látid Ambales burt úr landi þessu til Málpríants kóngs, og bid hann taka vara á hònum, ef hann heldur vid Sòmu Sidi, má hann láta hann lifa sér og mònnum sínum til Skémtunar, enn taki hann umskipti vitsku og vidfángs,
55 þá bid þú láta drepa hann. Þetta þókti kóngi allgott rád og lét búast vid ferdinni.

22 Capítuli.

Eg sem búid var til Ferdarinnar, gékk kóngur eirn morgun af Sæng sinni og rekkju Sveinar hans med hònum á brókar bekk ; og er hann heimleidis gékk, sá hann þrjá menn standa í miklum lióma, líkari eing-
5 lum en mònnum þó bar eirn lángt af hinum tveimur, svo konúngur feiladi sér á ad líta, enn þessi mikli madur kalladi á hann og baud honum ad koma. Kóngur lagdi sína Córónu af sier á jòrd, og fiell frañ á sína ásjónu til jardar, enn sá mikli madur reisti hann
10 upp, tók í hendur hañs og mynntist vid hann og mælti : Ríki þitt mun eg stadfesta med lángvarandi

were sought out by the sprite, and this is my dream."
All said 'twas a wondrous dream. " 'Twill come to
pass," the king said, " as I have long misdoubted me, that
Ambales will be this sprite : his death shall no longer
be delayed ; his wiliness has availed to put it off." The
queen said :—" Dost thou think thou wilt escape thy
death thereby, should he be slain? though he die thy
bane will live." All men said that the words of the
queen were true. Then the king's temper abated, and
he bade Gamaliel give counsel. Gamaliel said :—" I
counsel thee to send Ambales out of this land unto King
Malpriant, and bid him watch him : if he continue in his
present ways, Malpriant may let him live for the sport
of himself and of his men, but if he change toward
wisdom and good sense, bid him have him put to
death." The king deemed this counsel most wise, and
bade them prepare for the journey.

Chapter XXII.

AND now they were ready for the journey : but one
morning the king left his bed, and his pages with
him, for the "breech-bench;" and when he went back
again, he beheld three men in great splendour, more like
to angels than to men, yet one of them exceeded far the
others, so that the king was too abashed to look at them,
but the greatest of the three called unto him and bade him
come near, and the king put down his crown upon the
ground and fell prostrate to the earth, but the great one
raised him up and took him by the hands, and kissed him
and said :—" Thy kingdom I shall fortify with enduring

fridi og vissum lífdógum̄ ad leingd og velferd. Eg veit
ad þú hefur sett þér í Hug um fífl þad er þú hefur látid
hjá þér dvelja, aldrei skal grei þad þér granda, og ei mun
15 hann sér né ódrum til Sæmdar lifa, né hefndar Sorg auka,
Send þú hann austur í Skytja Tamerlaus kóngi bródur
þínum, hañ hefur nýlega mist marga menn í orustu er
hann átti vid Sarasenis, þú skalt láta ríki þitt filgja á
þennan hátt sem Gamalíel fyrr rédi þér, og til stadfestu
20 þínu lifi, ríki og magt, sem og líka mínum ordum, géf
eg þér þennañ ríkissprota, var þad hid tignarlegasta þíng,
og sem kóngur hefur vidtekid þessu ágjæta þíngi, hvarf
hónum liómi þessi og mennirnir, stód hañ þar eptir ber-
hófdadur med uppliptum hóndum grátandi lángann tíma ;
25 Sveinar hañs færdu hónum kóronu sína, giekk hann sídann
med gledi til Hallar og settist í Hásæti, sagdi hann mónnum sínum frá vitran sinni, sagdist sinn Gud nú fundid
hafa, og sýndi þeim hvórt teikn hans Særi filgt hefdi, sem
var sá tignarlegi Sproti, hann sagdi og hvórt rád hann
30 hefdi géfid sér um Ambales, og hvad hann hefdi um̄ hann
talad. Óll Hyrdinn qvad vid fagnadar lof, lét kóngur nú
búa þessa Ferd enn ei hina, og kallar fyrir sig Cimbal og
Carvel og baud þeim þessa ferd ad fara, þid skulud, seigir
hann, hjá Tamerlaus kóngi vera og hónum þjóna mz því
35 lidi sem eg þángad sendi. Þakklætis Hátid lét kóngur eñ
nú halda godum sínum, og var mikil gledi á Ferdum.

peace, and the days of thy life shall be long and prosperous. I trow thou art troubled in thy mind concerning a fool whom thou hast suffered to dwell with thee, but never shall that cur do harm to thee, nor will his life bring honour to himself, or to any man, nor need he make thee fearful of his vengeance, but send him east to Scythia, unto Tamerlan thy brother, who has lately lost a many men in battle with the Saracens: rule thou thy realm as Gamaliel has counselled thee: lastly, to vouchsafe to thee dominion and power, and to assure thee of my words, I give to thee this sceptre." It was the noblest thing to look on, and when the king received this glorious gift, the men of splendour vanished from his sight, and he stood alone there, his head bare and his hands uplifted, weeping for a long while. His pages brought to him his crown, and filled with gladness he went into the hall, and sat upon his throne and told the vision to his men; he said he had now met his god, and he showed them the token which had accompanied his sure word; it was a most glorious sceptre. He told them, too, the rede he had received concerning Ambales, and all that the angel said concerning him. The court spake praise and joyfully gave thanks; and the king bade them now prepare for this journey, and not for the former one, and he called Cimbal and Carvel before him and bade them to go on this journey: "Ye two," said he, "must stay with King Tamerlan and serve him with the host that I shall send thither." The king ordained then a thanksgiving festival for his gods once more, and there was great joy.

23 Capituli.

$\mathfrak{A}$ TILREIDÍNGAR tíma Ferdar þessarar, gékk Ambales
vestur um Fjallbigdir ad hitta vinkonu sína hina
gòmlu tròllkonu, eptir ad hann hafdi talad vid kóng í
Skikkjunni Tosta naut, hann kom í miklar Fjallhlídar
5 med háum Hòmrum, þar sér hann hvar eirn Risi fer, sá
bar tvo menn til baks og eirn í firir, þeir emjudu mjóg
er þeir sáu Ambales gánga, hann fer til Risans og mælti:
vinur! legg þú af vid mig byrdi þína ad ei þurfi eg ílls
ad neíta. Risinn mælti: ei hef eg fyrir meiri mòñum látid
10 enn þér, og ert þú heimskur, enn þú ert mér velkominn,
því þú ert Stikkja stór í mína máltíd, og ei skaltu erindis-
laus á burtu fara. Risinn hafdi Svedju mikla í hendi
og hjó hann til Ambalesar, enn hann brá sér undan og
hlióp hún í jòrd nidur, enn Ambales hlióp ad honum,
15 þreif í handleggina og stie í knésbætur hònum, og rikkti
fast ad sér svo Risinn biltist nidur, vid þad mikla fall
urdu honum lausir þeir tveir menn sem í baki vóru, enn
sá fékk bana er í Fángi hañs var, enn vopnid hraut úr
hendi hañs, stòkk þá Risinn á fætur og rédust þeir á
20 med grimd mikillri, var sú glíma laung med stórum
sviptíngum, hamadist nú Risin mjóg og þreýf Ambales
uppá bríngu sér, og bar hann sem barn væri til bigda sinna,
hvar sem þeir fóru, urdu eikur af Stofnum ad gánga,
gjòrdist nú Ambales léttur í hòndum hanns vard hann
25 mjòg óttaslegin, ei síst ad horfa á hañs grimlegu ásýnd;
þreýf hann nú bádum hòndum í Skégg Rísans sem huldi
brínguna ad belti nidur, skók hann þad og hristi svo
Háls hañs styrdnadi mjòg, var þá Risin komin ad Hellirs

Chapter XXIII.

WHILE this journey was being arrayed, Ambales went westward to the mountain-land to seek his friend, the old troll-woman. This befell after he had spoken to the king, clad in the cloak, the gift of Tosti. He came to a fell-side steep with mighty crags, and he saw how a giant strode forward with two men upon his back and one in front. They whined aloud when they saw Ambales approaching there. He went up to the giant and said to him :—"Friend, prithee lay down thy burden, that I may need no force." The giant spake :— "I have ne'er yielded to greater than thou; thou art needs a fool, but thou art welcome; thou'lt prove a goodly morsel for my meal, thy journey shall not be all in vain." The giant held in his hand a mighty glaive, and he heaved it at him, but Ambales drew aside and it stuck fast in the earth. Ambales rushed now at the giant, clutched at his arm, and pressed on his knee-bights, and pulled so hard at him that the giant fell adown, and through his fall the two men on his back got loose, but the one in his grip was killed withal, and the weapon dropped from out his hand. Anon the giant leapt to his feet, and they set upon each other with great fierceness. The fight was long and their tugging fierce. At one time the giant raged madly, and caught up Ambales to his breast, and bore him to his dwelling as he were a child ; and where they fared oaks were uprooted. Ambales was light in the giant's arm ; he was much afeard, and more so when he turned him toward his fearful visage. With both his hands he caught at the giant's beard which covered his body even to his waist, and he tugged at it hard so that his neck grew stiff. The giant was come by now to the doorway of the cave, and

dyrunum sínum, og vildi Ambales þar innkoma, vóru
30 nú umbrot mikil þeirra á milli, enn svo lauk, ad Ambales
reif alt Skegg af Risanum, þar med Skinnid og holdid
af kjálkunuɱ greip svo í eyru Risans sem mjóg vóru síd,
og speñti hañ so til baka, var nú Ambales komin inn
fyrir Hellirsdyrnar, í því heirdi hann þúngt til jardar
35 stígid, var þar þá komin Skiessañ vinkona Ambalesar og
þreif bádum höndum um lendar Risans, og kippti honum
lángt frá Hellirsdyrunuɱ, enn Ambal. hélt eptir á eyrunum,
vard honum þá litid í Hellirin, sá hann þar Sverd hánga,
greip hann þad ofan, hlióp ad Risanum og hjó í sundur á
40 honum qvidinn so inniflin féllu út, í því kom Tosti dvergur og veitti lid Skéssunni ad firir koma Risanum, enn
Ambales gékk í Hellirin og fann þar mikil audæfi, og
þar med Dóttur Risans fjógra ára ad aldri, hún grét
þúnglega Fódur sinn, því hún þóktist hann daudañ vita,
45 hún lá í eirnri gullbúinni Sæng, og var meñsk ad móderni
hafdi módur hennar látist nær hana fæddi. Ambales
tók meýuna í fáng sér, og færdi hana Skéssunni og
bad hana uppfóstra, hún lofadi því, fóru þaug so alt
til biggda kérlingar, og fluttu þángad audæfi Risans,
50 tók kérlíng þeim vel og vóru so þar um nóttina, seigir
hann nú kérlingu af Högum sínum, qvadst hann vináttu
hennar og filgdar von eiga vilja og bad hana sér gott
Ess og vopn senda med Tosta Dverg iñañ tveggja
mánada til þess lands er hann ætti til ad fara; þaug
55 lofudu honum þessu; bjóst hann nú til heimferdar, og
qvaddi kérlíngu og bad hana firir Mejuna Risadótter
126

he wished to force Ambales therein. There was a fierce
tussle between them then, and in the end Ambales pulled
off the giant's beard, and with it the skin and the flesh of
the jaws; then he grabbed at his ears, which were very
long, and pulled him aback. Ambales was now at the
doorway of the cave, and he heard heavy footsteps there,
and there came up to him his friend the ogress, and she
clutched with both hands at the giant's loins and pulled
him from the entrance of the cave, and Ambales was left
behind with the giant's ears in his hands. He looked
into the cave, and saw where a sword was hanging; he
pulled it down, and leapt at the giant and hewed his
belly asunder, so that the entrails fell out. At that
moment Tosti the dwarf appeared, and he helped the
ogress to deal the giant his death-bane. Ambales went
into the cave and found therein much wealth, and eke
the daughter of the giant, a child of four, who wept
greatly for her father, for as it seemed she knew that he
was dead; she lay in a golden bed; on her mother's side
she was of human kind, but her mother died in giving
birth to her. Ambales took the maiden in his arms and
bore her to the ogress, and begged her to foster her, and
she promised it. So they all went to the carline's dwelling, and carried thither the giant's wealth. The carline
gave them goodly cheer, and they abode there all that
night. He told her then how things fared with him, and
begged her for her friendship and her aid, and bade her
send to him within two months a goodly horse and
weapon by the dwarf Tosti to the land he was to
go to. They promised this, and he now got him ready
to go home, and said farewell unto the carline, and
begged her to care for the little girl, the daughter
of the giant, who said her name was Hair-brow.

er Hárbrá qvadst heita. Tók nú Ambales med sér Skikkjuna Tostanaut og lét hana í Skreppu sína; Signets
hríng gaf Tosti Dvergur honum, ad öllum merkjum
líkañ sem Signets hríngur kóngs var, skildu þeir so
60 med kjærleikum.

24 Capítuli.

Eɴɴ er sendimenn vóru albúnir, fékk kóngur þeim Dreka
allgódann, er átt hafdi Salman kóngur, hann var
med gylltum vedurvitum̃, stöfudu Segli og Stálslegiñ allt
ad Sjómáli, lét kóngur bréf í Höndur þeirra Cimbals og
5 Karvels, var þad á þennan hátt: "Lukka og velgeingni
sé med ydur og þínum þiónum Tamerlaus kóngur minn
bródir! Fólk þetta sendi eg ydur til lidveitslu, og eitt
Fífl er hér ad auki, gétid af Salman kóngi, á hvörju
eg bid þig vara ad taka, hvört nokkud adhefst til orda
10 edur verka þad mannlegt er, og sjáist þad, þá lát drepa
hann, enn prófist þad ei, meigid þér láta hañ lifa þér og
mönnum þínum til Skémtunar. Lif vel! Stigu þeir so
á Skip, og fór Ambales med þeim, gékk þeim ógreid-
lega, enn nádu þó um sidir Skytja, og komu ad vid
15 Hamra nokkra enn ei þær réttu hafnir, geingu þeir
þar á land, var þar firer ein eidimörk, um sídir komu
þeir ad einum kotbæ, þar var karl útistaddur, honum
vard ógott vid géstakomuna, enn þeir æddu inní hans
bæ óbodnir, kona hañs sat á palli og þjónusta hennar,
20 hún seigir gésti velkomna, Artes var hennar heiti,
hún bar kjöt á bordid firir gésti af Saudum, geitum
Svínum og Fuglum, og var þad Sundurskorid og vel
128

Ambales took away with him the cloak which Tosti had given him, and hid it in his bag. Dwarf Tosti gave him eke a signet-ring, for all the world like to the signet of the king, and so they parted with great show of love.

Chapter XXIV.

Now when the messengers were all ready, the king gave them a noble dragon-ship, which had formerly belonged to King Salman. It had golden vanes and wanded sails, and was all steel-bound down to the sea-mark. The king placed a letter in the hands of Cimbal and Carvel, which read as follows:—"Luck and prosperity befall thee and thy folk, King Tamerlaus, my brother! These people send I thee for thy succour, and with them send I eke a fool, begotten of King Salman, and I bid thee observe whether his conduct in word and deed be at all human; an it be, let him be slain, but if thou art convinced 'tis not so, then mayst thou let him live to make sport for thee and for thy men. Farewell!" So they went aboard. Ambales accompanied them, and things fared ill with them; but at last they reached Scythia, and they put in at a rocky strand, for there was no proper harbourage there. They went a-land; a wilderness stretched before them; after a time they found a small farmstead; the carl was standing without; he did not welcome his guests, but they rushed into the dwelling all unbidden. The carlin was sitting in the upper-loft, her wenches with her: she on her part gave the guests blithe welcoming: her name was Artes. She set before them on the board flesh of sheep and goats and swine and fowl, cut up ready into portions,

I

vel tilbúid, og grautur gjördur úr geitamjólk handa géstunū
25 med ödrum gódum tilfaungum. Ambales sat vid elld hjá
Húsfreyu og blés ad bröndum og tíndi agnir ad eldi,
Húsfreya horfdi á hann, og spyr hvad hönum bæri til
áhiggju? enn hann qvad sér sveingd granda, því Skip-
fólkid hefdi breitt ílla vid sig. Hún qvad so vera meiga,
30 enn munu þér þó fleiri ad auk . . . So bar hún hönum fædu
ad kostum nægilega enn hann neitti sem þurfti og qvad
þökk fyrir; vóru þeir þar um nóttina, lá Ambales undir
rekkju karls vid kubl hañs og þad annad sem kérling gat
á hann tínt; eñ ad morgni hielt Húsfreýa þeim aptur
35 sæmilega máltid, . . . Ambales og svo líka þótt hann væri
sér og bordadi einsamall, bjuggust þeir so í burtu og
luku launum fyrir gistínguna. Ambal. gaf Húsfreiu Stein
ágjætañ er gjæfu mañs jók, vyrdtist heñi hañs gjöf vid
hinna allra; fóru menn nú leid sína; vedur var hlýtt um
40 dagiñ, og áttu Sendimenn þessir dvöl hjá einu vatni, og
tóku middags vörd, og eptir máltid lögdust þeir til svefns,
Ambal. hraut miög þúnglega, enn sem allir voru í Svefn
komnir, stód han upp og festi ödrum̄ meiri Svefn, tók sídan
bréf þad er Cimbal hafdi, braut þad upp, rakti í sundur,
45 las, sídann batt hann þad vid Steinog kastadi útá vatnid svo
þad sökk þar nidur, Skrifadi sídan annad bréf í þess stad og
setti innsigli kóngs fyrir, og bjó so um sem ádur var, lagdist
so firir og hraut mædilega; enn er áleid dagjiñ, vöknudu
Víkíngar og geingu af Stad, enn Ambales lá eptir vid
50 ból sitt, geingu þeir þá til Hans og lömdu hann á fætur,
geingu so þadañ var þá Skam̄t eptir til kóngs hallar, og
130

and well served. Porridge made with goats' milk was eke prepared for the guests, together with other dainties. Ambales sat at the fire beside the housewife; he blew at the gleeds, and threw small chips into the fire. The housewife watched him narrowly, and asked him what it was that troubled him; he was suffering pangs of hunger, he said, for his crew-mates had treated him ill. She said belike 'twas so, but there was more behind. She then brought him food, and there was ample choice; he took whatso he fancied, and thanked her. They tarried there during the night, and Ambales lay beneath the goodman's bed, covered with his cloak and with such other garments as the carline Artes had got together wherewith to cover him. On the morrow the housewife regaled them all again with a goodly meal, the crew and eke Ambales, though he kept to himself and ate alone. They then prepared to depart, and gave gifts for their guesting. Ambales gave the good-wife a precious stone which always brought its owner luck, and she deemed his gift worth those of all the rest together. And so they went their way. Now the day was hot, and the messengers tarried beside a stream, and took their mid-day meal there, and after the meal they lay down to sleep. Ambales snored heavily for a while until the others were all fast asleep, when he got up and made their sleep even sounder, and took the letter which Cimbal carried with him, and broke it open and unfolded it, and read it, and thereafter tied it to a string, and threw it into the water, and it sank. He then wrote another letter in its stead, and set the king's seal thereon, and arranged all as before, and laid himself down again and snored wearily. And as the day wore on the vikings awoke and they went their way, but Ambales remained behind asleep in his lair. They went back to him and beat him and set him on his legs, and they all went thence together, and they were then not far from

CH. XXIV. er þeir komu þar, geingu þeir firir hann og qvöddu hañ, kongur tók því vel, þar eptir frambáru þeir sín eyrindi, og afhendtu kóngi bréfid, hvört hann medtók og las med
55 sjálfum sér, og er hann hafdi lesid bréfid, mælti hann : A annan veg hliódar bréf þetta enn þér hafid mér ádur afsagt, edur hvar er sá kóngs son sem eg er af Fástínus kóngi umbedinn ad eg mér fyrir Son taki ? Þeir qvádu þetta aungvañveginn so ásigkomid vera, og qvádu nú lígi fram-
60 borna. Kóngur mælti : aungvum banna jeg bréfid ad sjá ; lásu þeir þad sídann, er so var ordad sem hér seigir : Lukka og velgeingni sé med ydur og þínum þjónum Tamerlaus kóngur minn bródir ! Fólk þetta sendi eg ydur, er filgir þeim ágjæta kóngs syni Ambales, á hönum
65 er miñ kjærleiki, því hann hefur mér sekum vel reýnst og þjónad og til margra lífgjafa verid þá eg í daudans hættu staddur var, mínu Ríki hefur hann og mestan Sóma gjört med audæfum dírra hluta, og med því eg kann lítid hañs Sóma ad auka edur forframa ad veita,
70 þá sendi eg hann til ydar, bidjandi um hann sem mitt eigid barn, ad þér gjörid honuñ þann Sóma sem þess kjærasta, þér munud og víst reina ad eg sannindi mæli, ad hann mun ydar Ríkismagt Stidja, því hann er hinn mesti kappi, ríkur af vísdómi, og veit marga
75 leinda hluti firir, enn þeir meñ er hönum filgja, skulu hañs Sveinar vera, og ydvarri magt filgja og þjóna. Lifid med ágjæti og velferd ! Vid þetta urdu Sendimenn mjög hljódir, og undrudust slíka hluti.

the king's hall. When they came thither, they went before the king and greeted him. The king received their greeting well, and they brought forward their errand, and delivered the letter into the king's hands, and he took it, and read it to himself, and when he had read it all through he said thus: "The purport of the letter differs wholly from what ye have told me,—and where now is the prince whom Faustinus bids me take to myself as a foster-son?" Such was surely not the bearing of the letter, said they; else some lie had been brought to the king. The king said: "I forbid no one to read the letter." They read it and found it worded even as it is here related: "Luck and prosperity befall thee and thy folk, King Tamerlaus, my brother! These people send I to thee to·accompany the noble Prince Ambales, on whom resteth all my love; despite my guilt, he hath borne himself passing well toward me, and hath oft-times done me service, giving me my life when I was placed in very danger of death. To my realm, too, hath he brought great glory and rich stores of wealth. And whereas I know but little how best to advance his honour and to further his renown, send I him unto thee, beseeching thee, as if he were mine own child, to honour him as thy best beloved. Thou wilt soon discover that I speak but truth, for he will prove himself thy kingdom's stay; he is a mighty warrior, and rich in wisdom, and many hidden things can he foretell; the men who accompany him are to be his servants, though they should eke do homage to thy power and render thee some service." At all this the messengers were struck dumb, and they marvelled thereat greatly.

25 Capítuli.

Tamerlaus kóngur heimti nú af Jörlunum Svein þañ er hönum var sendur, ella qvad hann þeim straff búid, því væri svo hañ finndist ei, mundu þeir hafa myrdt hann fyrir ófundarsakir, verda nú Jarlarnir rádalausir, og geingu 5 úr Höllinni, og er þeir komu út, sáu þeir medal vaktaranna eirn ókénndan mann í hinum mesta Sóma, geingu Jarlar þángad og hneigdu enum ókunna tignar manni, enn spurdu ad Ambales, vaktararnir sögdu hann nefndi sig Ambales, og ekki hefdu þeir vid annan mann varir 10 ordid og hann hefdi þángad komid í þeirra ferd; gánga nú Jarlarnir miög lítilátlega inni Höllina, leidandi hann á milli sín berhöfdadir, og sem hann kom í Höllina, lúta honum allir, kóngur sjálfur Stód uppí móti hönum, enn Ambal. qvaddi hann mjög vyrduglega, kóngur tók vel 15 qvedju hañs, og setti hann hid nærsta sér, og sem þeir vóru setstir, spyr kóngur hann heitis og ættlanda, enn hañ seigir kóngi sem var, so og hvad honum hafi til nauda borid einkum Födurdrápid sorglegast, hvad hann sagdi sér óbætta Sök. Kóngur spyr: viltu hefna þíns 20 Födurs og Löndum þínum aptur ná? Ambales mæ: vildi Gud allra Guda þad veita, þá skildi eg hann Smánarlegum dauda deida, eñ vilje Gud þad ei, þá njóti hann þess rikis sem best. Kóngur mælti: af kjærleika vid þig, bidur Fástínus kóngur mig þér Sóma og vel-

Chapter XXV.

KING TAMERLAUS demanded now the youth who had been sent to him, or, said he, punishment was in store for them; forsooth, if it befell that he could not be found, belike they had murdered him through jealousy. The earls were all at a loss and knew not what to do, and they went forth from the hall, and there beheld among the sentinels a man of noblest mien; they knew him not. They went forward then and did obeisance to this noble warrior, who was all unknown to them. They inquired there concerning Ambales. The sentinels told them that that very man gave the name of Ambales; they had noticed no one else there; he had indeed come with them in their company. And anon the earls, dejected and humbled, with uncovered heads, entered the hall, leading Ambales between them; and as he came into the hall, all men bowed before him, and the king himself stood up to receive him, and Ambales greeted him right worthily, and the king received his greeting kindly, and seated him next to himself; and when they had sat down, the king asked his name and country, and he told the king all as it was; and he told him eke what had brought him to so sad a plight, namely, his father's cruel murder, whereof the guilt was not yet atoned for, said he. The king asked him: "Dost thou wish to avenge thy father and win thy lands again?" "If the God of all gods," said Ambales, "would but grant it, he should die a shameful death; but if God's will be not so, let him enjoy his dominion as best he can." The king said: "In his love towards thee, king Faustinus begs me to honour thee and to aggrandise thee."

135

gjördir ad veita. Ambales mælti : I aungvann máta er
eg þess maklegur af honum né ydur. Kóngur mælti :
Hvörsu skal med þína Filgjara fara er þig frá lífi logid
hafa? Ambal. mæ : þeir skulu sínu lífi halda í þañ
máta og med því móti ad þeir sverje ydur og mér holl-
30 ustu sína, er þó Carvel af mér daudans maklegur, því
hann er sekur í dauda Födur míns, þó skal hann þiggja
líf af mér vilje hann taka mína Trú og sverja mér
hollustu sína, geingu nú Jarlar fyrir kóng og Ambal.
med audmýkt, og sóru þeim sína Trú og Hollustu, hvad
35 kóngur leid og lét svo vera, gjördust þeir so Sveinar
Ambalesar. Var nú veitsla gjör med bestu kostum.
Kóngur hafdi Samneiti med Ambales og Jörlum báduñ,
enn Ambales, vildi ekki samneita kóngi, og í eingañ
máta hañs ádrykkju halda, eñ annara manna ádrykkju
40 þág hann ; Kóngur vard fár vid slíkt, leid svo daguriñ,
var Ambales og sveinum hañs filgt öllum í eitt Herbergi
miög veglegt, á midju gólfi þess var stóll eirn gjör af
marmara Steini, Sá Steirn var holur innann og, leini-
gángur í hann úr ödrum húsum þángad, plagadi kóngur
45 niósnar menn ad setja, sem heira máttu leindar ráda-
gjördir og nýmæli. Og er kóngs son gékk til hvílu, og
flestir vóru í Svefn komnir, þá tóku tveir vid hann til
orda : Hvörju sæta uñ skipti þín, aungvan hlut sáum
vér ólíkari enn þú ert sjálfum þér vordinn, því munu
50 álögiñ ein ollad hafa, þeir spyrja : hvad olli sérgjædi
þínu ad þú vildir hvörki eta né drekka yfir kóngs bordi ?
hañ mælti : þar eru margar ordsakir til, því braud-akur
136

"I am no wise worthy," replied Ambales, "of such kindness, neither from him nor from thee." The king said: "What shall be done with those that accompanied thee, who by base lying would have deprived thee of life?" Ambales said: "Let them live on this one condition, namely, that they swear fealty to thee and to me. Carvel deserves indeed to receive death at my hands, for he has guilt in my father's death; yet shall he have life from me, if he will but take my faith and swear fealty to me." And now the earls came before the king and before Ambales with humble demeanour, and they swore them fealty and allegiance, and the king was satisfied and assented. Thus became they the servants of Ambales. A banquet was now prepared with greatest splendour. The king and Ambales and both the earls were served together, but Ambales would not eat with the king nor respond to his wassail; with other men he drank; thereat the king was sorely vexed; and thus the day passed. Then Ambales and all his men were brought to a stately chamber; in the middle of the floor was a chair of marble stone; 'twas hollow within, and a secret passage led to it from other rooms. The king was wont to send spies thither to overhear secret talk and to gather news. Now when Ambales was a-bed, and when most of them were asleep, two of the men began thus to speak with him: "Wherefore this change in thee? We have never beheld anything more unlike thy former self than thou hast become; spells alone could have worked it." They asked him too: "What meant thy whim that thou wouldst neither eat nor drink at the king's table?"

kóngs er yfir daudra maña beinum og banværn, og því
át eg ei vid bordid, kóngur át af krásum afgudafórna,
55 hvad kristnuɱ sómir ei ad eta, enn því hielt eg ekki
ádrikkju kóngs, hvad þó mun mest forsmán virdst hafa,
ad hann er Hóru-Son, enn eg er í Hjúskap getiñ þeir
seigja: hvórjar Sakir tildrógu um mismun bréfanna?
hañ mælti: kóngur mun sjálfur skrifad hafa bréf hér
60 lesid sér ad óvitru, því til þess eru ólærdir ad blekkja.
þeir Spyrja: viltu hefnda leita vid kóng og svo Lóndum
þínum ná? hann mælti: hvad sem lukkan vill er mér
þekkast, enn hún kémur ei utañ af Gudi. Sídan fóru
þeir ad sofa, niósnarmadurin veik úr Steininuɱ og sagdi
65 kóngi hvórs hann var vís ordiñ; og sem hann heirdi
þád vard hann reidur, og qvad sá skildi smánarlegasta
dauda deja sem sér skóɱ mælt hefdi edur módur sína
hórkéñt, í því kom Ambales í Hóllina, og er kóngur
sá hañ, sefadist reidi hañs, og mælti: veitstu þaug upp-
70 tók hiá oss sem vond eru: aukir þú eda fram haldir
slíku, áttu ei lífs von. Ambales mælti: Sæmdarlaust er
vitrum mónnum sannindum ad reidast, enn ei láist
ydur þó þér vilied hylja módur lítiñ, þad er og annad,
Herra kóngur! ad hún mun ydur sem alla adra sínum
75 Skóɱum leint hafa, eñ ydur til advórunar hef eg svo
talad, því ydar brauds-Akur er orsók til drepsóttar sɱ
hér þrátt yfirgeingur af ódaun daudra manna beina upp-
sprottiñ, sé annars, þá er eg dauda madur. Kóngur lét
grafa til braud-akursins, þar reýndist þá urd mikil af
80 manna beinuɱ. þetta jók kóngi stórrar Sorgar, og ei
138

"There are various reasons," said he; "the king's corn grows over dead men's bones; wherefore 'tis poisonous, and so I did not eat thereof at the table: the king partook too of blood-offerings sacred to his idols, and it beseems not Christian men to partake thereof; but the thing that must have seemed most ill-mannered, to wit, that I did not drink with the king, had also its reason; he is the son of a whore, but I am born in wedlock." They asked him what might explain the changed wording of the letter. He said: "The king himself must have written the letter that had been read, not knowing what he had written, for the ignorant usually make strange errors." They asked him again: "Wilt thou take revenge against the king, and so obtain thy lands?" "Whatsoever fortune wills," said he, "I welcome; success comes but from God." They then went to sleep, and the spy left the chair, and thereafter narrated to the king all he had heard. And when the king heard it, he grew wroth, and said the fellow should die a shameful death who had spoken shame concerning him, and had called his mother a whore. At that very moment Ambales stepped into the hall, and when the king saw him his anger abated somewhat, and he said: "Thou knowest thy conduct has been evil from the beginning: persist therein or repeat it, and thy hope of life is gone." "'Tis ignoble," said Ambales, "for wise men to be angered at the truth; but I blame thee not for wishing to conceal thy mother's shame, or perhaps 'tis rather to be said, lord king, that she must have concealed her shame from thee as from others. Further, 'tis to warn thee that I have spoken, for thy cornfield is the cause of the dread pest so widespread in this region; it arises from the poison of dead men's bones. An it be not so, I am a man of death." The king then had the field dug up, and they found there a heap of dead men's bones. The king was greatly troubled thereat, but he was even more troubled concerning the matter of his birth. So he went to his mother's chamber to ask her

139

síst hriggdist hann af ætterni sínu, gékk hann þá í Sal módur sinnar og spyr hana fadernis síns, enn hún skipti litum af grimd og mælti : Reingir nokkur Sæmd vora? hafa ei ódöl þín ættkénnt þig, edur vilt þu hafna heidri
85 þínum og láta Lönd þín fyrir ord kóngs sonar þessa? Kóngur mælti : þú skalt hid sanna seigja verda, ella mun líf þitt vidliggja, og þótt ei sé Soldán kóngur minn Fadir, þá skalt þú þess ei gjalda, enn leinir þú því sem þú veitst sannara, þá skaltu þess gjalda. Kéllíng gjördist
90 stór í Skapi og vildi slá Son sinn kóngin enn hann hélt henni; Drottníng þessi hét Cemiría, og hafdi leingi lundstór og lostafull verid, hún mælti : Til ílls ertu af mér alinn, og ílla géldur þú mér mína daudlega qvöl sem eg leid þá eg þig fæddi, og fer þér síst mér slíka
95 svívyrdíng eigna, þá þreýngdi kóngur ad henni, hún mælti : íllt skal nú íllum bjóda, og er þér þad ei ofgott, þú þikist mínu lífi ráda, eñ eg skal þínu ráda, skaltu hér ekki leingur löndum né lífi halda því þú átt þaug ekki, og áttu þögn minni ad þakka heidur þiñ, eg skal
100 láta brædur þína vita ad Landid Schytja er þeirra erfda eign, þeir Skulu þínu lífi ei þyrma, og sína eign til sín taka. Hertogjeñ Artax á Indjalandi er Fadir þinn og hónum ertú líkur; einusinni hélt Soldan kóngur í her- nad, enn Artax gjætti landa á medan, og gat þig þá vid
105 mér, og láttu þér nú linda ad þú veitst hid sanna.

who was his father: she changed colour in her rage and exclaimed: " Is there any one here who misdoubts our honour? Have not thy possessions decided thy birthright, or wilt thou renounce thy good name and give up thy lands because of this princeling's word?" The king said: " Thou must needs tell me the truth or else thou losest thy life; though King Soldan be not my father, thou shalt not pay the penalty; but if thou concealest what thou knowest to be true thou shalt indeed pay for it." The woman then grew fierce of temper and rushed forward to smite her son, but he held her firmly; her name was Cemiria; she had long been of fierce temper and very lustful. " To my sorrow bore I thee, and ill requitest thou the deadly pang I suffered when I gave thee birth; and least beseems it thee to saddle me with such a shame." The king pressed her then, and she said: " Let ill requite ill; 'tis not too good a thing for thee; thou thinkest thou hast my life in thy hands, but I shall soon have thine in mine; thou shalt no longer hold sway here, nor have thy life, for thou hast no right to either, and my silence must thou thank for all thine honour. I shall let thy brothers know that the land of Scythia is their birthright. They will not spare thy life, and they will take what is theirs. The Duke Artax of India is thy father, and thou art like unto him. Once King Soldan went forth to the wars, and Artax ruled his lands in the meanwhile, and then he begat thee on me, and now be contented that thou knowest the truth."

26 Capituli.

SOLDAN kóngur á Indjalandi hafdi géfid dóttur sína
Artax Hertoga Födur Tamerlausar kóngs, og var
hañ þar í mesta ágæti. Kóngur vard mjög hliódur vid
rædu módur sinnar, enn þó lét hann hana í fridi og
5 gékk til Hallar og mælti til Ambal: ófagnad stórañ og
hugar raunir hef eg af þinni híngadkomu feingid. Ambal. mæ: Bætur liggja til alls, ekki muntu gjæfu þinni
sleppa fyrir mínar Sakir, eg skal þér þjóna med rád og
vilja, og ebla þitt Ríki sem eg best orka, og má, og ei
10 munu brædur þínir fá landid af þér tekid, því þeim
munu eldsglædur búnar til handa, enn Gud á Himnum
rædur öllu þessu. Kóngur mælti: vitur madur ertu, so
ad eigi veit eg þinn líka, mun eg því fastmæli vid þig
binda og lofun þiñi trúa. Gjördist nú kóngur gladur,
15 og lagdi mikin kjærleika á Ambales, og fékk honum í
Hendur landvörn, vann hañ jafnann Sigur og fékk ofur
Fjár, hann var vís og forspár og sóktu margir til hañs
rád og réttindi, gékk hann hid nærsta kóngi, og gjördist
nú hjá því sem firr öllum kjær og þekkur, jafnan var
20 hann áhiggjusamur og sidlátur í umgeingni, enn er hann
var med ödrum mönnum, var hañ hinn gladasti.

Chapter XXVI.

KING SOLDAN in India had given his daughter to Duke
Artax, the father of King Tamerlaus, and he was
held there in great renown. The king grew very silent
at his mother's speech, but he left her in peace, and went to
the hall, and said to Ambales: " Mighty sorrow and anguish
receive I from thy visit here." "There is," said Ambales,
a remedy for everything; and thou shalt not lose thy
bliss through me. I will serve thee with good counsel
and with right good-will, and strengthen thy realm as
best I may, and thy brothers shall not avail to wrest thy
realm from thee; coals of fire await them. God in
heaven orders all things!" The king said: "Wise art
thou, and the like of thee I know not, wherefore I would
make a covenant with thee, and will henceforth believe
thy promises." The king was soon of good cheer, and
laid great love on Ambales, and entrusted him with the
land's defence, and Ambales always gained victory and
won exceeding great wealth. He was wise and fore-
knowing, and many took counsel with him and sought
his judgment; he was next to the king. And now, in
contrast to his previous plight, he was dear and welcome
to all; yet was he always brooding, though his manner
to all men was gracious, and in the company of others
he was the cheerfullest there.

143

27 Capituli.

DROTTNING Cémiría lét nú bréf strifa til Sona sinna,
og lét þá vita um eignir þeirra, sem var Landid
Schytja, og lísti fyrir þeim án bligdunar sínum skómum
ad hún hefdi fram hjá kónginum hórast, baud hún þeim
5 Tamerlaus kóng frá löndum og lífi ráda, og lofadi sinn
Styrk þar til ad leggja, hún segir og af magt og vyrdingu
Ambalesar, og er Málpríant kóngur fékk sitt bréf, vard
hann allshugar gladr, fór því á fund Fást. kongs bródur
síns, og urdu þeir samráda í því ad herja á Ríki Tamerl.
10 kóngs. þá mælti Fástínus kóngr: þetta hefur minn
Gud mér fyrirsagt fordū, er hann lét Ríkissprota þenna
mér í Hönd til stadfestu míns ríkis og sinna firirheita.
Málpríant kóngur mælti: óvænt þikir mér þetta efni
vera, einkanlega vegna þess mikla kappa sem þar skal
15 komin vera miög nílega, og af þér sendur bródir! og
hefur þig stór heimska heimsókt ad þú létst hann lífi
halda, og vogadist til ad eiga hann yfir Höfdi þér; enn
Fástínus kgr. qvadst slíkt ekki hrædast mundi, og tjádi
honum vitran sína, dæmdu þeir sér þar firir fullkomlega,
20 Sigurin vísann.

Chapter XXVII.

QUEEN CEMIRIA had letters written to her sons, and let them know that the land of Scythia was theirs; she revealed to them without shame how grievously she had sinned against the king: she bade them plot against King Tamerlaus, against his land and his life, and she promised to help them therein: she spake also of the might and prowess of Ambales. Now when King Malpriant received this letter he was exceeding glad, and he went to meet his brother King Faustinus, and they were agreed together to win the realm of King Tamerlaus. Said King Faustinus: "My god foretold this in days gone by, when he placed this sceptre in my hands as a token that he would strengthen my dominion, and as a pledge of his promises." King Malpriant said: "The matter does not seem altogether hopeful because of the mighty warrior who is said to have come there but lately, sent even by thee, brother. Great folly must have possessed thee to let him have his life, and thou hast dared too much in having him over thy head." But King Faustinus answered that he was nowise afeard; and he then repeated his vision to Malpriant, and they both deemed that signal victory was assured them.

28 Capituli.

TAMERLAUS kóngur gjørdi herfør mikla til Grikklands og Ambales med honum; lét hann nú sækja Skip þad er hann kom þángad á, því hann vildi sjálfur í Herförum þessu Skipi Stíra, Eitt sinn var kóngur og
5 Ambales utan borgar, þá kom til þeirra madur lítill vexti, og qvaddi þá blídlega, hañ færdi kòngssyni Ess mikid og tignarleg reidtýgi, þañ Hest hafdi átt kóngur á Skotlandi er Játmundur hét, þessum sama Hesti hafdi Skéssann nád, og sendi hann Ambales; Sverd ágjætt
10 fékk komu madur honum, og vóru Eggjar þess í eitri herdtar, og umgjórd þess af kláru gulli, Spjót og brinju af Stáli ferfalda, hér med Skjöld vel vandadā, prídilegasta hjálm og Burstaung, hún hafdi þá náttúru ad jafnan saung í heñi nær þeim skildi Sigurs audid er hana bar,
15 allt vóru þetta ágjætir gripir. Kóngur frétti komu mann ad heiti; hañ qvadst Tosti heita hann gaf kóngi Sverd gott; kóngur þakkadi honum og spyr tídinda; enn hann seigir þeim um rádagjórdir þeirra brædra, ad þeir ætla med óvígañ Her ad tveim vetrum
20 lidnum ad herja á Tamerlaus kóng. Ambales mæ: svo seigir mér hugur ad ei muni þeim híngad komu audid verda, enn sídur Sigurs á kóngi þessa lands, enn í nedri Schytía munu þeir koma, og heñi munu þeir ráda meiga. Kóngur brosti þá lítid, geingu þeir sídan

146

Chapter XXVIII.

Now King Tamerlaus prepared to invade Greece with a mighty fleet, and Ambales aided him. He bade them find the ship wherein he had come thither, for he would himself take command thereof in this expedition. Now once when the king and Ambales were without the city, there came up to them a man of small size who greeted them joyously; he brought the prince a noble horse with brave trappings; the horse had formerly belonged to the King of Scotland hight Jatmund; this same horse the ogress had got possession of, and she sent it to Ambales. The stranger guest brought him eke a precious sword, the edge whereof had been hardened in poison; its sheath was all of bright gold; he gave him too a spear and a byrnie of fourfold steel, and eke a shield wondrously wrought, and a stout helmet, and a tilting-lance with this virtue, that a singing noise was heard therein whenever victory was fated for him who bore it; all these gifts were indeed precious possessions. The king asked the stranger his name: he said he hight Tosti; and therewith he gave the king a goodly sword. The king thanked him, and asked him what tidings he brought; Tosti then told him of his brothers' plans, that they had resolved to attack him with a mighty army when two winters had passed. "My mind presages," said Ambales, "that it will not be granted them even to come hither, much less to gain victory over the king of the realm, but in Lower Scythia they may perchance come, and they may lord it there." The king smiled a little thereat, and thereafter they went

147

heim til Hallar, fékk Tosti dvergur vyrduglegt Sæti.
[Kóngur lét búa mikiñ her til Grikklands herfarar, og
hefdi 90 skip mjög stór og ótal smærri skipanna. Ambales
stýrdi skipi sínu því er hañ kalladi fódur-naut sinn.
Tosti dvergur var med þeim. Kóngur hélt til Grikklands,
30 og tóku höfn, og hélt leidángur um alt Landid til höfud-
borgar og settu þar tjöld sin.] *

29 Capítuli.

FYRIR Grikklandi og ódrum kristnum kóngaríkjum
rédi sá keisari er Chrisólitus hét, hann sat í Cònstan-
tínópel, sem var Höfudborg Ríkisins, og hann med sínum
löndum vardveitti, hann átti í orustu vid þær þjódir sem
5 kallast Sarasenir, sem vóru hinir verstu Tírañar og vægdu
eingum hvörki úngbörnum né þeim í kör lágu, þeir sátu
um Constantínópel í 5 mánudi med 400,000 manna,
Höfdíngi þeirra hét Barastatis edur Bastíanus, enn ad
auk nafni Óttamañus, hann framdi hinar verstu Skañir,
10 hann tók þær Egiptsku meýar er höndla kunni, og
konur, og lagdi þær í sína Sæng, og hielt vid þær um
tíma, enn er hann girntist ei leingur hverja fyrir sig,
risti hann hennar qvid í sundur med knífi, og drap so
hvörja eptir adra; Hann hafdi 18 Slög haft vid borgar-
15 lídinn, og gjört mikid manntjón. Keisarinn lét læsa
öllum borgarhlidum, var hann þar inni, og í stærstu
neid komin. Tamerlaus kóngur og Ambales höfdu
sleigid sínum Tjöldum þriggja daga leid frá borginni.
Tamerlaus kongur qvad þar fyrir vera hid versta mann

* These lines, omitted for the most part in the MS., are based on the British
Museum MS.

home to the hall, where Dwarf Tosti received a right worthy seat. The king now put in order his huge fleet for the voyage to Greece. He had ninety great war-ships and many smaller craft besides. Ambales was captain of his own vessel, which he named Father-gift. Dwarf Tosti went with them. The king held on towards Greece, and at last they took harbourage there, and made raids on all the land round about, and pitched their tents over against the capital.

Chapter XXIX.

OVER Greece and other Christian realms there ruled the Emperor Chrisolytus, who dwelt at Constantinople, the capital of his empire. This city and all his territories he defended bravely; he maintained a hard fight with the people yclept Saracens, who were the cruellest of foes, and spared neither the young nor the bedridden. For five months they besieged Constantinople with four hundred thousand men; their leader hight Barastatis or Bastianus; his surname was Ottoman. He wrought most shamefully; he would seize Egyptian maidens and wedded women, all he could lay hands on, and did them outrage, keeping them for but a short time; when he cared for them no longer, he would disembowel them, and kill them one after the other. He had engaged in eighteen battles with the army of the city, and had caused great loss of life. The emperor gave orders that all the city gates should be kept shut; he himself remained within the city, reduced to the greatest straits. King Tamerlaus and Ambales had pitched their tents some three days' journey from the city. Before them, said King Tamerlaus, there was the vilest cur that men

149

grei er menn vita nú af ad seigja í öllum Heimi, so hvar sem hann nád hefur kónga Drottníngum og dætrū edur jarla, þá hefur hann þeim öllum Svívyrdíng gjört og sídarst drepid; í þessara tölu er mín Systir, hvörja hann firir þremr árum hielt í sinni Sæng í 3 mánudi,
25 sídann risti hann hennar qvid í sundur firir framann rekkjustokkiñ, og vildi eg honum yrdi þetta sitt nidings verk endurgoldid med smánarlegasta dauda, og þad var mitt erindi híngad í Land þetta, enn þó vil eg þín rád hafa og þitt fulltíngi. Ambal. mæ: þennañ kóng
30 muntu sigra, því reidi hins mikla Guds er og mun yfir hann koma, mun eg láta Tosta dverg skélfa þá med sinu lúdurs hliódi, því hañs lúdur blástur mun því valda ad þeir munu hrædast. Tók nú Tosti dvergur Ludur sinn, því hann bar þetta Horn á sínum hálsi, og blés
35 í hann 3 reisur, so ógnarlega ad þad heirdist um alt landid. enn sem Bast. kóngur heirdi Lúdurs hlióminn, vard hann mjóg óttasleigin, og spyr hvad menn haldi um hlíód þaug er í loptinu heirdust? enn honum var Svarad: þad er rödd Guds hinna kristnu manna sem
40 bodar þér hañs hefnd því þitt vond(t) athæfi hefur upp-vakid hañs grimd yfir oss, þú mátt senda í þá átt lands-ins sem hlíódid kom, ad ei komi Her ad oss óvörum, ef Ské má ad menn stíri hónum, enn ekki Gudanna þjónar, sendi þá kóngur 30. manna á niósn, foringi
45 þeirra hét Taulerus, enn er hann kom so nær ad hañ sá Herbúdir þeirra af Skytja, vard hann mjóg felmturs-fullur, og tók sér oljuqvist í Hönd og menn hañs, og

had ever known to tell of in all the world, for when he captured the wives or daughters of kings and earls, he perpetrated on them the basest outrage and then put them to death; "and of this number," said he, "was a sister of mine; three years ago he had her a-bed with him for three months, and then he cut her asunder at the bed's edge, and I would fain requite his craven cowardice with an ignominious death; this is my errand hither to this land, and I would fain have thy counsel and thine aid." "Thou wilt surely triumph," said Ambales, "for the wrath of the great God is kindled against him, and must overtake him. I will bid Dwarf Tosti scare them with the blast of his trumpet; that noise will surely avail to frighten them." Thereupon Dwarf Tosti took his trumpet,—he bore the horn a-hanging on his neck,—and he blew thereon thrice so terribly loud that it was heard over all the land. Now when King Bastian heard that trumpet-sound, he was struck with greatest fear, and he asked his men what they held of the great noise that was heard in the air. They answered him: "'Tis the voice of the God of the Christians, who announces thus to thee his vengeance; thy wickedness has awakened his anger against us. Thou shouldst forthwith despatch men to that region of the land from whence the sound has come, lest an army assail us unawares, if it chance that men have caused this noise, and not the servants of the gods." The king then sent thirty men to reconnoitre; their leader hight Taulerus; and when he came so near that he saw the tents of the Scythians, he was greatly afeard, and he and his men took olive-branches in their hands,

ridu med þad ad Herbúdunum, og var Taulerus vísad
til kóngs Tjalds, lét kóngur Ambales honum mæta í
50 Svörum soleidis: þú mátt þínum Herra seigja: ad
Tamerlaus kóngur af Schjytja sé yfir hann kominn
med sinn Her, til ad hefna á honum Svívyrdíngar
sinnar og dauda Systur sinnar og annara hans íllsku
verka og á hann aungvan kost lífs né vægdar, og vogje
55 hann sig ad verja, má hann oss mæta nær búin þikist,
Taulerus seigir hann muni ei slíkt óttast. Ridu nú
sendimenn leid sína og seigja kóngi sínum öll þessi
tidindi, lét þá kóngur búast strax til orustu, hann reid
því díri er Nomokey heitir, hann skipti sínum Her í
60 8ta Filkíngar, og lét helmíng þess gjæta borgar, enn þeir
flokkar sem til orustunnar fóru, ridu sumir Fílum og
ödrum dírum, lét hañ setja sínar Herbúdir nálægt Herbúdum Tamerlaus kóngs, blésu þeir sídann í lúdra sína
med miklu rembilæti. Tamerlaus hafdi sínū Her skipt
65 í þriár Filkíngar, var hann sjálfur firir eirnri, enn Ambales firir annari, Cimbal og Carvel firir hinni þridju.
Ambales vakti fyrstur víg og drap Hasarum födurbródur
hañs Bastíanusar, sídann réid hann í gégnum Filkínguna
frañ og aptur og drap fjölda manna, var nú enn hardasti
70 bardagi, og hlód Ambales valköstu í kríngum sig; Tosti
dvergur hlód og valköst stórann, og þókti hañs abl og
atgjörfi furdu gégna. Nú tók óvina Herinn ad flýa, og
höfdu látid 30,000, í þessari orustu, reid kóngur so heim
til borgar, lét kóngur og Ambal. blása öllum Hernum ad
Borgarhlidum og settu þar Tjöldinn.

and so rode to the tents. They led Taulerus to the tent of the king, and the king bade Ambales receive him as his spokesman. He addressed him thus: "Thou mayst tell thy sovran that King Tamerlaus of Scythia has come against him with his host to take vengeance for his cruel outrages, namely, for his sister's death, and for many a wicked deed besides: let him not hope by any chance for life or mercy: if he dare to defend himself, let him meet us whensoever he is ready." Taulerus retorted that he was not to be frightened by mere threats. And the messengers rode back and told these tidings to the king, and he ordered them at once to prepare for battle. The king rode the animal called Nomokey; he divided his army into eight divisions; half of his forces he left behind to defend the city; the troops went to battle riding on elephants and other beasts. The king ordered them to pitch their tents near the tents of King Tamerlaus, and they then blew their trumpets with great ado. Tamerlaus had divided his army into three divisions; he himself led the first; Ambales was at the head of the second; Carvel and Cimbal of the third. Ambales opened the battle by slaying Hasarus, the uncle of Bastian, and thereafter he dashed through the lines and slew a host of men. And now the battle waxed fierce. Ambales slaughtered men around him in heaps; Dwarf Tosti, too, piled great heaps of slain, and his strength and prowess seemed passing wondrous. Soon the enemy took to flight, and they had lost thirty thousand men in this battle; so the king rode back alone to the city. King Tamerlaus and Ambales then commanded the advance to be sounded to the city walls, and they pitched their tents there.

30 Capituli.

$\mathfrak{A}$D morgni bjuggust hvørjer tveggja til orustu, Tamerlaus kóngur mælti vid Ambales : Eg bid þig ad þú
vildir taka kóng þeñann til fánga, enn ei drepa edur
særa til Fjórlasta, heldur færa mér hann fánginn. Am-
5 bales lofadi honum þessu, tókst þár sídann hin hardasta
orusta, reid Bast. kóngur hardt fram og drap á bádar
sídur, honum filgdu 30. kappar, þeirra hinn mesti hét
Atríanus, hann var Gidíngakyns, og stódst eingin firir
honum, og þókti hann ósigrandi. Benkóbar hét annar,
10 var hann undan ytsta Skauti Heims, hann hafdi Risavóxt
og burdi, afar liótur, ad sjonum, þó verri ad raun, hañ
vann flest med góldrum og djófuls krapti, og Skaut ór
af hvórjum fíngri, og vóru flestir hræddir vid hann ; Tosti
dvergr sá nú risann og hans illskufullar adgjórdir, hann
15 mælti : íllt skal nú íllum bjóda, sídann fór dverguriñ í
leiptríng og manadi Risann til atgaungu ; Risinn vildi
dauda hans, og magnadi órvar sínar og vildi þeim á Tosta
skjóta, enn þær urdu þá fastar vid fíngur honum so ei
mátti med hæfa, Tosti hafdi órvamæli sitt á baki sér, átti
20 hann órvar þær sem alt mátti med hæfa þaed er kjósa
vildi, skaut hann nú tveimur af þeim, og kaus augu
Risans firir, fell dverginum þetta ad óskum og hittu bádar
hañs augu og hlióp daudi í Sárinn, vard þá risiñ ólmur,
og drap og deiddi á bádar hendur hvad sem fyrir vard,

Chapter XXX.

ON the morrow each side again prepared for battle. King Tamerlaus spake thus to Ambales : "Prithee, when thou takest the king prisoner, slay him not, nor deal him deadly wound, but bring him to me captive." Ambales promised so to do. A fierce battle then ensued. King Bastian spurred forward, and slaughtered men on either side of him. Thirty warriors went with him ; the mightiest of them was called Adrian ; he was of Jewish race ; none could withstand him, and he seemed invincible. Benkobar was the name of the second ; he came from the farthest region of the earth ; he was of giant's size, and had a giant's strength ; very ugly to look upon, yet uglier to encounter, he conquered by charms and by devil's crafts ; he shot arrows from his every finger, and folk were sore afraid of him. Dwarf Tosti saw the giant and knew his evil devices, and he said : "Evil shall now meet with evil." He went forward then like a lightning-flash, and challenged the giant to come forth ; the giant wished him dead and charmed his arrows, and assayed to shoot at him, but the arrows seemed fixed to his fingers, so that he could not ply them. Tosti had his quiver at his back, and therein were those arrows of his wherewith he might hit whatsoever he aimed at ; he shot two of these, aiming them at the giant's eyes : it befell according to his wish, and both arrows pierced the giant's eyes, and the wounds soon mortified : therefore the giant waxed furious, and smote and slew on either hand whatsoever was nigh :

bardi hann Reidhjörtinn ákaflega, og vard margra maña
bani ei síst í sínu eigin lidi, lömdu þeir hann og hañs
Reidskjót ákaflega med Spjótum og grjóti, þar til hann
hleýpti úr bardaganum, bardi hann nú sinn reidskjót
ákaft, so hann stökk og stedjadi sem fætur togudu, uns
30 hann rann af Skeidi ofañí eitt díki, lét þar bædi Risin
og reidskjóturin líf sitt. Ambales hjó og lagdi til beggja
handa so eingiñ stód vid honum, mætti honum Adrían
Júdi er bar merki kóngs, reidir hann þá Sverdid ad
Ambal. og kom á Höfudid svo daladist Hjálmurinn, og
35 honum lá vid óviti, Sló Ambal. aptur til hañs, og tók
sundur Skjöldin og af hægri höndina, Ambal. reid ad
hönum þreyf hann ór Södlinum og færdi hann Tosta
dverg, og bad hann græda ef vinnast mætti, þá var
orustan sem ákaflegust, og fiellu Heidingjar hrönnum,
40 mætir nú Ambal. Bast. kóngi í bardaganum, og lagdi
hvör til annars, eñ Ambales vo hañ upp úr Södlinum, og
reid med hann endilángar Filkíngar, þar til hann hitti
Tamerlaus kóng, og afhendti hann honum kóng þennañ,
sídan setti Tamerl. hann í fjötur, vóru sídan allir kappar
45 Bast. kóngs audteknir, Keisarin hafdi og í bardagan
komid, og ad feingnum Sigri, gaf Tamerl. kóngr hönum
frelsi, og landsvist, ásamt öllu Herfángi óvina sinna, og
bjó sídann sinn Her aptur til Heimferdar og lét í Haf,
fékk Ambal. og Tosti dvergur stórt lof firir sína frægd
50 og framgaungu alla, var Bast. kóngr settur í mirkvastofu og menn hañs utan Atían, hann var í gódu haldi,
og sór Ambal. trúnadar eid medann þeir lifdu bádir.

he fiercely lashed the beast he rode on, and became the bane of many men, his own not least; but the folk plied him and his beast with spears and stones, until he galloped away from the fight. He lashed his beast still more furiously, so that it sped on as fast as its feet would carry it, yet suddenly it swerved and stumbled into a ditch, where both giant and charger lost their lives. Ambales dealt cuts and thrusts on this side and on that, and no man withstood him, save Adrian the Jew, the king's standard-bearer, who encountered him and raised his sword to strike at him, and it struck Ambales on the head, crashing the helm, and he was well-nigh on the point of swooning; yet he dealt him a blow in return which sundered the shield and smote off his right hand; he then rode up to him and haled him from the saddle and brought him to Dwarf Tosti and bade him heal him, if that were still possible. Now the battle raged at its wildest, and the heathens fell in heaps, and Ambales met King Bastian in the fight and each made a thrust at the other, but Ambales heaved Bastian out of the saddle, and rode with him along the whole line of battle until he met King Tamerlaus, to whom he delivered him. Tamerlaus threw him in fetters, and presently all the chief warriors of King Bastian were easily taken. The emperor, too, had come into the battle, and when the victory was won, King Tamerlaus gave him his freedom, and therewith liberty to dwell there in the land, and he gave him eke all the booty of his enemies. Thereafter he prepared his host for the homeward journey, and they put forth to sea. Ambales and Dwarf Tosti got great praise for their deeds of prowess. King Bastian was put into a dark dungeon together with all his men, except Adrian, who was well cared for; he swore Ambales an oath of fealty as long as both should live.

31 Capítuli.

Í Þann tíma Tamerl. k. hádi stríd á Grikklandi, fjellu
Víkíngar inní Land hañs utan af Blálandi er
hietu Tarkus og Tambis, og hófdu gjört þar mikin
Skada med ráni og manndrápum, og ei þyrmdu þeir
5 úngbórnum né þeim í kòr lágu, eñ vóru med öllu í
burtu er kóngur kom heim, og láu þar skamt frá
med 60. Skipa, enn er kóngur spurdi þad, bad hañ
landvarnar menn sína ad leita hefnda vid þá; Ambal.
Adrjan, Cimbal, Carvel og Tosti Dvergur (fóru) med lid
10 á einu Skipi, og hieldu Strid vid Víkínga, var þad hórd
orusta og laung; Tarkus hitti Cimbal nærri Siglunni,
og lagdi til hañs Spjóti í qvidiñ, og útum bakid so
hann hékk fastur vid Sigluna; þetta sier Amb.: og eirir
illa, hlióp ad honum med nakid Sverd, og klauf hañ
15 ad endilaungu, nú sá Tambis fall Félaga síns, gjördist
hann þá ólmur og hjó á tvær hendur, Adrjan fór á
móti honum, og hjó af honum hóndina og fótinn, og
féll hann daudur nidur, feingu þeir þar mikid Herfáng,
samt Skip og miklar gérsemar; þakkadi Tamerl. kóngur
20 þeim mikillega firir þessa landhreinsun, og héldu so
heim öllum þessum Skipa flota.

Chapter XXXI.

Now while King Tamerlaus was away waging war in Greece, two pirates ravaged his land; they came from the East, from the land of Swart Men; they hight Tarkus and Tambis; they wrought great havoc by rapine and plunder; they spared neither the young nor the bedridden. When the king returned, they had already fled, and lay a short distance off with sixty ships. Soon as the king heard tell of this, he bade the defenders of his land wreak vengeance on them. Whereupon Ambales, Adrian, Cimbal, Carvel, and Dwarf Tosti manned a ship and waged fight with the pirates; it was a hard battle and long. Tarkus met Cimbal near the mast and hurled a spear at him, which pierced his belly and came out through the back, so that he was pinned to the mast. Ambales seeing this, misliked it much, and rushed upon him with a naked sword, and cleft him asunder from the head downwards. Now when Tambis beheld the fate of his fellow he grew maddened, and struck wildly on either side, and Adrian went against him, and smote off his hands and legs so that he fell down dead. They got there great booty, ships and much treasure. King Tamerlaus gave them exceeding thanks for ridding the land of this scourge, and so they took their homeward course with all that fleet of ships.

32 Capítuli.

DÓTTIR Tamerlausar kóngs hét Semríkandis sem fyrr
er gétid, hún var lík módur sinni, og ad öllum
kvennkostum hin ypparlegasta, hún hafdi fest Huga
sinn á Ambales, og kom þar svo um sídir, ad Ambales
5 vakti bónord til hennar vid kóng, og var þad strax
audsókt, var því þad fliótasta til brudkaups búist, fór
sú veitsla hid Skóruglegasta fram, vóru allir Höfdíngjar
utleýstir med gódum gjöfum, og ad öllu svobúnu hvarf
Tosti dvergur, og fór til ynnis síns, audugur ad fé
10 vordinn.

33 Capítuli.

TAMERLAUS kóngur sat ad veitslum hjá Landshöfdingj-
um á vissū tímum, og vóru þad 4 Mánndir er
hann var á þeim, og er byrjadist þessi reisa, tók hann
Bastían. k. med sér fjótradañ var hann dreiginn í
5 Hrosstagli, og streingdur vid eitt brotid hjól er mjög
gékk stopult, sat hann allsnakin á einum Stól mjög
þraungum, innañum hann allan vóru eggjar skarpbeittar,
frammi firir Stólnum let kóngur setja kosta drikk á
bord med dírmætri fædu, enn hann nádi aungvu þar
10 af, og þoldi samt hid mesta húngur, hendur hañs og

Chapter XXXII.

THE daughter of King Tamerlaus, hight Semrikandis, as has been said already; she was like unto her mother, rich in all the graces of womankind. She had set her heart on Ambales; and it came to pass that Ambales addressed the king her father and asked her of him; his suit was readily granted, and they prepared for the bridal with all speed, and the feasting was of the lordliest, and all the chieftains were sped with goodly gifts. And these things having taken place, Dwarf Tosti returned to his home, and he had become mightily wealthy in the meanwhile.

Chapter XXXIII.

AT certain seasons King Tamerlaus was wont to visit his chieftains to feast with them; he spent some four months in these revels. Now when he started on his royal progress, he took with him King Bastian fast in fetters, drawn at the tail of a horse, and tied to a broken wheel, which jolted along. He sat stark-naked on a narrow bench; its seat was all beset with sharp points; before it on a table the king bade them place the choicest drinks and the daintiest dishes; but King Bastian might not by any device reach thereunto, though he suffered direst pangs of

L

CH. XXXIV. fætur vóru vid Stóliñ reirdar; kóngur let hinar ágjætustu meýar dansa frañi firir Stólnum í einu línklædi;
undir hañs tól lét hann hárhvasst Sverd og lét binda 20
lód af blíe vid hans leindar lim; med þessum og ódrum
15 qvólum lét kóngur hann pína, enn því meira sem hann
leid því verri vard hann, til skapsmuna, Ambales vægdi
honum jafnan, og lét bera honum braud til lífsnæríngar á
hvórjum deigi, enn ad enduduñ veitslunuñ reisti kóngur
heim, og lét qvedja þings alla Hófdíngja, hvad vid Bast.
20 kóng gjóra skildi; enn þad kom óllum samann, ad Ambal.
skyldi þar firir sjá, bad kóngur hann þar dæma honum
þann dauda er honum síndist maklegur. þá mælti Amb:
ei mun lífs betrunar hañs ad bída, og er hann hefur so
mórg illverk adhafst sem mónnum er kunnugt, og má
25 hann hunds dauda deýa, so var Bast. k. heingdur, létu
þeir so um Snóruna búa ad hann skildi ei fliótt deýa,
lifdi hann marga daga í gálganum, lét hann so líf sitt
med mikillri Sneipu og stórum hórmū.

34 Capituli.

þEGAR Ambales hafdi verid med kóngi 3 vetur, mælti
hann eitt siñ vid kóng: Nú mun hendtugur tími
til þess vera kominn ad eg endi heitstreíngíngu mína,
og ná aptur fódurleifd minni, enn þó vil eg þitt leifi þar
5 til hafa. Kóngur mælti: eingin mótvilje er mér ad
áformi þínu, enn ei legg eg þér stirk til þessarar ferdar.

hunger, for he was bound to the seat both hand and foot. At the king's command the loveliest damsels danced before him, clad in a single linen raiment. Beneath him a sharp sword was placed, and a twenty-pound weight of lead was hung upon his lower limbs. With such-like tortures the king tormented him, and the more he suffered, the fiercer grew his mood. Ambales would always succour him, and every day he sent him bread wherewith to sustain his life. Now when the king's progress came to an end, he rode home again, and thereafter he called together all the lords of the land to take counsel with them as to what should be done with King Bastian. They were all of one accord, to wit, that Ambales should decide it; and the king then asked him to pronounce on Bastian the death he deemed most fitting. "There is no hope," said Ambales, "of the bettering of his life; and since he has wrought so many deeds of shame, as all men know, let him die the death of a dog." And so King Bastian was hanged, and the halter was so placed that he might not die quickly, but lived on for many a day upon the gallows, and at last expired in great shame and fierce agony.

Chapter XXXIV.

WHEN he had been with the king some three winters, Ambales spake thus to him: "The time has surely now come for me to keep my vow and regain my heritage, and yet would I first have thy leave thereto." The king answered: "Thy purpose is nowise contrary to my will, but I can give thee no help in this enterprise."

Cʜ.XXXIV. Ambales mælti : einskipa mun eg þángad fara á mínum
Dreka sem eg þadann med mér hafdi. Kóngur mælti :
ad sónnu er gjæfa þín allmikil, enn ekki er henni altjafnt
10 gott ad treýsta. Ambal. mæ : á gjæfuna treisti eg alls
ekki, heldur á gjafara hennar, Adrían skal so sem minn
pantur hjá ydur vera til þjónustu í min̄ stad. Kóngur
mælti : of fálidadur fer þú hjedan̄ frá oss ad þínu radi.
Ambales mæ : ei mun eg marga menn þurfa til hefnda
15 vid brædur þína, því þeim munu elds glædur búnar til
hefnda, enn Gud á Himnum rædur óllu þessu. Kóngur
mælti : hvór er sá Gud? edur hvad hefur hann heldst
ad verkum gért? Ambal. mæ : seigja skal eg þér þad
kóngur ef þú villt á hann trúa ; hann er sá lífsins andi
20 sem óllumm Sképnum géfur líf og andardrátt ; seigir
hann þá kóngi af óllum̄ hófudgreinum kristindómsins ;
og er hann hafdi lokid rædu sinni setti kóng hlíódan,
og undradist miög þvílíka hluti, enn sagdi þó um̄ sídir ;
enn mun eg vora Gudi tilbidja, því þessir hafa mier
25 leingi vel verid. Kvaddi þá Ambales kóng er hann
hafdi filgt honum til skips ; gékk hann þá um bord og
lét í Haf, gaf vel bir, lagdi hann undir Cimbrjam, og
hielt skipi sínu í djúpi sjáfar alt til Jóla. Þad var sidur
þeirra brædra, ad hvór hielt ódrum jóla veitslu, og átti
30 nú Málpríant ad sækja veitslu í Cimbrja til Fástínusar
bródur síns, var hann þar komin med miklu fjólmenni,
og ad því lidnu ætla þeir med Herfór í Schytía og taka
eignir sínar enn drepa Tamerlaus kóng ; enn kvóldinu
firir hinn 8da dag, lagdi Ambal. Skipi sínu á hófn upp,

"I shall go thither," said Ambales, "with but one ship, namely, with my 'Dragon,' which I erewhile brought with me from thence." "True thy luck is great," said the king, "but 'tis not safe to trust thereto always." "I trust not in luck," replied Ambales, "but in the Giver thereof. Adrian shall remain here as my hostage with you, doing service in my stead." The king said : "With too few men goest thou forth from us, if thou meanest to pursue thy purpose." "I shall not need many," said Ambales, "wherewith to wreak vengeance on thy brothers, for coals of fire will be ready for my vengeance, and all lies in the might of the God of heaven." "Who is this God ?" asked the king, "or what great thing has he wrought ?" Ambales answered : "I will tell thee all, O king, if thou wilt but believe in him. He is the Spirit of Life which gives life and breath to all created things ;" and so he recounted to the king the chief points of the Christian belief; and when he had finished his speech, the king sat silent, and wondered much thereat ; at last he spake thus : "I must still hold by our own gods, for they have acted kindly towards me this long time." Ambales bade the king farewell; he had accompanied him to his ship. He went aboard and put out to sea, and a fair wind brought him under the coast of Cimbria, and he held his ship out on the main all the time till Yule-tide. Now it was the custom of the brothers to invite each other to a Yule-feast, and it was Malpriant's turn to come to his brother Faustinus to a Yule-feast in Cimbria. And he had come thither with a great multitude of men. And when the Yule-feast had ended, the brothers were minded to make a war-raid upon Scythia, in order to seize their patrimony and slay King Tamerlaus. The evening before the eighth day of Yule Ambales brought his ship into the harbour,

enn festi þó ei skipid, og gékk eirn á land, tók hann á
sig annarlegan búnad, sm̄ vóru þær gjórfar allar er hann
ad fornu haft hafdi í Cimbrja, baud hann mónnum sínum
ad halda so lángt undañ landi, ad ei mætti sjá þá, skildu
þeir sín aptur vitja ad tveim nóttum lidnum, enn 8da dags
40 kvóldid gékk Ambales til eldaskála, hafdi hann kublinn
Drafnar naut ytst fata, enn þar innañundir Silki vodir og
grímu á Hófdi lióta so búna sem narrar tídkudu, gékk
hann ad hreisi, því er hann hafdi Spítur sínar í lagt ad
fornu, tók hánn þær þá allar og lét í Húdfat mikid, batt
45 so ei mátti glatast, bidleikadi hann nú vid þar til hā
vissi sér tíma hendtugan til Hallarinnar gánga; enn er
hañ heirdi sem mestañ glaum í Hóllinni, dróg hann nú
hlassid eptir sér ad hallar dyrunum̄, dira-verdir leifdu
hónum inngaungu, eñ er hann var innkomiñ, vildi hlassid
50 meira rúm hafa eñ dirnar gáfu, brá hann þá festinni um̄
bak sér og streittist vid slíkt er hann kunni, og sem
hlassid var laust vid dyrnar, enn hañ sjálfur vid gjætt-
irnar, tumbadi hann inná gólfid, var þad óhæg bilta,
vard af þessu allmikil gledi í Hóllinni, qvádu menn
55 þetta allmikla Skémtan og nú heldst í þarfir koma;
Fífl þetta tók nú ad brólta á fætur, og rogadi nú
hlassi sínu innar eptir, og komst med þad undir bord
kóngaña; eingin gaf gaum ad þessu edur meinti þar
mundi nokkud undirbúa, tók nú þessi þrjótur ad leika
60 ýmislega og láta óllum̄ ólátum̄, og vard mikid gaman
ad leikum hañs, átti hann gód vól matar og drykkjar,
enn so ákafur var hañ, ad hā tók sér loks hvíld undir

but he did not moor his vessel there. He went alone
a-land, wearing a disguising raiment, the very garment
he had formerly worn in Cimbria. He had ordered his
men to put off from the land at such a distance that they
might not be seen; they were to come to him again when
two nights had passed. On the evening of the eighth
day Ambales made for the hall; he wore over his clothes
the cloak that Drafn had given him; he had silken
raiment beneath; on his head he had a grotesque mask,
after the fashion of the fools of the time. He went
straight to the kennel where he had aforetime stored his
spits, and he took them all out, and put them into a
leathern bag, which he tied up so that none might be
lost. Then he loitered about until he deemed the proper
time had come for him to enter the hall. He heard a
loud noise of revelling within, as he dragged the load
after him to the doors of the hall. The doorkeepers
suffered him to enter, but though he himself passed in,
the load needed more room than the doorway would
allow; then he twisted the rope around his waist and
tugged at it with all his might, and at last the load was
got through; and when he was well within, he stumbled
upon the floor, and gave himself a nasty fall; and thereat
there arose great glee in the hall, and men said 'twas
good sport, and had come at the right moment. The
fool then made vain efforts to get upon his feet again,
and staggered with his load up the hall, so that at last
he got it beneath the table of the king: no one paid
any heed thereto, nor had suspicion that it meant more
than they saw. And then, like an ape, he began all
sorts of antics, and disported himself strangely, and
there was great glee at his pranks, and they gave
him good choice of meat and drink. And so he went
on unceasingly, but at last he took rest beneath

167

Ch. XXXIV. Hallar bekkjunum, enn ei var hañ þó heldur þar ydjulaus,
heldur dróg hann sem kjænast klædi þeirra sem á bekkj-
65 unum Sátu nidur umm gótinn og stángadi firir med
Spítunū enn ei hafdi hann þar lángar dvalir, heldur
jók hann Fólkinu á ný mikla Skémtan med sínum
narra látum, gjördust nú allir drukknir, so eingin gádi
ad sjálfum sér fyrir drykkjuskap og ofsakjæti, og er
70 mjög var náttad, sveif Fíflid ad Amba Drottníngu, og
varpadi einhvörju bindini í kné henni, enn hún brast
vid rjód og varpadi þessu ad Gamalíel, enn hann leýsti
til og fann þar bréf innañi, hann hugdi ad og las
bréfid hliódlega í eira Drottníngar merkti hún þá hvad
75 í efni var, og hóf grát mikin, og beiddist ordlofs ad
gánga í burtu, og qvaddi med sér Letam Drottníngu,
geingu þær so útaf Höllinni og allir þeir ed kristnir
vóru, eñ fíflid hielt samt á leikum sínum, so ei komst
athugje á burtför Drottnínganna, enn ad leiks lokum
80 brá gésturin sér ad Gamalíel, og bar hann sem hægast
mátti á Handlegg sér úr Höllinni, og sló sídann hurd
í lás, enn er hann Stökk útyfir Hallar dyrnar, gaus
eldur úr veski hañs er þar lá, so öll Höllinn vard Strax
í einu báli, enn þeir sem flýa vildu vóru fastir, var þar
85 þá emjan og óp mikid brann þá öll Hölliñ og alt fólk
er þar var inni, drápust kóngarnir bádir, þar med 2
Synir kóngsins af Spáni, og ad auki nær 2000 manna.

the benches of the hall. Nor was he idle there; stealthily he drew the robes of those who sat on the benches down through the holes, and pinned them to the other side with his spits. He did not stay there long, but came forth again and made sport for them with his fool's tricks. And soon all were so besotted that they were beside themselves with drunkenness and with mirth. When the night was far advanced, the fool made his way to Queen Amba and threw a bundle into her lap; she started thereat and turned red, and flung it to Gamaliel, who undid it, and found therein a letter which he read in a whisper into the ears of the queen; and then she saw what was toward, and she fell a-weeping, and asked leave to go away, and bade Queen Leta go with her; and so they passed out of the hall, and with them all the Christians who were there; but the fool went on with his pranks, so as to turn their minds from the departure of the queen; and when he was nigh bringing his sport to an end, their guest suddenly turned to Gamaliel, and gently carried him in his arms out of the hall, and slammed the door to, and even as he leapt over the threshold, flames burst forth from a bundle which lay there, and the hall was soon all ablaze, and those who would have fled were pinned fast to their seats, and there was great whooping and lamentation, and the hall and all the people therein were burnt: both the kings, and two sons of the King of Spain, lost their lives there, and some two thousand men besides.

35 Capítuli.

ᴇᴘᴛɪʀ þad Kóngarnir vóru daudir, gékk Ambales í Herbergi modur sinnar, og qvaddi hana med kjærleika,
vard hún honum þá allshugar feigiñ. Leta Drottníng
var þar, og bar lítinn Harm þó kóngur dæi ; þaug áttu ei
5 börn samañ og hjeldu menn þettad af brögdum vòlf-
unnar ad hún mundi um hann til qvenn manna búid
hafa. Gamaliel flítti ferd sinni í sitt herbergi, eñ ad
morgni bjóst Ambales til sjáfar og fann þar Skip sitt á
hòfn komid, tók þá Ambales upp sín tignar klædi gjeck
10 sidañ heim til borgar med lid sitt, gjekk Gamaliel þá á
mót hònum med virdíngu vóru þá 10 vetur lidnir frá
dauda Salmans kóngs : litlu sídar reid Ambales til Fjall
bigda ad hitta þá fjelaga Caron og Drafnar, fagna þeir
hònum vel, baud hann þeim heim til Borgar med sjer,
15 og fóru þeir heim med hònum med alt Sitt góts, Sidañ
ljet Ambales biggja eina Veglega Hòll miklu værni eñ
þá fyrri, Tosti dvergur var forsmidur þessa Verks, og er
þad var búid, ljet hañ þíng Stefna og lísti sínum eignar
Rjetti yfir landinu og òllum nálægum Ríkjuñ, Tóku
20 allir lands Hòfdíngjar því vel og var hann svo til kóngs
tekinn, Ambales konúngur héldt Drottníngarnar med
mestu Sæmd og vyrdíngu, sat kóngur þá tvo vetur, en
ad þeim lidnum, vildi hann austur í Schytjam halda, og
á þeim deigi sem kóngur vildi burt, sendi Skéssañ Tosta

Chapter XXXV.

SOON after the king's death, Ambales went to his
mother's chamber, and greeted her lovingly, and
from her very heart she was glad to see him. Queen
Leta was there with her, but she bore little sorrow
though her lord had perished; they had had no children,
and folk deemed that this had come about by the wiles
of the witch; she had perchance bespelled him with
regard to women. Gamaliel had already betaken himself
to his chamber. On the morrow Ambales went down to
the sea, and found that his ship had come into harbour;
then he took his robes of state, and went back to the city
with all his company; and Gamaliel came to meet him
with great worship; and ten winters had then passed
since King Salman's death. Some little space thereafter
Ambales rode to the mountain-ranges to meet his friends
Caron and Drafnar, and they greeted him well, and he
bade them return to the city with him, and they went
with him with all their belongings. Anon King Ambales
had a lordly hall built for himself, nobler far than the
former had been, and Dwarf Tosti was master-builder
of the work. And when it was finished, he caused an
assemblage of all the folk to be called, and he declared
to them his right to that realm and to the neighbouring
realms, and all the chieftains of the land acknowledged his
right, and so he was made king; but he still maintained the
two queens in greatest state and honour. Then he abode
at home for two winters, and when they were passed, he was
minded to fare east towards Scythia. On the day the king
was ready to depart, the troll-woman sent Dwarf Tosti

Dverg til hañs med ágjætan kóngs Skrúda, fékk Gamaliel í Hendur umsjón Ríkisins, á medan hann var
burtu, Sigldi hann sídan vída um heim þad Sumar. Eitt
sinn lagdi hann undir Eýuna Cýpern, festi Skipuñ, gékk
á land, og sá 18 Skip liggja ódrumeigin Eýar, Hólfdíngi
30 þeirra hét Hephesstus, hann var Víkíngur og íþrótta
madr mikill, og hafdi mikid lid, hann lagdi óllum sínum
Skipum ad Skipi Ambal. kóngs, enn hann gaf sig lítt ad
í fyrstu, og hudgu Víkíngar hañ mundi uppgéfiñ.

36 Capítuli.

VíKÍNGAR lietu all rembilega, og vildu veita uppgaungu
á Skip kóngs, enn Carvel vardi vinstri Sídu Skips-
ins, eñ kóngur vardi sjálfur hina hægri, og fiellu víkíngar hrónnum; þetta sér Hefestus, eyrir hann illa,
5 ridst um fast, og vard margra manna bani, þetta sér
kóngur, geingur til hans, og leggur Staunginni Tosta
naut fyrir brjóst honum gégnum brinjuna, og risti so
til med Sídu kappans, og vo hann svo upp á Stángar
oddinum, og festi Skaptid vid Vindás stokkinn, og
10 lét hann so í loptinu hánga, gékk so í burt og brá
vopnum sínum. Carvel mælti: hvar fyrer lætur þú
víkíngi þessum lífs frest? Kóngur mæ: því aungvañ
hef eg frægri fundid, því þad Hógg fekk eg af hónum,
ad eg fiell á bædi kné, og hefdi ei kubliñ dugad mér,
15 munda eg hafa lífid mist. Þeir drepa nú alla þá er

to him with a royal robe of state. To Gamaliel was delivered the regency of the realm while King Ambales was away, and so he sailed far and wide about the world during that summer. Once he lay off the island of Cyprus; he moored his ship and went ashore, and espied eighteen ships at anchor on the other side of the island. Their commander hight Hephestus; he was a pirate, a man of mighty prowess, and with him there was a great company. He set all his ships round the ship of King Ambales, who at first attempted to do little, and the pirates thought he had yielded himself to them.

Chapter XXXVI.

THE pirates carried things with a high hand, and were minded to board the king's vessel, but Carvel warded the left side thereof, and the king warded the right, and the pirates fell in heaps. Hephestus, seeing this, misliked it much, and rushed about wildly, and was the bane of many a man. The king observed it, and made for him, and thrust his pole, Tosti's gift, through the byrnie at his breast, and he ripped it to the warrior's side, and heaved him aloft at the point of the pole, and fastened the handle to the joist of the windlass, and left him a-hanging in the air, and then he went away, and took up his weapons. " Why grantest thou a respite to this pirate?" asked Carvel. " Because," said the king, " no warrior of mine is a doughtier than he, for such a blow got I from him, that perforce I fell on my knees, and had not my head-gear stood me in stead, I had lost my life."

Cн. XXXVII. mótstódu veittu, og tóku Skipiñ og fé alt. Nú gékk
kóngur til og sá Hefestum enn á Staunginni hánga
hálfdaudann, lét hann þá taka hann, leggja í hæga sæng
og sídañ næra; og sem hann mátti mæla, baud kóngur
20 honum líf, ef hann vildi sér trúa þjónustu veita. Hefestus qvadst þess fús vera, lét kóngur þá græda hann,
og bundu þeir vináttu sína med fastmælum, Sigldu so
til Schytja, og geingu á land, fagnar Tamerlaus þeim
vel, kóngr stardi miög á Hefestus, og spurdi hann nafns
25 og ættar, enn hann sagdi sem var, so og frá vigureign
þeirra Ambalesar kóngs og sín, fékk kóngur af því
stóran kjærleika til Ambalesar kóngs, ad hann hafdi
líf géfid Hefestus, því hann vissi hann sinn bródur vera,
þó heimuglegt væri, og mynntist orda módur sinnar, og
30 sagdi honum þetta í heimugleikum. Ambales kóngur
seigir honum frá afgángi brædra hanns, ad Ríkid væri
sitt vordid, enn Bálant kóngur mun Spanja ríki taka
vegna Drottníngar sinnar, og þad annad ad honum er
þad ad réttum erfdum tilfallid. Tamerlaus þakkar
35 honum allann þennan Sigur og Sæmdarauka.

37 Capítuli.

Að vetri lidnum mælti Ambales kóngur vid Tamerlaus
kg. nú mun hendtugur tími til þess vera komiñ ad
eg heim vitje, og ti(l) vorra landa aptur sigli. Tamerlaus
hliódnadi hér vid, og mælti: Ei mun tjá ad hindra ferd

Thereafter they slew all who opposed them, and seized the ships and all their belongings. Now as the king went his way he saw Hephestus still hanging on the pole half dead; he bade them take him down and lay him on a soft bed, and thereafter he had him well nursed. And when he was able to speak, the king offered him life, if he would but do him faithful service. Hephestus answered he was full willing thereto. So the king had him healed, and they bound their friendship with words of troth. Then they set sail for Scythia, and went a-land. Tamerlaus gave them goodly welcome. The king gazed hard at Hephestus, and asked him his name and kindred. He told him truly all, and he told him eke his dealings with King Ambales, and the king conceived great love towards King Ambales for having granted life to Hephestus, for he knew him to be his brother, though it had been kept secret, and he called to mind his mother's words, and told them him privily. King Ambales told King Tamerlaus of his brother's death, and how the realm was now his; King Balant would, however, still rule over Spain through his queen; though, he added, Spain had also fallen to him by right of inheritance. Tamerlaus thanked him for his victories and for all this accession of glory.

Chapter XXXVII.

AT the close of the year King Ambales said to King Tamerlaus: "The time has now come for me to go home, to sail back to my country." When he heard this, Tamerlaus was for a while silent; then he spake this: " It will not avail to hinder thy departure, though it will

Ch. XXXVII. þína, þó þad sé Skadi voru ríki, þridjúngur þessa ríkis heirir þínu valdi til sem er heimañfilgja dóttur minnar, og máttu sitja á því med oss, enn setja Skattþegna yfir lónd þín. Ambl. kóngr mæ: einginn rád hef eg í sjálfs valdi, heldur Gud sem rædur óllum vorum
10 stundum og Stódum hér í Heimi. leýsti Tamerlaus k. út dóttur sína med Stórmiklu Fé. Ambales setti Hefestus yfir þann hluta ríkisins í Schytja, sem drottníngu hañs til heirdi, og hér med baud hann honum Tamerlaus kóngi hollur ad vera, Ambales sendi Carvel eptir þeim
15 karli og kérlingu Artes sem hañ gisti fyrst hjá er hañ til landsins kom, urdu þaug bædi glód er þaug sáu Ambales kóng, og merktu hañs triggda hót vid sig, fékk hann þeim nægar vistir og miklar vyrdíngar. Filgdi Tamerlaus kóngur og Drottníng hañs Dóttur sinni til
20 Skipa, og var þar skilnadar ól drukkid, og vóru fæstir sem vatni gátu haldid, bádu hvórjer vel fyrir ódrum, og hafdi Ambales kóngur 6o Skipa, og fékk hinn besta byr, og er hann heim kom, baud hann óllum Hófdíngjum landsins til veitslu, var hún gjór med miklum kost-
25 nadi, enn ad henni endadri, vóru menn med gjófum útleýstir, Sat so kóngur í ríki sínu med fridi og gódri stjórnsemi.

needs impair our rule. The third part of this realm, the dowry of my daughter, owes obedience to thee; thou mayst well therewith make thy home in our midst, and appoint a tributary thane over thine own lands." "My own wish," said King Ambales, "counts for nought; all is in the power of God, who determines the days of our lives and our dwelling-places here in the world." King Tamerlaus sped his daughter from home with great store of wealth. Ambales set Hephestus over that portion of the kingdom of Scythia which belonged to his queen, and therewithal he enjoined upon him to be faithful to King Tamerlaus. He sent Carvel for the carle and the carline Artes, with whom he had stayed when he first came thither to the land, and they were right glad when they saw King Ambales, and perceived his token of kindness towards them; he gave them sustenance enow and showed them much honour. King Tamerlaus and his queen accompanied their daughter to the vessel, and the parting-ale was drunk, and few there could keep back their tears, and each wished god-speed to the other. King Ambales had sixty ships in all, and there was a fair wind, and when he reached home he summoned the chieftains of his realm to a feast; it was prepared at greatest cost; and when it came to an end, the guests were sped with goodly gifts. So the king abode in his realm in peace and with good governance.

38 Capituli.

EITT kvóld þá konúngur sat ad bordum, kom Tosti dvergur og qvaddi hann lítilátlega, og mælti : vinkona þín er nú sjúk vordin og nær ad Helju komin, og bidur hún þig ad finna sig ádur hún deir. Kóngur
5 brá skjótt vid og fór til bigda Kérlingar, var hún þá nær ómála ordin, enn kunni kóngur ad ráda þad af ordum̃ hennar, ad hún gaf Hárbrá fóstru sinni óll sín audæfi eptir sig, ad fráteknum þeim kostgripum er hún hafdi ádur kóngi géfid, og þad sem hún tilvísadi ad
10 sínum beinum filgja skildi, sást þad á hennar vidmóti ad hún unnti kóngi af alhuga, var hañ þar vid andlát hennar, sídan lét hann búa um bein hennar miög vyrduglega, og gjóra haug ad í dallendi einu fyrir nedan Fjallid, sídann bjóst kóngur heim og hafdi Hárbrá med
15 sér, og óll þaug audæfi sem þar vóru, og var þad stór mikid Fé ; Hárbrá var Jómfrú dægileg, Hefestus leit ástaraugum til hennar, og þar kom ad hañ hóf bónord til hennar vid kóng, og vard þad audsókt, og gjórdi kóngur brúdkaup þeirra med mesta Sóma, og ad því
20 endudu, bjóst Hefestus heim, filgdi kóngur þeim til Skipa, og gaf hónum ad skilnadi Sverdid Risanaut, og Sigldi svo Hefestus heim í Schytja, og hélt sínu Hertogadæmi inn til dauda Fódur síns, sídann tók hann ríkis stjórn eptir hann á Indjalandi.

Chapter XXXVIII.

ONE evening the king sat at his table, and Dwarf Tosti came to him and greeted him humbly, and said: "Thy woman-friend is now fallen ill, and at the point of death, and she prays thee to see her ere she dies." The king forthwith betook himself to her dwelling; she was nigh speechless then, but the king could understand so much of her words, that she bestowed all her wealth upon her foster-daughter Hair-brow, save such treasures as she had already given to the king, and such as she wished should bide with her bones. It could be seen from her looks how she loved the king with all her heart. He tarried there till she breathed her last, and he saw to it that her bones were right worthily bestowed, and he had a mound raised over her in valley-ground beneath the mountain. Thereafter the king prepared to return home, and he took Hair-brow with him, and all the wealth that was there, and it was a mighty hoard. Hair-brow was a comely maiden, and Hephestus cast longing eyes upon her, and at last he set forth his suit for her with the king: his prayer was readily granted, and the king gave her a noble wedding-feast. And when all was over, Hephestus prepared to go home; the king sent them off to their ships, and he gave Hephestus at parting his own sword, the gift of the giant. So Hephestus sailed home to Scythia, and held his dukedom till his father's death, when he succeeded him in India.

39 Capituli.

Þegar Bálant kóngur frétti fall Malpríants kóngs, kuñi hann ílla vid hagi sína, því Týris Drottníng eggjadi hañ hardlega þar til ad hefnt yrdi Fódur heñar, því bjóst hann nordur til þeirrar Ferdar med mikid lid, og 5 fór til Cimbrja, og sendi á kóngs fund. Ambal. k. mæ : vid of er þad, ad vid frændur skulum órlóg þreýta, enn hugsad hafdi eg ad Bálant kóngur skildi njóta Spanja ríkis, þá Málpríant kóngur væri frá því rádinn, enn koma mun eg á hañs fund, og skal hann þá fá ad þekkja 10 mig. Sendimenn fóru og seigja Bálant kóngi ord hanns. Ambales kóngur bjó sinn her út, og sem hann var komiñ á leid, mætir hónum madur, sá síndist komin á sinn efri aldur, hann qvaddi kóng vyrduglega, kóngur horfdi mióg á hann, og Spyr hañ ad nafni? hann qvadst Tellus 15 heita. Kóngur mælti : gjörla kénni eg þig og þekki þann ad vera sem leingst vardist med Fódur mínum, og skaltu mér velkominn vera, og slíkan Sóma þiggja sem þú ert verdur. Tellus mælti : ódru er nú ad gjegna, og skulum vid þar fyrst til verda sem heldst er naudsýn 20 til. Sídann ridu þeir til Herbúda Bálants kóngs, og skipudu lidi sínu, vóru þessir heldstu kappar Ambalesar : Gamalíel, Caron, Drafnar, Adrjan, Tellus, Carvel, Tosti dvergur og Sonur hañs. Ambales k. bad þá, ef Bálant kóngur Sigradist, ad granda ei lífi hanns, heldur færa

Chapter XXXIX.

Soon as King Balant heard of King Malpriant's fall, he was troubled as to his own fate, seeing that Queen Tyris egged him on to avenge her father. So he prepared to journey northward with a great host, and went to Cimbria, and sent men to hold speech with the king. King Ambales said : "Far be it from us that we kinsmen should try issues with each other, for I had resolved that King Balant should enjoy the realm of Spain when King Malpriant had ceased therefrom, but I will come and meet him, and he shall get to know me." The messengers departed and told King Balant the words of Ambales. King Ambales arrayed his host for going forth, and when he was come on the way, there met him a man who seemed sunken in age; he greeted the king worthily, and the king asked him his name. He said his name was Tellus. "Surely I know thee," said the king; "I know thee to be the man who so long fought for my father, and thou shalt be welcome to me, and have all the honour thou art deserving of." "Other things have now to be looked to," said Tellus; "we must first go thither where the need is greatest." Thereupon rode they to King Balant's camp, and they drew up their lines, and the chief warriors of Ambales were the following : Gamaliel, Caron, Drafnar, Tellus, Carvel, Dwarf Tosti and his son. King Ambales bade them, if King Balant should be vanquished, not to hurt him fatally, but to bring him

CH. XXXIX. sér hann fjötradañ. Ambal. k. reid í heirnar færi vid
Bálant k. og mælti : ósæmilegt er okkur Stríd ad halda so
nánir sem vid erum ad ætt, og hef eg aungva gyrnd á
þínum dauda né audæfum, og ei skyldir þú fyrir brek
Drottníngar þinnar farid hafa þessa Ferd ef mín rád haft
30 hefdir, enn ei mælist eg undann þér þó eg sé lidfærri; enn
það skaltu vita, ad ei hefnir þú Málpriäts kóngs í þessari
Ferd hvad sem þér verdur til qvennfadmlaganna þá þú
kémur heim aptur. Vid þessi ord vard Bálant kóngur
miög reidur, og Svaradi aungvu, eñ lét blása til bardaga,
35 og tókst hin hardasta orusta, fiellu nú meñ Bálants kóngs
hvör um̃ annan þverañ; því eýrir Bálant kgr. illa, reid
framm og ridst um fast og felldi fjölda manna, þetta sér
Carvel, og reid á moti Bálant kóngi, og áttust þeir vid,
Carvel hjó til kóngs og klauf Skjöldinn og brinjuna,
40 og fékk kóngur Sár á lærid; kóngur hjó aptur til Carv.
og tók af Hjalminum og Brinjunni á Brjóstinu, þar med
fildgi vinstri höndiñ og Hesturin sundur í bógunum̃; þá
hlióp Carvel ad kóngi og hió um þverar Herdar hönum,
og reif brinjuna, og í suñdur Södulinn og Hestinn, og
45 fékk kóngur mikid Sár á rassiñ, kóngur hlióp ad honum
og hjó á öxlina og klauf svo nidur, fiell Carvel þá
daudur; þetta leit Drafnar, reid ad Bálant kóngi, var
hann þá á annan Hest kominn, Drafnar þreýf kóng af
Hestinum og lagdi hann fyrir framann sig, og færdi
50 hann Ambales kóngi, var hann þá í fjötur settur, lét
Ambales kóngur halda upp Fridar skyldi, og fara hver-
tveggi í sínar Herbúdir, því ad qvöldi var komid.
182

to him in fetters. King Ambales rode within hearing distance of King Balant, and said : "Unseemly is it for us to be at strife, so near as we are to each other in kinship; I desire not thy death, nor covet I thy wealth. Thou wouldst never have ventured on this enterprise, despite thy queen's desire, hadst thou taken my word. I cry not off from this enterprise, though fewer men are mine ; yet know thou wilt not avenge King Malpriant on this journey of thine, whatever be the welcome in store for thee in thy wife's embraces, when thou returnest home." At these words King Balant was passing wroth, yet he answered not, but bade them blow the battle-blast. A fierce fight ensued, and King Balant's men fell in heaps, one after the other. Things boded ill for King Balant, and he rode forward, and rushed about wildly, and felled a multitude of men ; and when Carvel saw him, he spurred towards King Balant, and they fought together, and Carvel hewed at the king, and clave his shield and byrnie, and the king was wounded in the thigh. The king in his turn hewed at Carvel, and clave his helmet, and cut the byrnie on his breast, so that his left arm was struck off with the blow, and his horse was cut through at the withers. Then Carvel leapt at the king, and dealt him a blow athwart the shoulders, and ripped his byrnie, and cut a-twain his saddle and his horse at the same time, and the king got a mighty wound in the buttocks. The king then rushed at Carvel, and smote him in the shoulder, and it clave so deep down that Carvel fell dead. Seeing this, Drafnar rode at King Balant, who had now mounted another horse, and Drafnar seized the king from off his horse, and laid him prostrate before him, and brought him to King Ambales, and he was put in fetters. Thereupon King Ambales bade them raise the shield of peace, and they each went to their camps, for the day had worn to evening.

40 Capítuli.

CH. XL.

Um morgunin baud Ambales kóngur mónnum Bálants kóngs heim med sér, og þad þádu þeir gjarnsamlega, enn sem þeir vóru heim komnir, mælti Ambales kóngr vid Bálant kóng: Hvórja kosti viltu nú af oss taka?
5 Bálant k. mæ; óll mín lífs kjór eru nú í þínu valdi. Ambales k. mælti: Eg vil ad þú haldir lífi þínu og svo ríkjum þínum med því móti ad þú látir trú þína og kristnir lónd. Bálant k. mæ: ei mun eg þad til vinna, og ekki til lífsins þann átrúnad ad láta sem eg nú hefi,
10 því mínu ríki hefur meiri lukka heppnast sídañ eg sida skipti hafdi. Ambal. k. mælti: Hvórninn ætlar þú þér muni gánga á þeim eilífa tímanum? Bálant k. mæ: þeinkir þú þinn Gud mínum Gudi sterkari ad hugsa sínum dírkendum fyrir betri Sælu, þad muntu
15 mér ei trúlegt seigja kunna, Skulum vid því hætta þessari þráttan, er þad best ad hvór deíe uppá sína Trú. Ambal. kóngur vildi honum þá ei í neinu naud þreýngja, enn qvaddi Hófdíngja Landsins á rádstefnu, hvad gjóra Skyldi vid Bálant kóng, allir qvádu hann
20 dauda verdann, enn Ríkinn óll Ambales kóngs. þá mælti Greifi Gamalíel: Ekki er þetta lángt frá sónnu talad, þó sýnist kóngi vorum gott til gánga þó hann samaumkan hafi med Bálant kóngi frænda sínum, því þad er Guds þolinnmædi ad hafa yfir sindugum mónnum,

184

Chapter XL.

ON the morrow King Ambales bade King Balant's men wend home with him; they welcomed the bidding. Now when they were come home, King Ambales said thus to King Balant: "What terms wilt thou take of us?" King Balant said: "All my life's fate is in thy power." "'Tis my will," said King Ambales, "that thou have thy life and eke thy realms on this condition, that thou yield me thy fealty and Christianise thy lands." "Thereto I cannot bring me," answered King Balant; "not even for my life's sake can I give up the faith I hold, for better fortune has befallen my realm since I changed my faith." "How think'st thou," said King Ambales, "it will fare with thee in the life eterne?" King Balant answered: "Think'st thou thy God is stronger than my god, winning nobler salvation for his worshippers? Thereof thou wilt never convince me. Let us then leave off this wrangle, for it is best that each one die in his own faith." King Ambales in nowise would press him then, but he called the lords of the land together to counsel him as to what should be done with King Balant; they all said he well deserved death, and that all his land should belong to King Ambales. Then spake Count Gamaliel: "The words spoken are not far from truth; yet his kind heart leads our king to have compassion upon King Balant, his kinsman; 'tis indeed God's nature to be long-suffering with sinful men,

185

ef verda mætti ad betrun kynni ad ské, og líka ad straffa ríki þessarar veraldar med ógudlegu yfirvaldi til ásetts tíma, því þikir mér rádlegt, kóngur! ad þú Guds vegna í hlut leggir líf og dauda kóngsins, og hafir so það Gud kýs honum til handa. Þetta þókti kóngi og
30 Höfdíngjum allgott rád; vóru sídann hlutir í Skaut lagdir, fiell lífsins hlutur yfir kóngin, var hann svo leýstur og fékk stórann kjærleika til Ambales kóngs, og sór eid med fastmælum ad reýnast hónum triggur í öllum hlutum inn til daudans; Sigldi sídann heim í
35 Spanja, og var fátaladur lánga tíma. Týris Drottníng frétti hann ad sökum og Sigur kjörum. Enn hann bistist vid og mælti: opt lukkast ílla áeggjan qvenna; því óhægt er audnu manninn ad sigra, þar sem eg vid Ambales kóng frænda minn átti í hlut, á eg honum
40 best ad launa, og ei reini eg ad vinna það til þinnar vináttu framar ad vera óvinur hañs, því hefdu frændur þínir lifad, þá hefdir þú ekki Spanja ríki feingid, hvört Ambales kóngur á med réttu, enn ann mér halds og eignar á því, og þá eg var af honum fángadur, þyrmdi
45 hann lífi mínu, hvad eg mundi honum ei gjört hafa hefdi mér Sigur yfir hónum heppnast, skal eg aldrei vid hann kjærleika slíta á medann eg lifi, og so vil eg ad þú gjörir med mér. Drottníng qvad so vera skildi, og hieldu þaug sídan kjærleika vid Ambales kóng medann þaug lifdu.

in the hope that things may take a better turn, yea, and to scourge the kingdoms of the world with ungodly sway, for a time at least; wherefore methinks it were a wise course, sir king, that thou shouldst, for God's sake, submit to lot the life of the king, and do even as God chooses for him." To the king and to his chieftains this counsel seemed excellent. So lots were then thrown into a cloth, and the lot of life fell to the king. And he was thereupon released, and he conceived great love for King Ambales, and he swore an oath with words of sooth to prove faithful to him in all things until death. Thereafter he sailed home to Spain, and he was of few words for a long time. Queen Tyris questioned him as to the cause of his silence, and eke what sort of victory he had won. But he grew cross-grained thereat and said : " Oft the egging on of women turns out ill; 'tis no easy thing to overcome a favoured mortal, when such a man as my kinsman, King Ambales, is to be dealt with. I owe him greatest gratitude, and to gain thy good-will, ne'er will I risk so much again as to become his foe; for had thy kinsman lived, thou wouldst never have gotten the realm of Spain, which rightly appertains to Ambales, to whom I owe the rule and ownership thereof, and whereas I was his captive, he has spared my life. I would not have done the same for him had victory fallen to my lot, and I shall never forsake my love towards him as long as I live, and I desire that thou join me therein." The queen said it should be even so, and thereafter they maintained their love towards King Ambales as long as they lived.

41 Capítuli.

GODFREIR hét kóngur á þeim dögum er stýrdi Vallandi,
var hann nú gamall vordinn, hafdi hann bædi verid
megtugur og hinn mesti Riddari, og var Ambales bræd-
rungs sonur kóngs; kóngur átti eina dóttur, hún hafdi
5 blind borinn verid, og var enn nú blind; Lönd hañs
vóru stórlega á sókt af Tirkjum og ödrum þiódum ómild-
um, hlaut hañ því opt Styrk ad þiggja af ödrum
nálægum kóngum, og vard það því af rádi Höfdíngja,
sérdeilis Páfans í Rómaborg, er hét Jóhannes þridje, ad
10 Godfreir gaf Ambales kóngi Ríkid eptir sig, enn hálft
medan þeir lifdu bádir, enn ádur enn Ambales af Cimbría reisti, kallar hann Tellum firir sig, og spyr first,
hvar hann hefdi allañ þann tíma verid er Fástínus hieldt
Cimbrja? eñ hann sagdist á Eidimörku biggd hafa hjá
15 eirnri konu er Ísodd hiet, hún var í mörgu vel ad sér,
og er hún nú fyrir tveim vetrum daud, enn þá eg spurdi
þína híngad komu, vilda eg heldur þér þjóna enn einmana
búa þótt eg nógan aud hafi. Kóngur mæ: góds ert þú
af mér maklegur, vil eg þig hér ad kóngi gjöra, og þetta
20 ríki þér til halds í hendr fá, og tak til Egta Letam
Drottníngu, því henni munu karlmenn ei spillt hafa.
Tellus mæ: gott er mér þínu rádi ad filgja; og svo
gjördist hann kóngur yfir Cimbrja, og drakk brúdkaup
sitt til Letam Drottníngar, var henni og sjálfri þetta

Chapter XLI.

IN those days lived a king hight Godfrey; he ruled over Gaul; he was now an old man; in his time he had been a doughty warrior and valiant; Ambales was second cousin to this king. The king had a daughter who had been born blind, and was still blind at this period. Now the king's lands were cruelly ravaged by the Turks and other barbarous tribes, and therefore he was oft-times forced to ask aid of neighbouring kings; and it came to pass by the counsel of great potentates, especially of the Pope of Rome, who hight John the Third, that Godfrey bestowed on King Ambales his whole realm after him, and half thereof while they both lived. But before Ambales set out for Cimbria, he called Tellus before him, and asked him first where he had dwelt during all the time that Faustinus held sway over Cimbria. He said he had been dwelling in a wilderness with a certain woman hight Isold; she was withal a woman of goodly parts, but she had been dead then these two years; "and when I heard of thy coming hither, I would fain rather serve thee than dwell alone, albeit I have wealth enow." The king said: "Well hast thou deserved of me, and I will make a king of thee, and give this realm into thine hands, and take thou Queen Leta for thine own wife; her, I trow, men have not befooled." Tellus said: "Right gladly will I follow this thy bidding;" and so he was made king over Cimbria, and he drank the bride-ale with Queen Leta, and belike to her herself

kjært; enn Amba Drottníng fór til Vallands med Syni sínum, enn sem Ambales kóngur hafdi ríkt 10. ár í Wallandi, andadist sá nafnfrægi Greifi Gamaliel, og bar Ambales kóngur mikinn trega eptir hann. Ambales kóngur átti þrjá Sonu vid Drottníngu sinni, hét hiñ firsti 30 Salman, annar Godfreir, þridje Gamalíel, eñ dætra nöfn eru hér ei skrifud; Stírdi sídann Ambales kóngur ríki sínu til daudadags, enn hañs Son Godfreir tók þad ríki eptir hann.

Endum ber so þessa Sogu af Ambales kongi,
sem ádur nefndist
líka Amlodi.

it was a welcome thing. But Queen Amba went to
Gaul with her son; and when King Ambales had ruled
in Gaul ten years, the famous Count Gamaliel breathed
his last, and King Ambales bore great grief for him.
King Ambales had three sons by his queen, the first
hight Salman, the second Godfrey, the third Gamaliel,
but the names of his daughters are not recorded here.
Thereafter King Ambales ruled his realm unto his dying
day, and his son Godfrey took the realm after him.

Thus end we this Saga of King Ambales,
who erst was also
called Amlode.

APPENDIX.

Ambales Rímur.

I. RÍMUR AF AMBÁLES EPTIR HALLGRÍM HALDÓRSSON: Isl. Bokm. 273. 8vo.

. . . . . .

SALMAN kie(-ndur) digða dyr,
 Döglings arfeñ þriðie.
21 Þesser báru þundar stáls
þroska vitsku pryðe,
snarpa lund og sn(-ille) máls,
snögt yfer aðra lyðe.
 22 Sagañ greiner sikling stryð,
sárt að Elleñ neiðe,
leið so frañ uñ lánga tyð,
Loks í friðe Deiðe.
 23 Reckar skifttu Rykuñ þeim,
Ræsers eftter dauða,
vösku liðe uñar Eim,
og oturs giallde Rauða.
 24 Spania velde Haukur hyr,
hiellt með vaska dreinge,
þó varð luckañ þeingil Ryr,
þyðu svifttest gei(nge).
 25 A Hans Ryke heiðeñ her,
hielt (með) kölldu stryðe,
lietu christner lyf og fier,
landeð gótz og pryðe.

26 Af Sciutia Soldans son,
seggiuṁ varð að grande,
háðe stryð uṁ heimdalls kvon,
hölda vo með brande.

27 Malpryant hiet millding griṁur,
magnaðe villu Ránga,
christna meñ með kvöl og Riṁur,
kugaðe bender spánga.

28 Þykeð tok með Rausnuṁ þá,
Recka þrutu gæðe,
syðar verður sikling frá
sagt i þessu kvæðe.

29 Balant frægur beitte hiör,
banaðe heiðnuṁ lyðe,
Hispania orku ör
að sier tók með (pryðe).

30 (C-)umbra vellde (hilm-)er (hyr),
hlaut (með) frægð og sóma,
Salman kóngur dáða (dyr),
Drafnar þaktur lióma.

31 Vinsæll (þ)ótte vyser fróður,
veitte giafer meinge,
(eñ) i stryðe stiggur og óður,
stódst þá við hönuṁ Eingeñ.

32 Hoskur giæter viðreks vyfs,
veifaðe hiörnuṁ Rauða,
sigur hlaut i sóknuṁ kyfs,
segge hió til dauða.

33 Firðuṁ veitte fiarðar bál,
fræguṁ meingið uñe,
kappa lyður kiærn við stál,
kiesiu þiente Ruñe.

34 Eina meÿ er Amba hiet,
af Fracklande góða,
Dögling feste og dreinguṁ liet,
Dyra veitslu bióða.

35 Flest að vilia filkir (þá),
fiell sem villde kiósa,

hölldum̄ veitte hornalá,
og hrañar Eisu liósa.

36 Seima gierður siður bar,
sóma Rausn af lyðe,
Greifa Dótter vitur var,
vafiñ ment og pryde.

37 Virðing stór og hefðeñ há,
hyru þiente vyfe,
uñe gramur auðar gná,
Eins og sínu lyfe.

38 Fædde sveinbarn fallda vör,
fram̄ (þá) stunder lyða,
Sigurð nefnde sverða bör,
siklings þióðeñ blyða.

39 Hilmer Rykur helga trú,
hiellt með vaska lyðe,
Eingiñ fanst á jggiar frú,
Öðling iafn að pryðe.

40 Drottníng tiggia (dyr) og sviñ,
digg með hegðan góða,
Óliett varð i añað siñ,
Eikiñ báru glóða.

41 Grams i Ryke galldra norn,
greint er Ein sig hielde,
brögnum̄ þótte bragða forn,
bist i siñu velde.

42 Stór ættuð var strákleg frú,
Styfeñ skálka lykie,
alest hafðe auðar brú,
upp y Garða Rykie.

43 Öðlings frúr þä ólu börn,
oftt til heñar vitia,
sókt var snóteñ galldra giörn,
greitt til þierra að vitia (sic).

44 Vereð hafðe vyða um lönd,
virðing Ecke dvynar,
fieck þvi óðum̄ fallda strönd,
fie og leiptur Rynar.

45 Amba Drottníng Ecke liet,
hið jlla sækia kvende,
þar af grimt um þagnar flet,
þióstur völvu brende.

46 Gribbañ filtest grádug móð,
grim̄ i siñu Rañe
buðlúngs heim til borgar óð,
bistur galldra svañe.

47 Rækalls þy af Reiðe brañ
Ram̄lega þúng að bragðe,
Drott(n)íng hyra filkiers fañ,
fóleð þañ veg sagðe.

48 Hagur þiñ og lyfsens lán,
leikur i stæðstum̄ blóma,
að þier hverfur auðnu Rán,
sem Eiðer þynum̄ sóma.

49 Kóngur þiñ skal kyfs af öñ
kalldañ hreppa dauða,
með virða sveitum̄ (va-)ls i hröñ
vegs þá Efne nauða.

50 Buðlúng Eingiñ byte sverð,
bardaga þó Reine,
það mun vöfðum̄ giltre gierð,
gilfa verða að meine.

51 Son þiñ lyka sviftest brátt,
sætu lyfsens geinge,
mun á gálga heing(d)ur hátt,
harmureñ so þig streingi.

52 Gramsson sá þú geingur með,
girt af nauða kyfe,
synest fibl með sviplegt gieð,
samt mun hañ hallda lyfe.

53 Óvirðter þú ylla mig,
auðnu sleppter þiñe,
sárleg skaltu sorgar stig,
siá af beiðne miñe.

54 Sorgande varð siklings frú,
syst má gleðiñar nióta,

þeingil sagðe þorna brú,
þessa Ræðu lióta.

55 Reiðeñ svall uṁ siñu ból,
sorg nam briósteð þreingia,
þetta griṁa galdra fól,
gilfe bauð að heingia.

56 Drottníng fieck so digðug Rææðt,
við dreifer gullsens Rauða,
vort mun Ecki böleð bætt,
þó byðe norneñ dauða.

57 Sætañ biður sikling nú,
sæmder heñe að bióða,
ef böl vort villde bæta sú,
brigðlind hringa tróða.

58 Mællte Reiður milding þá,
mál sem heirðe þetta,
Ey má vondur ande sá,
ánauð miñe lietta.

59 Frá vyser geingur ve(-ig-)a slóð,
völvu hitte skiæða,
se(-l-)i(-añ gulls a-)f sorguṁ (móð)
so t(-ók)eñ að Ræða.

60 Veita skillde virðing þier
vefian kólgu bryma,
Ef sitia vilder sviñ hiá mier,
uṁ sængur legu tyma.

61 Ey kvaðst munde þiggia það,
þiófsleg galdra friggia,
búeñ sagðest brátt i stað,
burt af höllu tiggia.

62 Þoo kvaðst nornen jlsku ör,
afttur fiña kvende,
þá sætañ ætte sængur för,
syna firer hende.

63 Síðañ skillde sviplegt fljoð,
vid seliu mundar faña,
sást því döpur seima slóð,
sorg vill gleðena baña.

199

64 Sá kom dagur sagt er frá,
sóttar Drottníng kiende,
óvart þángað öllum þá,
aftur nornen vende.

65 Nornen veitte þiónkan þá,
þyðre seliu tviña,
fædde sveinbarn falda gná,
filkirs artug kviña.

66 Sveinen bar i siklings Rañ,
Seggia drótten nyta,
Ecki vilde öðling þan
augum synum lyta.

67 Þesse syndest þroska stór,
þó ey dægilegur
nauða döckur nadda þór,
nockuð sómatregur.

68 Ecki villde öðling mætur,
augum völvu lyta,
sá hún aungvar sáttar bætur,
af sviñum geimer Ryta.

69 Þaa syna Endte sængur för,
Selian oturs giallda,
bióst hin grima bauga vör
burt þaðan að hallda.

70 Burt þá vilde bragða forn,
af buðlungs Rañe gánga,
fan að mále ferleg norn,
fryða seliu spánga.

71 Jlla spáðe eg um þin hag,
Eikin kraka sáða,
fæst það Ecki færst í lag,
forlög þessu Ráða.

72 Son þin ungur veiga vör,
virðing stæðstu byðe,
Eflaust verdur alma bör,
ættar sinar pryðe.

73 Burtu vykur hreckia hrat,
sem hölldum varð að meine,

dávæn eftter drottníng sat,
og dillaðe ungum̄ sveine.

74 Synu nafne siklings frú,
so nam Rádugh breita,
Ambales liet auðarbrú,
unga sveiniñ heita.

75 Þroska mikeñ þesse hlaut,
þótte menta tregur,
fremda lytt af náme naut
nockuð skindelegur.

76 Sigurður fremd og sóma hlaut,
af siklings völldu meingie,
luckañ studde laufa gaut,
lyfs meðañ Endtest geinge.

77 Afleið tyme ytum̄ sá,
iña greiner letra,
filkiers arfar fundust þá,
fim̄ og tyu vetra.

78 Sveimar heim að sagna vör,
súða Dvalins karfe,
Gillings falla giölldeñ spör,
af góma Rámu starfe.

END OF THE FIRST RIMA.

II. RÍMUR AF AMBÁLES EÐA AMLÓÐA EPTIR (?) PÁL BJARNARSON: A.M. 521e. 4to.

Mansöngr.

RÓMUR máls um raddarsal
reiður í burtu vendi
hvörn eg alt að heyrnardal
hjeðan frá mjer sendi.

Þó mjer væri list sú ljent
ljóða kvörn að hræra,
orðasnild eða eddument
inn í þau að færa,

Þar frá gjörist mjer horfinn hugur;
hjer um fátt eg ræði;
hvorki er í mjer dáð nje dugur
að drýgja mærðar sæði.

Gefast mjer lítil gleðinnar faung
grúfi' eg í sorgar sæti,
hörmúng lífsins hörð og laung
hindrar alla kæti.

Líkama hreysið lamið og veikt
lystíng so frekt tærir
þó fær meira brjóstið beygt
bölið það hjartað særir.

Sá sem reynir soddan þrá
samlega veit hann fleira;
hirði eg ekki að herma frá
hugraun þeirri meira.

Minn þó kæmist hugurinn heim
að hreyfa mærðar formi

fer mjer líkast fugli þeim
sem flýgur á móti stormi.
    Enn þó hann í ákefð frekur
áfram vilji streyta
vindurinn hann úr hófi hrekur
so hvíldar þarf að neyta.
    Haft hef eg oft í hugsun það,
þá hægði á stygðargeingi,
að ævintýrið uppteiknað
öld í ljóðum feingi.
    Eins má dæmin ill og góð
öld í nyt sjer færa ;
citthvað gott kann þegna þjóð
þeim af skynja og læra.
    Leingi' eg ekki mansaungs mál
mitt að þessu sinni
því skal birla boðunar skál
og brögnum skeinkja á minni.

END OF MANSÖNGR.

    Forðum kóngur ríki rjeð,
reindur að magt og sóma,
Cimbría, so skýri eg skeð,
skal það veldið róma.
    Sagður kóngur Salman hjet,
sá var Donreks arfi ;
Spanía kóngs sem lýði ljet
lúta í vopna starfi.
    Sá fjekk kóngur sóma nægð
sínum á æsku aldri,
auðnan nóg og alskyns frægð
örva þjenti baldri.
    Buðlúng átti bræður tvo,
báðir eldri vóru,

Haukur og *Báland* hjetu so
herrarnir máttar stóru.
Þegar faðir þeirra frá
þessum heimi leiddist
Haukur Spaniam hlaut að fá
honum sá arfur greiddist.

Ekki leingi lifði hann
landinu því so hjeldi,
annar kóngur illur vann
undir sig það veldi.

Mildíng sá hjet *Málprýant*
magtar stór með geiri,
tignaði þessi *Terúgant*
og töfruð goðin fleiri.

Enn *Báland* annar bróðir þá
bragna stýrði meingi,
harla ríkur *Hispaniá*
og hjelt það ríkið leingi.

Sálman kóngur kænn við rönd
Cumbría löndin fríðu;
þessi góðu og litlu lönd
liggja á Vallands síðu.

Páfans trú og reglu ráð
ræsir trú eg að hjeldi,
og öll þau lönd sem um er tjáð
utan *Spania-veldi.*

Olli þessu ilsku gramur
sem inn tók það með stríði,
enn *Sálman* kóngur sómasamur
sín hjelt lönd með prýði.

Vitur og tryggur, vænn og sterkur
var sá hirðir dáða,
góðgjarn, ljúfur, mildur og merkur
mönnum gott að ráða.

Sinn kónglegan hefðar hag
hjelt so meður snilli
að sitt færði lof í lag
landsins enda á milli.

204

Óvínum sínum grimmur gramur
gjarn að beita vigri
hjelt sá jafnan filkir framur
frægð og mesta sigri.
  Únga fjekk hann auðargná [úngra, MS.
afbragð var sú fljóða,
kónga ættum fornum frá
af *Fracklandinu* gó a.
  Hennar faðir var greifi gildur,
Geirmanus að nafni,
Sá hjet *Ambá* svanninn mildur
sæmdra kvenna jafni.
  Kóngurinn unni refla rein
ræktar stór í máta,
so að ekkert mátti mein
á móti henni láta.
  Samfarirnar þeirra því
þótti hin mesta æra,
þeirra hvílu það skeði í
að þúng-búin varð kæra.
  Sú kom tíð sem var til von
að vífið kóngi fæddi
frábæran og fríðan son
fljóðið reifum klæddi.
  Nefndi *Sigurð* niflúng ríkur
niðjann sinn hinn fríða ;
þessi gjörðist þengli líkur
þegar að stundir líða.
  Ári síðar yndishrein ;
ástum kóngs ei slefti,
lífs ávaxtar gæfugrein
gull-hlaðs eikin hrefti.
  Þar i ríki þeingils var—
þó ei komin af flögðum—
völvan ein sem vísdóm bar
vönd í mörgum brögðum.
  Sú var liddan lyndisstór
so lýðum þótti á ýki ;

hennar ætt og fæðíng fór
fram í *Gardaríki.*

Því við drottníng, þess eg get,
þykkju fyltist dækja,
þá auðgrund fæddi ekki ljet
ilsku fljóðið sækja.

Nornin hafði norður um heim,
þá nauða sóttir mæddu,
höfðíngskonum þjónad þei
þegar þær börnin fæddu.

Þykkju sinnar kaldan korg
með kýngju trú eg hún herði,
Sjer í kóngsins breiða borg
bráða reisu gerði.

Hitti drottníng heiftum skift
hún með þúngu bragði,
hvíla búin var hrínga nift
við hana nornin sagði :

"Þú skalt vita," völvan kvað,
"veraldar magt og sóma
muntu hljóta að missa það
mætan heiður og blóma."

"Þegar að buðlúng beitir vigur
og berst við heiðna lýði
missa skal hann mætan sigur
mestan heiður og prýði.

"Laus mun hann verða löndum frá
lífs í fári nauða ;
so mun og líka sonur þinn fá
sáran og harðan dauða."

"Enn þann son sem fæðir frú
fífl skal öllum sýnast ;
með þeirri skrift skal þorna brú
þína um ævi pínast."

"Haft hef eg oft hjá herrum náð
og haldin mesta ágæti,
aldrei var eg so illa smáð
sem af ukkar stærilæti."

"Drambið mun og dreissið vest
dvína í fári nauða,
þjer skal sætan þykja best
þinn að kjósa dauða.''
Þá vífið forlög vita fjekk
sem völvan á hana lagði,
hún frá henni grátin gekk
og gjörvalt kóngi sagði.
Stórlega reiddist ræsir þá
og ræðir við hirðmenn sína :
"völvunni skuluð þið vondri ná
með vestum dauða pína."
"Bætt er ekki bölið að heldur,"
burðug drottníng tjáði,
" meinum einginn veit hvað veldr
nema völvan úr þeim ráði."
''Við skulum láta' hana vera oss hjá
og virðíng nokkra hljóta,
so að vorum sorgum þá
sjáist ráð til bóta."
Þeingill mælti þorns við ey :
"þú munt ráða verða,
enn aldrei mun það arma grey
auðnuna mína skerða."
Drottníng gekk, sú hrygðir hlaut
hilmirs út af ranni,
völvunnar til, því brátt á braut
búinn var stygðar svanni.
Drottníng talar við dúka þöll :
"dýra vil eg þjer bjóða
veislu að þyggja í vorri höll,
vist og allan góða."
''Þar til mitt er fóstrið fætt,
fárinu so það hnekki,"
á þann veg nornin þá fjekk rætt :
" þiggja mun eg það ekki."
"Þín mun eg vitja," völvan kvað
vikin úr stygðar svíma,

"og yfir þjer sitja eftir það
um þinn sængur tíma."
    Skrafinu ljettu þanninn þær;
þaðan nornin vendi ;
sú kom tíð að sjóla kær
sóttar drottníng kendi.
    Aftur kom þá auðar brú
öðru vísi í bragði,
og jóðsjúka filkirs frú
í fagra hvílu lagði.
    Vitug sat yfir vella hlíð,
vífið sóttin mæddi,
sú var þjáníng sár og stríð,
sveinbarn eitt hún fæddi.
    Yfrið stór enn ekki fríður,
með ásján þeigi hvíta,
sýndist öllum sveinninn stríður
og sviplegur að líta.
    Völvan þjenti þorna vör
til þarfar alt hún greiddi,
síðan að liðinni sængur för
sætu úr hvílu leiddi.
    Gjörði fátt við gamla snót,
gramur orðum býta,
eingin sýndi ástar hót,
nje augum vildi líta.
    Nornin því í bræði brann
og brjóstið af illum anda,
drottníng slíkt til raunar rann
við ríkan stýrir landa.
    Nafnið vildi nýtum svein
niflúng ekkert greiða,
og so kærleiks aungva grein
af sjer láta leiða.
    Þetta öllum þótti ófrægð,
það hvur öðrum sagði,
enn alla drottníng ástar nægð
á úngan son sinn lagði.

Völvan dvaldi vífi hjá
vikurnar fjórar tvennar
umbun fjekk og æru há
eftir vilja hennar.

Síðan sig í burtu bjó
með bestu faung og færi;
drottníng vildi að þorngrund þó
þar enn leingur væri.

Á þann dag sem orðlof fjekk
á burt reisa skyldi,
í barnahúsið brúðurin gekk
beint og kveðja vildi.

Drottníng hitti dregla rein,
dýr með ástar hendi,
upp tók þann hinn ýngra svein
og á brjóst sitt vendi.

Nornin mælti : "stúruð stilt
á stóra manndygð þína
minnast væri mjer nú skylt
og mesta trygð að sýna."

"Fyr aungvum hef eg so illa spáð
sem yður í minni bræði,
ekki verður því aftur náð
eru það lítil gæði."

"Forlögunum öllum einn
eflaust hygg eg valda,
þó skal ekki þessi sveinn
þín í öllu gjalda."

"Þú skalt gefa nýtum nafn
nærri þínu heiti,
því hann mun verða þokka jafn
þjer að nokkru leiti."

"Lítt mun stoða lofunin tóm
ljúfum beitir sverða,
allrar sinnar ættar blóm
eflaust mun hann verða."

Kóngsins börn og kurtis frú
með kossi myntist viður ;

O

II. Rímur
eptir Pál
Bjarnarson

so var haldin seima brú
hún sáldaði tárum niður.

Síðan burtu völvan veik
vikin úr stygðar skugga,
þó sat eftir brúðurin bleik
barninu sínu að rugga.

Þúngum anda brúðurin bljes
af bölinu raunar efna;
úngan son sinn *Ambáles*
auðþöll gjörði að nefna.

Þessir sveinar þaðan í frá
þroska gjörðust bráðir,
ólíkir að öllu að sjá
örvaviðirnir tjáðir.

Sigurður var frægur og fríður,
framur í menta greinum,
lystugur og lyndis stríður,
og ljet sig ei fyrir neinum.

Enn Ambáles var öllum þrjótur,
og aungvum vildi hlýða,
og ásýndar yfrið ljótur
so ekkert mátti prýða.

Fætur stórar hafði og hendur
hans ei fanst þar jafni
af því var hann af öllum kendur
Amlóði að nafni.

Ára fjöldañ áfram bar,
um annað ei sagnir letra,
tyggja synirnir töldust þar
tíu og átta vetra.

Líst mjer ekki ljóða kver
leingur saman að stíma,
stuðla málið stofnað þver,
stendur þanninn ríma.

END OF THE FIRST RIMA.

III. RÍMUR AF AMBALIS
KVEÐNAR AF

Læsing hlés, * hvar *laugir tveir* †*
með Lóðins *prýddu sprundi* ‡
úr § og *mein* ‖ *þar mundar þreir*
marar reif ¶ hjá lindi.

FYRSTA RÍMA : FERSKEYTT.

Mansöngr.

1 Kjalars dælu knörinn má
  kreika máls af strindi
  Býleifs skafla unnar á
  æstur beslu vindi.
2 Skuli eg mastra Týrs á tjörn
  Týleiks hundi fleyta
  Móðsognirs eg mér á börn
  má til fulltings heita.
3 Norðri og Suðri nýráðs hró
  Nikars snekkju leiði
  fram úr hrófi þagnar þó
  þunds að Ránar heiði.
4 Hlunnana Austri hafðu til,
  Hléfreyr vörina ryðtu,
  Draupnir ýttu á dverga hyl,
  en Dvalinn mastrið bittu.

---

* þ. e. íss = *i*.   † tveir legir = *ll*.   ‡ = ár = *a*.
§ = *u*.   ‖ = stunginn kaun = *g*.
¶ = læsing hlés = *i*; alt nafnið er því : *Illaugi* = *Illugi*.

5 Byrinn aukið Gjöll og Gjálp,
   en gustur seglin . . .*
   Galar ára gerðu í dálp,
   en Glói austu að . . .*

6 Af leiru máls svo liðaður
   Litars knör . . .

   .   .   .   .   .
   .   .   .   .   .*

7 Neins ei virðir Norðra lið
   nú mitt boð útgefna,
   þessir fyrst að þegja við
   þá skal aðra nefna.

8 Brags að efna Bragi smíð
   beindu af anda þínum,
   æða Kvásirs iðan fríð
   yljaðu gómi mínum.

9 Standi álfar starblin(d)er
   og styrki að kvæða lögum,
   ásar og dísir alt eins sér
   anni að hlynna brögum.

10 Lýður Herjans þræla þó
   þögn mér gjaldi laka
   Býleifs ferju Brokks á sjó
   býst eg við að aka.

11 Lag til kvæða liðugt mér
   ljóðanornir sendi;
   efnið fræða frá eg hér
   fara nú að hendi.

12 Alt sem þankinn æskja má
   eins á sjó og landi
   sinn mér ljóða sannan hjá
   sé nú dag eflandi.

13 Hjálpar ekki um bót á brag
   að barma sér hjá þegnum,
   því skal mönnum mærðar slag
   miðla og sprundum gegnum.

* The MS. is here illegible.

14 Fyrir sjónir lýða sagan ein
   sezt í hætti ljóða ;
   þeim sem hlýða hverfi mein
   og hugarins angrið móða.
15 Þó skáldin víða birti brátt
   Boðnar lög fram k(n)úinn
   hef eg aldrei hennar þátt
   heyrt í ljóð upp snúinn.
16 Þó eg réttan rauna stig
   ráfi í höllu vinda
   af fræði sögunnar fýsir mig
   forman óðs að mynda.
17 Sögunnar dæmi sannar það
   sorg nær gistu lýðir,
   hversu römmum rauna vað
   raknar úr um síðir.
18 Kvíða ekki hjálpar hér
   hvað sem móti geingur ;
   meyja söngur þanninn þver ;
   þiggi hann faldaspeingur.
19 Sögunnar vitja byrjar beint,
   beygðu að heyrnar ranninn,
   faldasól, með hugvit hreint ;
   hefur efnið þanninn.

END OF MANSÖNGR.

20 Donrek nefni eg dögling einn
   drakons gæd[dan síki]
   Spania stýrði hilmir hreinn
   helztu kónga líki.
21 . . . milding mætr
   með Cimbria réði,
   rétt [að lögunum gaf hann] gætr,
   grand svo aungvum skéði.

22 Efnis betri upplýsing
öldin hér svo fái,
hvar þau lönd um lygru hring
liggja þess hún gái :

23 Frá eg tvö hin fyrstu sé
Frakkalands nær gröndum
í suðvestast Evrópe
af öllum hennar löndum.

24 En land Cimbria, les eg bert,
liggur þessum fjærri :
Eystrasaltið vestanvert
við með eyjum smærri.

25 Sagt er Japhets sonur var
sá með Gómers nafni,
frón sem numdi fyrstur þar,
frægstu kónga jafni.

26 Eptir sig þar innan lands
ættstofn leifði fríðan ;
Gemeria af heiti hans
hauðrið nefndist síðan.

27 Fólks og tíma talan nær
tungna jókst með blandi
Cimbria hét Sviðriks mær
af sveitum þar búandi.

28 Í frá Gómer ættmenn hans
einir Cimbrar hétu
og nafn af sér til daga Dans
draga hauðrið létu.

29 Ættmann Gómers Óðins frú
einn þar við sig kendi,
Dan hét sá, en Danmörk nú
Dvalins nefnist kvendi.

30 Ríkti hann þar sem lofðung lands
og leifði orðróm fríðan ;
dregið nafn af heiti hans
hefir frónið síðan.

31 Tignast mektum Tvíblinds mær,
tignar stjórnin hana,

214

    tignaðrar svo til vor nær
    tignin hveðru Dana.

32 Þegar gerðist saga sú,
    sem í ljóð hér færi,
    í Spania ríki þeingils þrjú
    þá hygg eg að væri.

33 Gylfi einn í Granadá
    Gínars kvinnu réði,
    í Arragonia annar þá
    Ónars stýrði beði.

34 Í Kastilia vísir var
    vel hvað hefst í minnum;
    Spania land við þeingil þar
    þríhlutað vér finnum.

35 Voru ríki þeingils þrjú
    það um langar stundir,
    lofðung einn sem leingi nú
    legið hafa undir.

36 En Cimbria þá, sýn ef er
    sagan, vil eg hyggja,
    væri eitt, það virðist mér
    af veldum kónga þriggja.

37 Og hana á Spanskra lýða lóð
    líta enn nú megi,
    en Tartara Danmörk tæki' inn þjóð
    trúað fæ eg eigi.

38 Vafinleiki veldur því
    sá villir heita landa
    þessum bo . . . í
    Óðinn sögunnar blanda.

39 Til þess er sögu sk . . .
    . . . og gaf út forðum
    flyt eg óð og fremst sem . . .

40 Donrik einvalds innist gramr
    yfir Spania veldi;
    ræsir sá í rómu tamr
    risa og blámenn feldi.

41 Greifar bæði og barónar
  buðlung dýrum þjóna,
  hristu í mundum Högna skar,
  hans þegar messur tóna.

42 Mestur kappi milding var
  mekt og afl berandi,
  á gulli auðs og gnægð óspar
  gjöfum þjóð sæmandi.

43 Vitugr, hægur var og blíðr
  virðum sátt bjóðandi,
  grimmr, óvægur, geysistríðr
  gotnum mótþægjandi.

44 Summu stóra stillir af
  strjálum rauðum fjarðar
  fátækum sá gylfi gaf
  gautum linna jarðar.

45 Silvia hét fremda fjáð
  fylkis ektakvinna;
  kóngsins studdi ríkdóms ráð
  ristin gulls hin svinna.

46 Angurs rauna mýkti móð
  mengrund dáð eflandi;
  Hauks var gylfa hringþöll jóð
  Holsetu af landi.

47 Sjóli átti syni þrjá
  við sævar loga gefni;
  prýddi afl og auðna þá;
  ýta svo eg nefni.

48 Salmon bæði og Haukur hægr
  Héðins mey við undu,
  Bálant hristi brandinn frægr,
  nær byljir Flárs á dundu.

49 Söguna þegar svo fram á
  segist vera geingið
  arfar höfðu þeingils þá
  þroska og aldur feingið.

50 Ellihniginn kraminn kör
  kóng á Spönsku láði

216

säran dauða af sóttarför
síðan hreppa náði.

51 Fjörráðs gyðju ílt við am
andar banns sá kendi,
Hallinskíða gyldan gram
geymir síðan kvendi.

52 Döglings arfar ríkis ráð,
reifðir snildum, jóku
skiptust þeim með skötnum láð,
skýrir kongdóm tóku.

53 Spania hlotnast Hauki vann
hilmis eptir dauða;
með seggjum friðinn semur hann,
en sóaði efling nauða.

54 Hispaniam, birt er beint,
Bálant hreppa náði,
en Cimbria fær sagan greint
Salmon kóngur þáði.

55 Jötna gladdi málið mál
mála gemlis njóta,
runnar létu stála stál
stála sæva brjóta.

56 Donriks arfi Haukur hel
heiðnum fyrir tiggja
fleins við starf, þó færi ei vel,
frægur varð að þiggja.

57 Af Skidia ættaðan
innir fræðið sjóla,
sem fylkis drýgja fjörrán vann
fyrr í járnaskóla.

58 Malprýgant hét sjóli sá,
sem að fella náði
hara dýran fjörvi frá,
en firða landsins þjáði.

59 Hilmir þvíngar harðráður
hölda villu megna,
álma þíngi ótrauður
opt þó hefði að gegna.

217

60 Spania fólk til heiðni hart
  hnepti og þrældóm stríðan
  fylkir sá með fólsku djarft,
  fróni stýrði síðan.

61 Bálant skýrum óðar orð
  ætti frá að greina,
  hreystin gæddi hjörs við morð
  horskan bendir fleina.

62 Ríki stýrði sínu sá
  saddur heiðri klárum ;
  seggjum lands þar Sjóli hjá
  sældaði Freyju tárum.

63 Í hildar stormi sízta sátt
  sýndi hann óvinum
  sjóli var með sinnið kátt
  sæmd bjóðandi hinum.

64 Sínu ríki Cimbria
  Salmon kongur stýrði,
  blámenn lægði og burgeisa
  brands, þegar skúrum ýrði.

65 Hárs í byljum reyndi rönd
  runnur drakons bóla ;
  mistu gotnar auð og önd
  ört fyrir vopnum sjóla.

66 Hvar sem vakti Héðins mey
  hilmir ríkmannligur
  fyrða hrakti fleins við gey,
  fékk því jafnan sigur.

67 Málmarunni megnfrástum
  margir vildu þjóna ;
  höldar unnu hugástum
  hirðir dýrra fróna.

68 Fríða meyu lofðung lands,
  ljóma Hárs sá beitir,
  frægur ekta fékk til bands ;
  fljóðið Amba heitir.

69 Gæfan sjóla gekk í vil,
  girð(um) ektabandi ;

greifadóttir baugs var bil
af Borgundialandi.

70 Germanus hét faðir fljóðs
fremd og hreysti vafinn ;
þá var runnur funa flóðs
fjörs í banni kafinn.

71 Sjálfur unni seima gná
sikling vafinn dáðum ;
lýða meingi lands í krá
laut að hennar ráðum.

72 Spök í geði, vinsæl var
vefjan frænings reita ;
vizku nægð og blóma bar
bauga lofnin teita.

73 Sú í mörgu dýrleg drós
döglings bætti efni ;
hvíluverkin lofðungs ljós
lítast baugs á gefni.

74 Á tíma réttum seima sól,
sorgar leyst frá böndum,
sjóla fagurt sveinbarn ól,
sízt með efnum vöndum.

75 Lofðung dýrum laukahlíð
lætur sveininn færa ;
Sigurð nefndi þjóðin þýð
þeingils arfann skæra.

76 Kristna trú fékk sjóli sett
svinnu að rækja meingi ;
páfans fylgdi reglum rétt
ræsir vel og leingi.

77 Skjöldung djarfi skrímirs svar
skeinkti randa þundum ;
fylkis arfa fóstur var
feingið vanda bundnum.

78 Eptir það varð öðlings fljóð
aptur barnshafandi ;
völva ein, er magnar móð,
mildings bjó í landi.

219

79 Af meiri ættum menskra norn
   mundi komin vera,
   býsna skyn á brögðin forn
   bar með lundu þvera.
80 Grimm í æði, siðug sízt,
   seiddi ærsl að mönnum ;
   ótta meingi vakti víst
   og veifaði galdra hrönnum.
81 Súkans friðla á galdra gjörn
   gisting fékk sér valið,
   þar herramanna höfðu börn
   horskar kvinnur alið.
82 Víða sú í virðing höfð
   var á Norðurlöndum ;
   illum spám af kyngi kröfð
   kastaði máls úr gröndum.
83 Yrpan glæpa sveipuð súð
   sanntalað er væri
   niflungs þar í neðstu búð
   nettasta verkfæri.
84 Við karlinn gamla kyrtla laut
   koma vel sér gætti,
   ráð og efni þann nær þraut
   þá hún strax úr bætti.
85 Um forlög barna fleipra mart
   fýtons hennar kraptur
   gerði, en auð og gullið bjart
   að gjöfum þáði hún aptur.
86 Fyrri þegar fæddist snar
   fylkis arfinn gildi
   ekki kölluð völvan var
   veigs að þjóna hildi.
87 Feikna bræði fyllast réð
   fálan galdra rúna,
   svo fjölkyngi mestu með
   magnar fólsku búna.
88 Rétt af inni róms þinga
   ritin galdra nærði,

svipljót versins særinga
sjóla á hendur færði.

89 Þegar téðan tíma fljóðs
tiggja á var liðið
getur fitin galdra skrjóðs
grams til borgar riðið.

90 Kveitan vestra konstra hams
kemur sízt þá varði,
þegar dvaldi drottning grams
í dýrum eplagarði.

91 Hún þar finnur hilmis sprund
hrekkjafull nam róma :
Leikur nú þín lífsins stund
ljóst í mestum blóma.

92 Lífsins þessa lán gjörvalt
og lukku efling hreina
þú skalt missa þetta alt,
þitt nema fjörið eina.

93 Þinn mun kongur fleins við fár
falla í eli randa ;
dapur ört fær dauðinn sár
döglings fjöri granda.

94 Óvinir munu yndis kárn
auka hirðir fróna
buðlung eingin bíti járn
beint við hildar sóna.

95 Hygg eg lukkan hilmir greið
héðan (af) trauðla styðji,
herfilegan hér með deyð
hreppir ykkar niðji.

96 Alla kæti útrýmer
aðþreingjandi nauðin,
lífi betra þá skal þér
þykja sjálfur dauðinn.

97 Fífl skal öllum sýnast sá
sonur með þú geingur,
af honum svo ei þinn má
eyðast hrygðarstreingur.

98 Fyrri aldrei fíls um láð
   fátækum né ríkum
   mundi eg vera af mönnum smáð
   mínum eða (yðar) líkum
99 Þanninn lætur konstra kát
   kallsi verstu linna;
   fyrsta lasinn Fjölnis bát
   foldu sel eg tvinna.
100 Byrðing móðan Báleiks hyl,
   burt er sagna gróðinn,
   virði góða valin til
   víðis loga slóðin.
101 Ræðusmíðið ljóma lind
   lægis niður brotni,
   mæðu kvíðir góma grind,
   greina kliður þrotni.

END OF THE FIRST RIMA

ÖNNUR RÍMA: AFHENT.

Mansöngr.

1 Dvalins læt eg húna hauk í hyrjar vindi
   setjast fram af sagna strindi.
2 Liðið suðra vantar víst að velja leiði,
   kenni eg þessa kráks um heiði.
3 Mart á brestur, bifurs ferju bilað hróið,
   ei því verður áfram róið.
4 Brákast reiði, bönd frá súðum brotin falla,
   Fjölnis skeiðin flýtur valla.
5 Frekari nauðsyn fær mér störf þau fast á stríða
   heldur en bifurs bát að smíða.
6 Frost með hríðum, hreifing storma og hlaupin jaka
   hamla því að hreifist staka.
7 Heims til láta svo er sem mig svipi stundum,
   mér það hamlar geðs í grundum.
8 Af minstum skamti með ólátum menn fram ana
   eptir heimsins vondum vana.
9 Minstur hluti mannkyns er þar má til dreyma,
   sem munn og hendur gá að geyma.
10 Baktal auka, banna, ljúga, brígzla, ragna
   og annara hrösun yfir fagna.
11 Frömdu margir formæling og fyrnsku ljóta,
   fyltir lundu heiptar hóta.
12 Þó að halli þessu nú hjá þundum skjalda
   manndygðin því má ei valda.
13 Mörgum frá því mestan part eg meina hnekki
   að gera ilt, þeir geta ekki.
14 Sönglið galdra sjálft bevísar sögu stefið
   illa raun hvað getur gefið.

15 Máske hafi á bikar bergt í bragði köldum
   annara jeg af ilskuvöldum.
16 Mætti af stáli munnur gjör sá meinti öllum
   brydda heims á glæpa göllum.
17 Ágirndin, sem hverjum hrekk fær hærra geingið
   heit af dygð nú hefir feingið.

· · · · · ·*

END OF MANSÖNGR.

18 Álaganna yrpan skilst við öðlings kvendi,
   en beðja kongs til borgar vendi.
19 Tækilegum tíma á með trygða gildi,
   nær fylkirs kvinna fæða skyldi,
20 Góðsemd vafið gylfa fljóð með geði svinnu
   sækja lét þá konstra kvinnu.
21 Í dýra sæng þá drottníng lagði drillan rúna;
   fljóðið sveinbarn fæddi núna.
22 Vífin furðar vöxt á ungum vísis arfa
   hörunds með ófríðum farfa.
23 Broddhærðs var með blökkumanna bragði kynsins
   yfirlitur unga prinsins.
24 Augna var hans yfirbragð þó ílitshreina
   dægilegt sem djásn gimsteina.
25 Beðjan hara buðlung svinnum barnið sendi;
   ræsir mestrar reiði kendi.
26 Nær sjóli lítur sveininn á í sinnu hlíðum
   fyltist hann af forsi stríðum.
27 Ekkert nafn vill ungum sveini öðling veita
   haldinn sorg um hyggju reita.
28 Aungva heldur svinnum sæmd vill sveini tæra,
   barnið skipar burt að færa.
29 Kvinnu þá, sem konstraversum kunni býta,
   vísir augum vill ei líta.
30 Hilmis drottníng hér af gisti hryggðar æði,
   til sjóla völvan safnar bræði.

Deest unum folium. The catchword is "sinn."

31 Vefju dýrri völvan þénti vastar bríma
   og leiddi af sæng á settum tíma.
32 Dýran sóma drottníng sjóla drillu valdi,
   þrjá mánuði þar hún dvaldi.
33 Hilmis drottníng hana út með heiðri leiddi
   [Rín]ar ljósa gnægtir greiddi.
34 Völvan . . . aptur vinskap sýndi
   hana við svo hatri týndi.
35 Beint þann dag sem burtu norn sig búa skyldi
   fylkira drottníng finna vildi.
36 Með sinnis kælu sjóla til í salinn barna
   reikar snótin rúnagjarna.
37 Barnið yngra buðlungs fljóð þar brjóst á lagði ;
   hana við svo völvan sagði :
38 Þér eg einni afreiðzt hef með illspá sagna,
   orðin vel sem ekki þagna.
39 Mögulega má ei bætast meinið kalda,
   fast því settu forlög valda.
40 Máttugur sá einn sem er því öllu ráða
   æðstra kann með efling dáða.
41 Skylt mér væri þó á þig með þægð að minnast
   og á trygðir fús að finnast.
42 Þessi sonur þinn, hvern fæddan þú nú hefur,
   þér í raunum gleði gefur.
43 Hvað sem nú um hilmirs niðja helzt og meinast
   annað síðar sveit mun reynast.
44 Sinnar ættar sómi beztur sá mun verða
   og óvinanna orku skerða.
45 Þér og móður þínum föður þundur fleina
   líkjast mun, það lýðir reyna.
46 Af þínu nafni hals sé heit að hálfu dregið ;
   þar af bregða ekki eigið.
47 Tillögur þó mínar minst hann megi stoða,
   honum frið og heill eg boða.
48 Konstra vítið kvinnu grams nam kveðjur vanda
   hrygðum spent í hyrjar anda.

P

49 Hilmirs drottníng heilla bað og hennar kundi,
   grátandi svo gekk frá sprundi.
50 Ambalis var siklings son af sjóla sprundi
   nefndur, við sá nauðir undi.
51 Þeygi * líkir þeingils arfar þóttust mönnum
   í lista nægð og sóma sönnum.
52 Sigurður prýdi sonar bar með sóma skýran,
   menta nægtir huldu hýran.
53 Geðstrangur og vinsæll var sá vísdóm unni,
   hrósuðu flestir hjálma runni.
54 Ambalis var ólíkur að öllu honum,
   ræmdur lítt hjá karli og konum.
55 [Óge]öslegur, öllum þrjózkur öðlings niður,
   flestum [mönnum] féll því miður.
56 Gotna eingin ræktust [ráð á ræsi]s kundi,
   sem góðs til honum gagna mundi.
57 Mildings kundur mjög útlima mundi þrekinn
   flest æfandi fíflabrekin.
58 Nafni breyta náðu menn á nadda þundi,
   gylfa er mælt það geðjast mundi.
59 Hilmir jafnt og hirdin snjalla hrannar glóða,
   þundinn kallar þann Amlóða.
60 Eykst svo tíðin Ambalis varð ára níu,
   vitnast Sigurðr vetra tíu.
61 Fyrst um sinn eg frá þeim Dvalins ferju beiti;
   fleiri menn upp fræðið leiti.
62 Soldan nefnist sikling gæddur sævar ljóma,
   Scidia stýrði sviptur sóma.
63 Milding þessi Macons dýrkun mesta framdi
   goðanna sig á göfgun tamdi.
64 Átti þessi arfa þrjá við eisu fjarðar
   gefni, alla hetjur harðar.
65 Hét hinn elzti hentur næsta hjörs í starfi
   Thamerlaus tiggja arfi.
66 Malpríant var niflungs niðji nefndur annar,
   fleins í hríðum bót sem bannar.

* þeiged, MS.

226

IV. AMBÁLES RÍMUR SALMANSSONAR, ORTAR AF ÞORVALDI SIGMUNDARSYNI:

ISL. LANDSBÓKASAFN 72. 4to.

II. RÍMA.

ENN vil Vindólfs ara kló
ýta fram á Boðnar-sjó
hverninn sem mér vegna vill
viðrinn fars er mjög lítill.

Á háttum rímna eg hef ei skil,
Hjarandi mér drakk ei til,
þegar honum Gunnlöð gaf
góða drykkinn kerinu af.

Stóru skáldin virtu vel
Valgauts metið hyggju þel,
Boðnar þegar veitti vín
vestur fengið gestum sín.

Hlæja þessir helzt að mér,
hróðrar þegar iðka kver,
vitrir svo sem von er á,
varla kann eg þetta lá.

Annar hópur ýta hér,
eina stund þó hlýði mér,
lastar fast mitt ljóðaspil,
lesið fram af raddar-hyl.

Þriðju hlýða efnið á,
ef ella skilið meining fá,
um hróðrinn ekki hirða par,
hverninn sem að kveðið var.

Fjórði manna flokkur hér
forvitnast um mærðar-kver,
Eddu-greinum hælir heitt
og hugsar ekki um efnið neitt.

Hópinn fimta hef eg séð
sem hirðir ekki örgum með
ljóða-söfn að lýta frí,
lasta þá sem kveikja á því.

Sjötti skilur ekki orð
Eddu-greina máls um storð,
en ef kent er ekki par,
alúðlega það lofar.

Á sjöundu eg hef séð
óbærilegt reiðigeð,
hreyfi nokkur halur snar
hróðri sér til skemtunar.

Hafa þeir í hyggju snart,
hann muni kveðit nógu mart,
ef þeir heyra eitthvað það,
ei sem koma skilning að.

Í veröldinni vandlifað
virðum er í hverjum stað,
sumir brugga sorgar-dans,
sem þó látast vinir manns.

Þeirra búin glæpa-gjörð,
galdra samt í nauðum hörð,
nornin sem eg nefndi fyr
nógan gjörði rauna-styr.

En þó drottníng allt fyri það
illu flagði náðar bað,
þegnum skjöldung skipa réð (*beiða* hdr.)
skyldi' hún deyja píslum með.

Mansöngs rénar þáttur þver,
því að sagan eptir fer,
á hana gengur ekki par,
efnið hefst svo rímunnar.

IV. Rímur
eptir þor-
vald Sig-
mundarson

END OF MANSÖNGR.

Þraut mig áðan Þundar-vín,
þar sem völvan motrar-lín
sæng af leiddi svo með kurt,
síðan vildi halda á burt.

Drottníng henni góðar gaf
gersemar ag jötna-skraf,
í mánuði þó hún þrjá
þorna dvaldist eyju hjá.

Daginn þann sem burtu bjóst
barnið vildi kveðja ljóst,
hafði drottníng hugar-þrá,
hélt þeim unga sveini á.

"Engum hef eg utan þér
ofreið orðið," nornin tér,
"illa fyrir yður spáð,
engin get þó séð til ráð.

Forlög gjöra þjáning þér,
þína manndygð skyldugt er
mér að virða og minnast á,
mikla dygð eg fann þér hjá."

Ei þín gjalda að öllu skal
yðar sonur kóngs á sal,
sinnar ættar sómi hann
Sannlegana verða kann.

Gef þú honum göfugt nafn,
get eg hann munu seðja hrafn,
eptir þínu auðar-brú
á hann nefnast heiti nú.

Lítið stoðar lofan mín ;
lofðungs son og hringa-lín
kveðja síðan völvan vann
og veg svo (v. vísis) burt af salnum rann.

Öðlings son hét Ambales
engum líkur sitt með vés,
ólust synir öðlings þar
upp með frægð sem líklegt var.

Sigurðr fríður vaskur var,
vel geðaður, orku-snar,
framur mjög og frægðar-gjarn,
frábærasta kóngabarn.

Ambales á allan veg
ósélegur þótti mjeg,
nokkuð gott ei nema vill
né neinum hlýða skapmikill.

Útlimastór yfrið var,
engum manni líktist par,
Amlóði því örva-grér
af öllum lýðum nefndur er.

Fengið hafði átta ár
öðlings sonur lyndis þrár,
en Sigurður tíu til,
til nú enn þá genguz vel.

Soldán nefni eg öðling einn
-átrúnaður þeygi hreinn-
sagt er átti sonu þrjá,
sem að ríkti' í Skyþiá.

V. RÍMUR AF ÞEIM NAFNFRÆGA KONUNGI YFIR VALLANDI AMBALES SALMAÑS SYNI:

ORDTAR AF A Þ LAGAFELLI E J MIKLA S HOLTSHREPP.

I. FYRSTA RÍMA : FERSKEYTT.

1 ÁSA hara horna lá
    hagyrks fram á borðum
    bendir hjara baugs og ná
    bjóðist nú sem forðum.

2 Vantar mig, þó bjóði brátt,
    bjórinn Óðins megna,
    hugsa eg þá í aðra átt
    öðru starfi gegna.

3 Fornjóts anna flóða hjört
    fram á láðið bylgja
    setja skal, ef andinn ört
    yrpu vildi fylgja.

4 Sízt er þó til ferða fær
    Fjalars ranga jórinn,
    hjá mér einginn halur rær,
    háreistur er sjórinn.

5 Stýrið vantar vizkunnar,
    vænt er seglið þeygi,
    aungvar feimast árarnar
    á því leku fleyi.

6 Saumslitin og brotin borð
    bundin klampar (?) * saman,

      * Illegible.

að fara á þessu þangs á storð
þyki mér ekki gaman.

7 Einn eg rölti samt á sjó,
sízt mun annað hlíta,
alt vantandi árakló
eingir vilja nýta.

8 Fyrst að eingan mentamann
mér þénandi fæ eg,
heilög ráði hamingjan(n)
hvort að landi næ eg.

9 Kóngur sá, er kendi mér
krappa fílnum stýra,
heim að landi hjálpir tér,
hætturnar mun rýra.

10 Mér fyrst kendi mentirnar,
mér þó bili hugir,
mér ei granda mæðurnar,
mér hans andi dugir.

11 Hátt lof greiðist hilmir þeim
heims á breiðu völlum,
lífgar, deyðir, lénar seim
laufa meiðum öllum.

END OF MANSÖNGR.

12 Æfðan frækleik um eg get
í Spanía landi
dögling þann, er Donrek hét
dr(e)ifði japa sandi.

13 [Hann] Spanía hauðri réð,
historíur spjalla
að Kimbría átti með
öðling frí af galla.

14 Eylöndum og meingi með
milding stýrði frægur,
þar til honum þjóna réð
þegna ótal sægur.

15 Skráð er, margir skattkóngar
skjöldung þéntu fríðum,

232

hraustir jarlar, hertogar
hratt með fleiri lýðum.

16 Vörðu þessir vísir með
valin lönd og ríki
hreysti mest var honum léð
hvergi fanst hans líki.

17 Ráðugur og vitur var
vísir gjafa mildur,
lýð fátækan forsorgar,
fyrðum hjálpar gildur.

18 Setina drotning döglings er
dúðuð linna sandi
hilmirs fræga Hauksdótter
Holsetu frá landi.

19 Þessa drotning þæga fá
þótti kostur happa;
áttu hjónin arfa þrjá,
alla mestu kappa.

20 Haukur, Bálant hétu tveir,
hraustur Salman líka,
hilmirs arfar hófu geir,
hvergi fann öld slíka.

21 Þegar andast dögling dýr
dögum saddur þægur
Spanía erfði Haukur hýr,
hilmir gerðist frægur.

22 Hispanía buðlungs bur
Bálant fekk að erfðum,
skýr þar gerðist skjöldungur,
skatna stýrði mergðum.

23 Í Kimbría kynt er varð
kongur Salman fjáði,
smálönd mörg og eyja arð
eptir föður þáði.

24 Haukur bróðir hans með prýði,
hver eð Spanía réði,
feigur hari féll í stríði
firtur auð og gleði.

25 Halur sá, er hann deyddi
heiðingi var mesti,
fólk af kristni kúgaði,
kongur gerðist vesti.

26 Malpríant hét öðling æfur
ættaður frá Skitía
seinna viður söguna kræfur
sviður kemur tíja.

27 Buðlungs arfa Bálant þann
birtir um í sögum,
stýrði Hispanía hann
helju fram að dögum.

28 Salman kongur situr að
sínu ríki fríðu,
vitrir segja virðar það
Vallands austursíðu.

29 Hreystimaður mesti var
mikið stórhugaður
fylkir glaður fríðleik bar
fyrðum velþokkaður.

30 Ef að reiddist dögling dýr
dróttum óhreppandi
var hann þeim, en vinum hyr
vel og þá gleðjandi.

31 Stjórnsamur og þægur þar
þeingill meður sóma
elskaður af öllum var
ullum jötna dóma.

32 Greifadóttir drotning þæg
döglings af . . .*
Burgundía fríð og fræg
Frakka burt úr landi.

33 Kongs af ættum vífið var,
vafin japa slóða
Amba hét, sem ástirnar
öðling sýndi fróða.

* Words omitted in MS.

234

34 Milding unni menja rein
    meður ástar hita
    svo að hennar mátti mein
    mäta (!) einginn vita.

35 Herra sínum hlýðin var
    hlökkin elda Rínar
    skynsöm dýra dygðirnar
    drottning æföi sínar.

36 Bæta gerði ræsis ráð
    rörust foldin spenna,
    ýtar feingu allir tjáð,
    afbragð væri kvenna.

37 Yndislega buðlungs blíð
    beðjan ólétt verður,
    sveinbarn eptir talda tíð
    tvinna fæddi gerður.

38 Skjöldungs arfi skírður var,
    skapaður dáfallega,
    sá fékk heiti Sigurðar
    sifja hlynur trega.

39 Svaf hjá fylkir fríð á kinn
    Fofnis bóla gerður
    þar til ólétt annað sinn
    öðlings frúin verður.

40 Valva nokkur djörf, ódæl,
    dvaldist þar á láði,
    öllu meingi óvinsæl
    ýtum forlög spáði.

41 Forn í skapi flegðan var,
    fór um löndin víða,
    og hjá kóngum alstaðar
    upphefð þáði fríða.

41 Úr Garðaríki gríður var
    getin af háum ættum,
    stolt og heiptug brögðin bar
    búin orma gættum.

43 Jóð þá fæddu frúr um heim
    fylkira og jalla

valvan þessi var hjá þeim
vitur forlög spjalla.

44 Salmans frú í fyrra sinn
fæða þegar náði
var ei boðið völvu inn,
við það reiðast gáði.

45 Forsmáð þóttist vera vís
valva stríð í lundu,
hefndir spinna heiptug kýs
hilmirs tvinna grundu.

46 Þegar aptur þeingils kvinna
þunguð varð í náðum
valvan gerði vífið finna
víst að fjandans ráðum.

47 Í lystigarði ljúfust var
lofðungs frú í gleði;
valvan hana hitti þar,
heiptug þanninn téði:

48 Lukka þín og lífleg æfi
lízt mér nú í blóma,
menja ströndu mest þó hæfi
missa þennan sóma.

49 Óvinonum umsetin
eg þess bið og segi:
drepinn verði vísir þinn,
vopnin bíta þeygi.

50 Þér um spái þinn arfann
þær um sömu tíðir
smánarlegust helja hann
hremmi burt frá lýði.

51 Þegar soddan þjáning sker
þig við nauða kífið
dauðinn verður þægri þér
þá en mæta lífið.

52 Í lífi þínu ljótan hal,
læt eg það við klínast
þegar vex upp virðum skal
versta fíflið sýnast.

53 Fyrri var eg forsmáð ei,
  þó færi um löndin víða;
  hljótið þið nú Hárs á mey
  hefndir þess að bíða.

54 Drambið ykkar dofni nú,
  drjóla beðja ræddi;
  burtu vendi síðan sú;
  sorgin drottning mæddi.

55 Hitti gram, og harma ber,
  hrakspárnar um getur;
  reiður skipa fylkir fer
  að fanga völvu tetur.

56 Smánarlegum dauða drós
  deyja skal, hann téði;
  öðling reiðum aptur ljós
  anza drottning réði:

57 Batnar ráðið, þeingill, þey
  þó að látir deyða
  fólsku trylda falda ey,
  fæst ei græðing neyða.

58 Valvan ráð við sorgum sér,
  sagði drottning fríða.
  illum fjanda, öðling tér,
  einginn skyldi hlýða.

59 Aptur brúður anzar glatt
  öðling reiðum þjóða:
  við skulum finna hana hratt,
  henni sæmdir bjóða.

60 Veizlu þiggja biðjum brátt
  brúði dygða snauða,
  þá mun brögðótt baugagátt
  bætur gera nauða.

61 Anzar vífi upp á það
  öðling reiður sveita,
  Satan beiddi sinn í stað
  sætu lotning veita.

62 Drottning síðan drillu fann
  döpur mjög af trega,

en við hana sig með sann
sýndi þó blíðlega.
63 Bæta vil eg buðlungs tér
beðjan þá við hina
alt, er gerði þykkju þér,
þægða-frú og vina.
64 Vinsemdir og veizlu með
völvu bauð að þiggja,
hennar svo að hressist geð
heim í stað hjá tiggja.
65 Sittu þar í sæmd hjá mér,
sætan hatri sleppi,
þar til fóstrið fæði hér,
fögnuð svo eg hreppi.
66 Aptur sprundi anza vann
illmælanna vífið :
soddan þiggja sízt eg kann,
seint þitt græðist kifið.
67 Þegar jóðið fæðir fín
foldin orma skrefa,
ósókt kem eg þá til þín,
þarftu slíkt ei efa.
68 Skildu vitur vífin að,
valvan burtu geingur ;
drottning fór í döglings stað,
döpur var ei leingur.
69 Meðgaungunnar talda tíð
tiggja frúar þrýtur,
var þá komin valvan blíð,
vífið fögnuð hlýtur.
70 Þá við drottning sýndi sig
sæmilega blíða,
aðhlynningu ástúðlig
auðgrund veitti þýða.
71 Sveinbarn fæddi falda hlíð
fagurt sízt að líta,
hörund svart, en hárin stríð
hlyn á litlum rýta.*

* i.e., ríta.

72 Ásýnd hafði illa mjeg
  arfinn frúar svarni,
  augun voru óhýrleg
  í því ljóta barni.

73 Drottning lætur, dygð er ann,
  dögling sveininn færa,
  svo að fagni sjálfur hann
  sínu jóði kæra.

74 Þegar barnið ljóta leit
  lézt hann reiður vera,
  sjóli skipar svör með heit
  sveininn út að bera.

75 Ekkert nafn gaf öðling víst
  ungum viði ríta,
  en þó vildi allra sízt
  augum völu líta.

76 Valvan þá um rænu rið
  reiði þunga kendi ;
  af því hrepti sorga sið
  siklings ektakvendi.

77 Valvan þjónar vífi trú
  vel sem þörfin beiðir
  þar til að hún fylkirs frú
  fríða sæng af leiðir.

78 Drottning býður dregla brú
  dvelja hjá sér skyldi
  svo leingi með sæmd og trú
  sjálf er kjósa vildi.

79 Þetta sízt eg þiggja má,
  þá nam valva svara ;
  beið þó mánuð brúði hjá,
  burt svo vildi fara.

80 Ferskeytt leiðast leingri mér
  ljóð ; þó neyðir píni
  örva meiðum aðra hér
  Austra skeið eg sýni.

II. Önnur Ríma : Bragsneitt.

1 Þrjóta náði þundar vín um þykkju kóra,
  þegar vildi valvan fara
  við að skilja brúði hara.

2 Brjóstlagt hafði barnið unga buðlungs kvinna;
  valvan hrygðist vizkusanna,
  við þá ræðir dygðasvanna.

3 Eingum hef eg ofreiðzt manni utan saka,
  nema þér mín foldin flíka,
  fólskan þá mig trylti ríka.

4 Spáð hef illu þorngrund þér, ei þarf að neita,
  má þó ekki bölið bæta,
  brúði fyrst eg náði græta.

5 Forlögonum fyrða ræður frægsti hari,
  ekki neitt eg að því geri,
  angur þó mitt sinnið beri.

6 Skylt að minnast mér er þó á manndygð hreina
  mér sem gerði mesta sýna
  móðu glossa hlökkin fína.

7 Sonur þessi svarti þinn með sinnið trylda
  ekki skal að öllu gjalda
  illra föðurs hefndar valda.

8 Sinnar ættar sómi verður sendir fleina,
  honum gef þitt heitið fína,
  hann mun líkjast ætt í þína.

9 Hvað eg segi hrína skal á hlyni branda;
  vil eg, tjáði vefjan linda,
  við þig, drottning, trygðir binda.

10 Gersemar og gullið bjarta gaf þá henni
   vizku prýdda vísirs kvinna,
   valvan gáði þakkir inna.

11 Kysti barn og frúna fríða fríuð vanda;
   brátt svo náði burtu venda
   búin skarti valvan kenda.

12 Mildings frúin mædd þar eptir mása náði;
  forlög sín hún syrgja réði,
  sára neyð því bar í geði.

13 Svanninn mætur síðan lætur sveininn skíra,
  Ambales þá ýtar heyra
  ungur nefnist viður geira.

14 Ólust báðir upp með virðing arfar sjóla,
  ólíkir þó, allir tala,
  ullar væri nöðru bala.

15 Sigurður var fríður, frægur, fróður, slyngur,
  hámentaður hjörs við angur,
  hygginn, glaður, reiðistrangur.

16 Ambales mjög ófrýnlegur öllum sýndist,
  óþekkur og reiðinn reyndist
  rétt sem fífl, en vizkan leyndist.

17 Öðlings niður aungum hlýðir örva runni,
  hrekki sýndi hverjum manni,
  harðsinnaður kongs í ranni.

18 Ekkert læra öðlings vildi arfinn stríði,
  fálátur og fúll í æði,
  freklega þó vaxa næði.

19 Útlimirnir allir voru ógnastórir,
  aungum líkur álfi geira,
  ámátlegur sjá og heyra.

20 *Amlóði* var upp nefndur hjá öllu meingi,
  líka sjálfum af lofðungi
  lukku firti sveinninn ungi.

21 Þeygi segir þeim af meira þar til dýru
  trú eg átta vetra vóru
  vísirs niðjar þroskastóru.

22 Fylkis land í friði var og fríðir þegnar;
  annað kemur efni sagna;
  um það verður ljóðin magna.

I. A.M. 521c. 4to.

HIER biriar sögu af Ambulo eður Amloða enum heymska I Capitul. Donareck ħ : kongur sem rieði firer spania kimbria og Curlandi og óðrū mörgū þióðlöndū ħñ var øðugʳ af | gotzi oᶜ fielmeñúr af folki og morgum völldū undirsatūm ħm þientu margir undirkongar hertugar og Jallar, sem ħm | aðstoð veittū með storri framkūæmd lóndiñ að veriạ og øðæfū að safna var ħ oᶜ sialfʳ hiñ mesti kapi og forsiall. H vʳ stor ov | inū sýnᵐ eñ liufʳ og lytilátʳ vinū synū vitugur i radū þūj ħm vʳ stör viska länuð ħn vʳ ölmusu giaʳ og gaf mᵐ störar giafir. Selina | ħᵗ drott : ħnz bæði voru þøg mióg gómul orðiñ þä saga ʄzi giórðist. Sini ätti ħ þriá við dro : siñi hū var dottir Haukz kˢ a hol | setulūdi og eftir ħm hiet ħz firsti sonʳ. Añar ʄra son ħᵗ Baland eptir feður f s. þriðie h : Salman aller vᵒ ʄr mickler firi sier að | afli oᶜ aðgiórvi og fullvagsta þä hier var komið söguñi oᶜ sem donrek k. deiði skiptust lönd. . . .

II. A.M. 521A. 4to.

SAGA af amlóða eður Ambalase.

Donrik hiet kongūr sem rieðe fyrer Spania | Hysana Cimbrija eður Cumbria og lóndūm hier | óðum og borgūm nærri Spania. Hañ var audugʳ | af fie mecktugūr af folki og stormeñi Radvit | ugur stiorn samur órlatur af gotze ljufúr vi | nūm synūm eñ strangūr ovinūm og hielt | sitt ryki með storūm heiðri, Hañ var for | siall og sigūr sæll J orūstūm og haði marg | ar orūstūr við heiðnar þioðer, hañ hafði christnra maña trú og var under Pafans | reglūm og so vorū óll hans lond. Donrik | kongūr hafði drottingu att ættaða af Smä- | londūm dotter Hauks Jalls af heñar nafni | greynir ecki, við heñi hafði kongūr þria so | nū gieteð sa ellsti

242

hiet Haukur eftter | moður fóður synûm, añar Baland hiñ | þriðie Salman
þesser aller bræður vorû är | borner ordner er i sogû fra seiger, þeir voru |
aller mikler meñ fyrer sier sterker að af | le stor hûgaðer vygvaner og
þeir mestû bar | daga meñ ollûm ovæger i skape. . . . |

III. A.M. 521ᴅ. 4to.

SAGAÑ af Amloða Harðvendelssÿne.

Efter það að kong Hóttûr deiðe, tök Hrærekûr kongdöm effter, þä
fiellû undañ danmerkûr Rÿke, svensker kúrlenðsker og Zlavonia, og óñûr
fleire ûmliggiande lönd, sem til forna hófðû vereð undergiefeñ og skattgild
og vildû nú vera frÿ f' óllûm tollûm og ärlegû skattgiallde, þûi baðð
Hrærekûr kgʳ ût almeñinge af danmórk i leiðangûr og ämiñte að þeir
villdû fóðûrlandsens vegna iñleggia stör mañdöms sticke og viðrietta afftûr
það ûndañ var geingeð, so fóðûrlandeð næðe sÿnûm riettûgheitûm, þær
ûndañ fóllnû svenskû og kûrlendsku þiöðer settú ifer sig kong og dröû so
á möte Hrær: k: i tveñûm flockum, añañ settû þeir i launsätûr, eñ með
añañ forû þeir fram ä vÿgvölleñ Eñ sem Hrær: k: fornam þesse svik,
lagðe hañ sÿnûm skipûm að lande og villde ecke verða miðt ä millûm
óvinaña þar aðrer vorû i laûnsätrenu ä lande, Eñ aðrer hieldu til siös með
allañ skipaflotañ, hañ fiell hastarlega ifer þä sem ī laûnsätrenû voru og
fellde þä so giórsamlega, að þar komst ecke eirn lyfss ûndañ. Skipa hereñ
forûndraðe störlega, hûað syna filgiara tefðe so leinge, þûi hañ visse ecke
eñ þä að Hrær: k: hafðe lagt þä að velle og læckað þeirra opsa, þui kom
þeim äsamt að hallda ä móts við Hrær: k: og vita ä hûórn veg lûckañ
skiffte sier. Y her þeirra var eirn Ógnarlegʳ Rise, þegar hañ sier þañ
danska her kallar hañ härre röddû til beggia partaña seigiande. Mier
sÿnest räðlegt að hófðingiar vorer setie grið og frið ä bäðar sÿður Eñ
utvelie siñ mañ af hûórûm að hallda Einvÿge sÿn aa ä millûm. . . .

VII. Ex-
tract from
Thor-
lakssons
Amloða
Saga

ÞEGAR Amlóði Harðvendilsson sá hvörsu hans föðurbróðir hafði framið þetta óguðlegt morð og hórdóm, varð hann óttasleginn um sjálfs síns líf, og uppá það hann kynni að forða sjálfum sjer, þá stilti hann so bæði orð og gjörðir að allir meintu hann vera hálfvita; hann lá sífeldlega í saur og skarni og jós ösku um sig allan með mestu óskikkanlegheitum; öll hans orð og verk voru dárleg og gikks-leg og alt hans framferði leit so út sem hann væri kominn af einum narra; hann sýndist líkari vansköftu skrímsli enn nokkrum manni; stundum lá hann í ösku og beit kol, enn stundum tálgaði hann trjespítur, beygði þær í lögun sem fiski aungla, og gjörði þar á agnúa, og sveið so endana í eldi. Þeir spurðu hann að hvað hann gjörði; hann svaraði: "Eg skerpi mín spjót, að hefna með dauða föður míns." Margir hjeldu þetta fyrir dár og heimsku, enn sumir sem djúphygnari voru misþeinktu hann og meintu hann ekki so galinn sem hann ljeti, heldur mundi hann skýla sinni visku undir dáruskap og þreyskleika, og því tóku þeir sín ráð saman að þeir skyldu setja hann í heimuglegan stað, og láta hjá hönum eina dægilega jómfrú, og vita hvort hann upptendraðist ekki til óley-filegrar elsku með henni, því það er mannsins meðfædd náttúra, að hann kann ekki að dylja sinn vilja nær hann veit sig í heimuglegum stað, og meintu þar fyrir ef Amlóði hefði nokkurt forstand mundi hann láta sig yfirvinna með girnd lostaseminnar. Á meðal þeirra sem Amlóða fylgðu var einn sem upp með honum hafði alist alt frá barndómi. Hann þeinkti á gamlan kunníngs skap og gaf honum eitt heimuglegt teikn að hann skyldi vara sig, því hann vissi það mundi kosta hans líf ef þar fyndist nokkurt forstand með hönum. Þetta formerkti Amlóði. Og sem þeir báðu hann að stíga á hest sneri hann bakinu fram enn fánginu aftur, og festi beislið við stertinn, eins og hann vissi ekki annars, enn hesturinn

244

skyldi stjórnast með taglinu. Öllum þótti spottlegt að sjá þar hesturinn
hljóp fram og aftur, og maðurinn sem à baki sat stýröi með stertinum.
Þegar þeir komu nokkuð fram á veginn mætti þeim einn úlfur. Amlóði
spurði hvað það væri, þeir sögðu honum það væri úngur foli; hann
svaraði: "Soddan fola hefur Feingi fáa í sínum garði." Með soddan
orðum óskaði hann straffs yfir sinn stjúpfödur að úlfarnir og þau greindu
villudýr skyldu hefna á hönum sýns föðurs dauða, og taka af hönum góss
og ríkdóm, lönd og lýði, sem hann hafði maklega forþjent. Síðan komu
þeir með hann niður að sjávarströndu og sáu þar liggja sveif af hafskipi
sem þar hafði áður brotnað þeir segja: "Hjer finnum vjer stóran hníf."
Amlóði sagði: "Þá heyrir þar til stórt stykki sem þessi knífur skal í
brúkast." Hann meinti efunarlaust hafið, í hvörju sveifin þjenar skipinn
best. Þeir báðu hann að skoða það hvíta mjöl sem lægi með sjávar-
ströndinni. Amlóði sagði: "Það er malað með vindmylnu, enn sú hvíta
froða er skúm af öli." Þeir hlóu að hönum, enn hann sjálfur þrésaði sitt
forstöndugt tal. Þegar þeir komu lángt fram á skóginn skildu þeir hann
einan eftir so hann því djarflegar skyldi forgrípa sig á stúlkunni sem þeir
höfðu þar áður láteð, og skyldi hún koma óforvarandis til hans, so sem af
veðurs ráði: Hann hefði og vissulega forgripið sig á henni hefði ekki
hans gamli stallbróðir varað hann við og gefið hönum vist teikn þar uppá.
Hann tók eitt laufviðar blað og stakk í gegn um strái og ljet so fljúga
þángað sem Amlóði stóð. Enn sem Amlóði sá það fornam hann strax að
þar voru svik á ferðum. Hann tók stúlkuna til sín og gekk nokkuð
leingra áfram, alt þángað til þaug komu í nokkurs konar hulstur, þar sem
einginn sá þaug. Þar bað hann hana að hún vildi aungvum segja hvað
millum þeirra fram færi. Þessi stúlka hafði upp alist með Amlóða í frá
barndómi, því duldi hún með hönum alt það er hann vildi, og hún vissi
að hönum mátti til gagns koma. Nú sem þeir fóru heimleiðis með
Amlóða spurða þeir hann að uppá spje hvört hann hefði hrært nokkuð við
stúlkunni. Hann svaraði já. Þeir spurða hann fram vegis hvar það
hefði skeð, hann sagði: "A húsbust, hesthófi, og hana kambi." Þeir
gjörðu sköll að þessu og spurðu stúlkuna að því, enn hún neitaði og
vildi það ekki meðkennast. Hvör maður trúði hennar orðum eftir því
að einginn af þeim sem í skóginum voru hafði sjeð hvað skeð hafði;
þar kom ogso hans trúr stallbróðir og spurði hvört hann hefði orðið var
við nokkra sending? Amlóði sagðist vel hafa fornumið það sem hefði
komið fljúgandi fram fyrir hann með strá í rumpinum þar að hlóu þeir
aðrir, enn hans stallbróður hagaði soddan forstöndugt svar. Þegar þeir

kunnu ekkert að formerkja af hönum annars enn hann væri einn vitleysíngur, ráðlagði einn af Feingis ráðgjöfum að hann skyldi enn þá reyna til við Amlóða hvört hann væri aldiðis afsinna. Hann sagði Feingi skyldi láta sem hann vildi lángt burt til merkilegra útrjettínga, og læsa Amlóða einúngis með sinni móður í einhýsi og láta einn mann vera þeim óvitanlega í leyndum, að heyra hvað þaug segðu sín á millum; því væri nokkurt vit í honum þá myndi sonurinn eflaust ekki dylja þess móðurina. Þessi sami Feingis ráðgjafi lofaðist sjálfur að vakta uppá þeirra samtal. Feingi eftirfylgði hans ráðum og ljet sem hann vildi reisa nokkuð lángt í burt. Amlóði og hans móðir voru bæði innilukt í einni stofu, enn Amlóði óttaðist það sem í sannleika var að einhvör mundi heimuglega vera tilsettur, að njósna eftir þeirra samtali; því hljóp hann fyrst sem hann alminnilega plagaði hrínginn í kríngum alt húsið og veifaði kríngum sig hanðleggjunum sem öðrum vængjum og gól sem einn hani; Hann hljóp upp á hálminn sem lá í húsinu þar skálkurinn hafði sig undir falið og var þar ýmist að stappa upp eður niður so hann feingi þess betur skynjað hvört nokkuð kvikt væri þar undir hulið, og sem hann formerkti að þar var eitthvað þess háttar, greip hann sverð og rak þann í gegnum er sig hafði þar undir hulið. Hann dró hann síðan undan hálminum, og hjó hans kropp í smá stykki, því næst sauð hann þaug í heitu vatni, og kastaði þeim ofan um eitt heimuglegt salerni, þar svín voru niður undir. Þar eftir vendi hann til sinnar móður, hver eð grjet yfir hans heimsku og galinskap, og segir til hennar: "Ó þú argvítuga hóra, sem hefur tekið í faðm þann sem myrti þinn kæra herra og húsbónda, og gjörði þinn einasta sön föðurlausan; í þessu hefur þú sjálf opinberað þína vanartugu náttúru, að þú snöggt gleymdir þínu fyrra egtarhjarta; þú skalt og fyrir víst vita að eg gjöri mig ekki galinn fyrir aungva orðsök, því eg veit fyrir víst, að sá sem ekki sparaði sinn eiginn bróður, hann brúkar aungva miskunsemi við sína aðra náúnga. Það er og einginn galinskapur að forvara sitt líf og velferð með heimsku; míns föðurs dauði er mjer æ fyrir minnum, hvenær sem eg fæ hefnt hans; allir hlutir kunna ekki að útrjettast á einum tíma, þar heyrir til stór forstöndugheit að fanga þá hörðu og ómenskusömu týranna. Það er forgefins þó þú grátir yfir mínum galinskap, enn viljir þú sorga, þá grát heldur þína skömm og vanæru; eður þóknist þjer það betur að þegja og láta ekkert á þjer festa? Með soddan skörpum orðum og ströffunum vendi hann sína móður til dygðanna frá ódygðunum, frá óleyfilegum kærleika og blóð skömm, er hún hafði samlagað sig með Feingi, og til síns föðurs fyrri elsku og kærleika.

246

VIII. BRJÁMS-SAGA.

(EPTIR A.M. 602E. 4to. EPTIR HILDI ARNGRÍMSDÓTTUR LÆRÐA.)

ÞAÐ var einu sinni, að kóngur og drottníng rèðu fyrir ríki sínu; þau voru rík og voldug og vissu varla aura sinna tal. Þau áttu eina dóttur; hún ólst upp sem flest önnur sögubörn. Þar bar hvorki til titla nè tíðinda, frètta nè frásagna, um þann tíma, nema logið væri. Karl og kerlíng bjuggu í garðshorni, þau áttu sjö syni og eina kú til bjargar; hún var svo væn, að hana þurfti að mjólka þrysvar á dag, og gekk hún sjálf heim úr haganum um miðdegið. Það var einu sinni, að kóngur reið á dýraveiðar með sveina sína. Þeir riðu hjá nautaflokki kóngs, og var kýr karls þar saman við. Kóngur mælti til þeirra: "Væna kú á eg þarna." "Ekki er það yðar kýr, herra," sögðu sveinarnir, "það er kýr karls í kotinu." Kóngur mælti: "Hún skal verða mín." Síðan reið kóngur heim; en er hann var seztur til drykkju, mintist hann á kúna, og vildi senda menn til karls að fala hana fyrir aðra. Drottníng bað hann að gjöra það ekki, því þau hefðu ekki neitt annað til bjargar. Hann hlýddi því ekki og sendi 3 menn að fala kú karls. Karl var úti og börn hans öll. Þeir skiluðu frá kónginum, að hann vildi kaupa kú karls fyrir aðra. Karl mælti: "Mèr er ekki mætari kýr kóngs, en mín." Þeir leituðu fast á, en hann lèt ekki af, þángað til þeir drápu hann. Tóku þá öll börnin að gráta, nema elzti sonurinn, er hèt Brjám. Þeir spurðu börnin, hvar þau hefði tekið sárast. Þau klöppuðu öll á brjóstið, nema Brjám, sem klappaði á rass sèr og glotti. Drápu þeir þá öll börnin, er á brjóstið klöppuðu, en kváðu það gilda einu, þó hitt greyið lifði, því hann væri vitlaus. Kóngsmenn geingu heim, og leiddu með sèr kúna, en Brjám gekk inn til móður sinnar og sagði henni tíðindin, og bar hún sig illa. Hann bað hana að gráta ekki, því þau tæku ekki mikið upp á því; hann skyldi bera sig að gjöra svo sem hann gæti. Það var einu sinni, að kóngur var að láta smíða

247

skemmu handa dóttur sinni, og hafði hann feingið smiðnum gull, að gylla hana innan og utan. Brjám kom þar með fánahátt sinn. Þá mæltu kóngsmenn: "Hvað leggur þú hèr gott til, Brjám?" Hann svaraði: "Mínki um mælir mikinn, piltar mínir," og gekk síðan burt. En gullið, sem þeim var feingið til að gylla með, mínkaði, svo það dugði ekki meir en til helmínga. Þeir sögðu kóngi til. Hann hèlt, að þeir hefðu stolið því og lèt hengja þá. Þá fór Brjám og sagði móður sinni. "Ekki áttirðu svo að segja, sonur minn," segir hún. Hann mælti: "Hvað átti eg þá að segja, móðir mín?" Hún svarar: "Vaxi það um þrjá þriðjúnga, áttirðu að segja." Eg skal segja það á morgun, móðir mín," svaraði Brjám. Hann fór svo heim. Morguninn eptir mætti hann þeim, er báru lík til grafar. Þeir sögðu: "Hvað leggur þú gott hèr til, Brjám?" "Vaxi um þrjá þriðjúnga, piltar mínir," sagði hann. Líkið óx svo, að þeir mistu það niður. Brjám fór heim og sagði henni frá. Hún mælti: "Ekki áttir þú að segja það, sonur minn." Hann svarar: "Hvað átti eg þá að segja, móðir mín?" "Guð friði sál þína, þinn dauði, áttir þú að segja," mælti hún. "Eg skal segja það á morgun, móðir mín," mælti hann. Hann fór um morguninn heim að kóngshöll, og sá hvar rakkari einn var að hengja hund. Hann gekk til hans. Rakkarinn mælti: "Hvað leggur þú gott hèr til, Brjám?" Hann svaraði: "Guð friði sál þína, hinn dauði." Rakkarinn hló að þessu, en Brjám hljóp heim til móður sinnar og sagði henni. Hún mælti: "Ekki áttir þú að segja svo." "Hvað átti eg þá að segja?" sagði hann? Hún svaraði: "Hvert er þetta þjófsgreyið kóngsins, er þú ferð nú með, áttir þú að segja." "Eg skal segja það á morgun, móðir mín," segir hann. Fer hann þángað morguninn eptir, og var þá verið að aka drottníngu kríngum borgina. Brjám gekk til þeirra. "Hvað leggur þú hèr til gott?" sögðu þeir. "Er þetta nokkuð þjófsgreyið kóngs- sins, er þið farið núna með, piltar mínir?" Þeir atyrtu hann. Drottníng bannaði þeim það, og sagði, að þeir skyldu ekki leggja neitt til dreingsins. Hann hljóp heim til móður sinnar og sagði henni frá. Ekki áttir þú að segja svo, sonur minn," sagði hún. "Hvernig átti eg þá að segja?" sagði hann. "Er þetta nokkuð heiðurslífið kóngsins, sem þið núna farið með, áttir þú að segja." "Eg skal segja það á morgun, móðir mín," mælti hann. Fór hann þángað um morguninn, og sá tvo menn vera að birkja kapal; hann gekk til þeirra. "Hvað leggur þú hèr til gott, Brjám?" sögðu þeir. "Er þetta nokkuð heiðurslífið kóngsins, sem þið farið nú með, piltar mínir?" mælti hann. Þeir sveinðu honum. Hann hljóp heim lit móður sinnar og sagði henni frá. Hún mælti: "Farðu ekki leingur

248

þángað, því eg veit aldrei nær þeir drepa þig." "Ekki drepa þeir mig,
móðir mín," sagði hann. Það bar svo við einhverju sinni, að kóngur bauð
mönnum sínum að róa til fiskjar, og ætluðu þeir að róa á tveimur skipum.
Brjám kom til þeirra, og bað þá flytja sig. Þeir hæddu hann, og skipuðu
honum burt; þó spurðu þeir hann, hvernig hann ætlaði, að veður mundi
verða í dag. Hann horfði ýmist upp í loptið eða niður á jörðina og mælti:
"Vind og ei vindi, vind og ei vindi, vind og ei vindi;" en þeir hlóu að
honum. Reru þeir svo á mið og hlóðu bæði skipin. En er þeir fóru í
land, gjörði storm, og fórust bæði skipin. Bar nú ekkert til tíðinda, fyrr
en kóngur hèlt veizlu öllum vinum sínum og vildarmönnum. Brjám bað
móður sína, að lofa sèr heim, að vita, hvað fram færi í veizlunni. Þegar
allir voru seztir, gekk Brjám út í smiðju og fór að smíða spýtur. Þeir,
sem komu þar, spurðu, hvað hann ætlaði að gjöra við þær. Hann svaraði:
"Hefna pápa, ekki hefna pápa." Þeir mæltu: "Þú ert ekki óþesslegur."
Síðan fóru þeir burt. Hann stálsetti spýturnar allar í oddinn, læddist inn
í stofuna, og negldi niður föt allra þeirra, sem við borðin sátu, og fór svo
burt. En þegar þeir ætluðu að standa upp um kveldið, voru allir fastir,
og kendu hver öðrum um, þángað til hver drap annan, svo einginn varð
eptir. Þegar drottníng heyrði það, varð hún mjög hrygg, og lèt grafa
hina dauðu. Brjám kom heim um morguninn og bauð sig til að verða
þjónn drottníngar. Varð hún því fegin, því hún átti ekki mörgum á að
skipa. Fórst honum það vel, og svo kom, að hann átti kóngsdóttur, varð
síðan kóngur og settist þar að ríkjum, og lagði af allan gapahátt. Lýkur
svo sögu þessari.*

* "Þessi skröksaga er uppskrífuð eptir Hildi Arngrímsdóttur í Hvammi Anno
1707" stóð á handritinu með hendi Árna Magnússonar. Sbr. Dr. Maurers Isl.
Volkss. 287-290.

IX. CONCERNING SNÆBJÖRN:

FROM THE LANDNÁMABÓK.

IX. Concerning Snæbjörn

SNÆBJÖRN son Eyvindar austmanns, bróðir Helga magra, nam land milli Mjóvafjarðar ok Langadalsár, ok bjó í Vatnsfirði; hans son var Hólmsteinn, faðir Snæbjarnar galta; móðir Snæbjarnar var Kjalvör, ok váru þeir Tungu-Oddr systrasynir. Snæbjörn var fóstraðr í Þingnesi með Þóroddi, *enn stundum var hann með Tungu-Oddi eða móður sinni.* Hallbjörn son Odds frá Kiðjabergi Hallkelssonar, bróður Ketilbjarnar ens gamla, fekk Hallgerðar, dóttur Tungu-Odds; þau váru með Oddi enn fyrsta vetr; þar var Snæbjörn galti. Óástúðlegt var með þeim hjónum. Hallbjörn bjó för sína um várit at fardögum; enn er hann var at búnaði, fór Oddr frá húsi til laugar í Reykjaholt; þar váru sauðahús hans; vildi hann eigi vera við er Hallbjörn fœri, þvíat hann grunaði hvort Hallgerðr mundi fara vilja með honum. Oddr hafði jafnan bœtt um með þeim. Þá er Hallbjörn hafði lagt á hesta þeira, gekk hann til dyngju, ok sat Hallgerðr á palli ok kembdi sér; hárit fell um alla hana ok niðr á gólfit; hon hefir kvenna bezt verit hærð á Íslandi með Hallgerði snúinbrók. Hallbjörn bað hana upp standa ok fara; hon sat ok þagði; þá tók hann til hennar ok lyftist hon ekki; þrisvar fór svá; Hallbjörn nam staðar fyrir henni ok kvað:

> Ölkarma lætr erma
> eik, firrumk þat,'leika,
> Lofn fyr lesnis stafni
> línbundin mik sínum.
> Bíða man ek of brúði
> (böl görir mik fölvan;
> snertumk harmr í hjarta
> hrót) aldrigi bótir.

Eftir þat snaraði hann hárit um hönd sér, ok vildi kippa henni af pallinum, enn hon sat ok veikst ekki. Eftir þat brá hann sverði ok hjó af henni höfuðit, gekk þá út ok reið í brutt. Þeir váru þrír saman, ok

250

höfðu tvau klyfjahross. Fátt var manna heima, ok var þegar sent at
segja Oddi. Snæbjörn var á Kjalvararstöðum, ok sendi Oddr honum mann; bað hann sjá fyrir reiðinni, enn hvergi kvezt hann fara mundu. Snæbjörn reið eftir þeim með tólfta mann, ok er þeir Hallbjörn sá eftir-reiðina, báðu förunautar hans hann undan ríða, enn hann vildi þat eigi. Þeir Snæbjörn kvámu eftir þeim við hæðir þær er nú heita Hallbjarnar-vörður; þeir Hallbjörn fóru á hæðina ok vörðust þaðan; þar fellu þrír menn af Snæbirni ok báðir förunautar Hallbjarnar; Snæbjörn hjó þá fót af Hallbirni í ristarlið; þá hnekti hann á ena syðri hæðina ok vá þar tvá menn af Snæbirni, ok þar fell Hallbjörn; því eru þrjár vörður á þeiri hæðinni, enn fimm á hinni; síðan fór Snæbjörn aftr. Snæbjörn átti skip í Grímsárósi; þat kaupir hálft Hrólfr enn rauðsenzki; þeir váru tólf hvárir. Með Snæbirni váru þeir Þorkell ok Sumarliði, synir Þorgeirs rauðs, Einarssonar Stafhyltings. Snæbjörn tók við Þóroddi ór Þingnesi, fóstra sínum, ok konu hans, enn Hrólfr tók við Styrbirni, er þetta kvað eftir draum sinn:

> Bana sé ek okkarn
> beggja, tveggja,
> alt amorlegt
> útnorðr í haf,
> frost ok kulda
> feikn hverskonar;
> veit ek af slíku
> Snæbjörn veginn.

Þeir fóru at leita Gunnbjarnarskerja ok fundu land; eigi vildi Snæbjörn kanna láta um nótt. Styrbjörn fór af skipi ok fann fésjóð í kumli ok leyndi; Snæbjörn laust hann með öxi; þá fell sjóðrinn niðr. Þeir gerðu skála ok lagði hann í fönn. Þorkell, son Rauðs, fann at vatn var á forki, er stóð út í skálaglugg; þat var um gói; þá grófu þeir sik út. Snæbjörn gerði at skipi, enn þau Þóroddr váru at skála af hans hendi, enn þeir Styrbjörn af Hrólfs hendi; aðrir fóru at veiðum. Styrbjörn vá Þórodd, enn Hrólfr ok þeir báðir Snæbjörn. Rauðssynir sóru eiða ok allir aðrir til lífs sér. Þeir tóku Hálogaland ok fóru þaðan til Íslands í Vaðil. Þor-kell trefill gat sem farit hafði fyrir Rauðssonum. Hrólfr gerði virki á Strandarheiði. Trefill sendi Sveinung til höfuðs honum; fór hann fyrst á Mýri til Hermundar, þá til Óláfs at Dröngum, þá til Gests í Haga; hann sendi hann til Hrólfs vinar síns. Sveinungr vá Hrólf ok Styrbjörn; þá fór hann í Haga. Gestr skifti við hann sverði ok öxi, ok fekk honum hesta tvá hnökkótta, ok lét mann ríða um Vaðil alt í Kollafjörð, ok lét Þorbjörn enn sterka heimta hestana. Þorbjörn vá hann á Sveinungseyri, því at sverðit brotnaði undir hjöltunum. Því hældist Trefill við Gest, þá er saman var jafnat viti þeira, at hann hefði því komit á Gest, at hann sendi sjálfr mann til höfuðs vin sínum.

X. MÝVATNS-SKOTTA.

(EPTIR NORÐLENZKUM SÖGNUM Í HANDRITI SÈRA BENIDIKTS ÞÓRÐARSONAR
Á BRJÁNSLÆK.)

X.
Mývatns-
Skotta

EINHVER nafnkendastur draugur á norðurlandi var Mývatns-Skotta
á sinni tíð, og eiga Mývetníngar margar sögur af afreksverkum
hennar. Frá uppruna hennar er svo sagt, að galdramaður nokkur hafi
eitt sinn búið á Grímsstöðum við Mývatn, og hafi hann átt ílt útistandandi
við mann einn yfir í Köldukinn. Á laugardaginn fyrir páska eða hvíta-
sunnu kom flökkustúlka að Grímsstöðum. Bóndi tók vel við henni og
fylgdi henni í eldhús; kona hans var þá að færa hángiket upp í trog.
Bóndi þrífur lánglegg úr troginu, rèttir að stúlkunni, og segir henni að
èta. Stúlku-aumínginn tekur feginshendi móti ketinu, og ètur með góðri
lyst. Þegar hún var mett orðin, býðst bóndi til að fylgja henni til næsta
bæar. En þegar þau koma að á þeirri, sem rennur milli bæanna, tekur
hann stúlkuna, kastar henni í ána, og heldur í fætur hennar, meðan hún
er að kafna. Stúlkan hafði, eins og þá var títt, skautskuplu á höfði, og
snaraðist skuplan á hnakkann, meðan hann hèlt henni í kafinu. Þegar
hann þóktist viss um, að stúlkan væri dauð, dró hann hana úr kafinu og upp
á bakann, magnaði hana síðan með fjölkynngi sinni, og sendi hana svo til
að drepa manninn, sem hann þóktist eiga varhefnt við. Þegar draugur
þessi sást á ferð síðan, dínglaði skuplan á hnakka hennar, og er þaðan dregið
Skottu-nafnið. Skotta fór sendiförina, og vann það, sem fyrir hana var
lagt; kom aptur og sagði bónda, að hún hefði banað manninum, og spurði
hvað nú skyldi vinna. Bóndi sagði henni, að hún skyldi fylgja ættarskömm-
minni, og það gjörði hún, og vann margt til meins ættíngjum þess, sem
hún drap fyrst. Hún hèlt til við Mývatn, því þar voru niðjar manns
þessa. Í mæli var það, að hún hefði valdið raunum Illuga Helgasonar,
þess er orti Ambalesrímur; því bæði gat hann stundum ekkert kveðið

252

tímum saman fyrir ásókn hennar, og misti konur sínar vofeiflega, og varð
sjálfur geðveikur og vesall á seinustu árum sínum, og var alt þetta kent
Skottu. Í mansaungum fyrir Ambalesrímum minnist Illugi á böl sitt, og
er þar þessi vísa ein í:

> " Er eg svo merkjum ánauðanna undir staddur,
>   og einhverri á óstund fæddur,
>   að yndi trautt má verða gæddur."

Víða fór Skotta um bygðir, og var það sagt, að hún fylgdi Mývetn-
íngum, og þóktust margir sjá hana, sem skygnir voru, á undan komu
þeirra, en sumum barst hún í drauma. Frá því hefir verið sagt, að kerlíng
ein, sem fóstraði barn, sat uppi um nótt í rúmi sínu, en barnið nam ekki
af hljóðum; kerlíngu þókti þetta venjubrygði, og kom henni þá í hug, að
barnið mundi sjá eitthvað óhreint. Fer hún því að litast um, og sèr, hvar
Skotta situr á auðu rúmbóli yfir í baðstofuenda; rær hún sèr þar og er að
skæla sig framan í barnið; en kerlíng gat sèð þetta, af því glaðatúnglsljós
var í baðstofunni. Beið kerlíng þá ekki boðanna, leggur barnið í rúmið,
en tekur kolluna sína, og ætlar að fæla með því drauginn. Þegar Skotta
sèr tiltæki kerlíngar, stekkur hún ofan, en kerlíng sendir kolluna með
öllu, sem í var, á hæla henni; heyrir hún þá, að Skotta segir: "Það mátti
ekki minna kosta." *

* I Þíngeyarsýslu er sú sögn til um uppruna Skottu, að bændur tveir hafi búið
á Arnarvatni við Mývatn, og væru galdramenn, og mikill og illur kur í milli þeirra.
Einn vetur bar svo til, að stúlka varð úti í hríðarbyl þar vestur á heiðinni, fyrir
vestan Helluvað. Annan bóndann grunaði, hvað stúlkunni leið, fór um nóttina
vestur á heiði, og vakti hana upp, áður en hún var orðin köld. Síðan fór hann
með hana heim um morguninn, lèt hana fara á undan sèr inn í bæinn, og sagði
henni að drepa sambýlismann sinn. Hún fór inn, og bóndi litlu síðar. En
þegar hún kom inn, settist hinn bóndinn snögglega upp í rekkjunni, og skipaði
henni að taka þann, sem á eptir henni kæmi, og það gerði hún. Greip hún þá
þann bóndann, sem hafði vakið hana upp, og fleygði honum sem sopp innan um
baðstofuna. En hinn sat kyr í rekkjunni og hló að. Þó lèt hann hana ekki
gera út af við sambýlismann sinn, en ætt hans fylgdi hún eptir það. Svo stendur
í handriti frá sèra Jóni Kristjánssyni á Yztafelli, og ætla eg það sè hönd Bjarnar
Jónssonar á Finnstöðum í Kinn.

XI. ILLUGA-SKOTTA.*

(Eptir handriti Gísla Konráðssonar.)

XI. Illuga-Skotta

ILLUGI hèt bóndi, og bjó á Arnarvatni, norður við Mývatn ; hann var talinn margfróður. Þá bjó á Gautlöndum bóndi sá, sem Magnús hèt Hallsson ; hann var skáld og haldinn fjölkunnugur. Hann kvað níðvísu um Illuga, og hèt hann því þá, að hefna þess á Magnúsi. Það var einn dag, að Illugi kom að Gautlöndum ; stóð þá Magnús yfir fè, en konur sátu inni í baðstofu við tóvinnu. Baðstofunni var svo varið, að þar voru götupallar lángsetis. Illugi fór inn í baðstofu, og talaði við kvennfólkið um stund, og stóð upp við rekkju Magnúsar, á meðan hann stóð við. Um kvöldið, þegar Magnús kom heim, og gekk að rúmi sínu, spurði hann, hvort nokkur hefði komið um daginn. Kvennfólkið neitaði því, og mundi ekki, að Illugi hafði komið. Magnús trúði því ekki, og spurði enn ítarlegar um gestakomu. Sagði þá stúlka ein, að Illugi á Arnarvatni hefði komið. Magnús sagði, að sig hefði grunað það ; greip hann þá hund sinn, og fleygði honum upp í rúmið, og drapst hundurinn, en Magnús sakaði ekki. Þegar Magnús háttaði um kvöldið í rúmi sínu, fann hann þar fyrir sèr eitthvað í konulíki með skuplu á höfði. Honum þókti hún ákaflega leið, og að Illugi mundi hafa sent sèr kvenndraug þenna til óheilla, og til að drepa sig. Tók hann því það ráð, að magna drauginn og senda Illuga hann aptur. Við þetta óx draugnum svo mikið afl, að Illugi átti fult í fángi með hann, en þó er sagt, að hann bryti báða handlegi draugsins ; því hann var svo rammur, að hann var þreifanlegur. Draugurinn fylgdi leingi eptir það Magnúsi og fólki hans, og var kallaður Illuga-Skotta. Galdra-Ari, Jónsson prests greipaglennis, magnaði Skottu að nýju, og sendi hana aptur Illuga Helgasyni skáldi, sonarsyni Illuga á Arnarvatni. Gerði hún bæði honum og öðrum margt ílt, og er sagt hann verði sig mest

* Er að líkindum sama og Mývatns-Skotta.

254

fyrir henni með kveðskap.   Sagt er, að svo stæði á því, að Ari sendi Illuga
Skottu, að einu sinni kom Illugi á bæ Galdra-Ara, en milli þeirra var
óþokki nokkur.   Ari sat í eldhúsi og vissi Illugi það; kom hann upp á
eldhúsgluggann og kvað níðvísu um Ara; ekki er þess getið, að þeir ættust
fleira við að því sinni.   Eptir það sendi Ari Illuga Skottu, og kvaldi hún
hann jafnan um nætur, svo hann gat lítið sofið, eða ekkert.   Illugi þessi
bjó á Syðri-Neslöndum við Mývatn, og átti Ingibjörgu fyrir konu.   Hjá
þeim var bróðir Ingibjargar, sem Jón hèt, miklu eldri en hún, og gat hann
leingi varið Illuga fyrir Skottu, meðan hann varð ekki ellihrumur, og er
sagt, að hann beitti að eins afli við hana, því hann var bæði stór og sterkur.
Um þetta leyti bjó Haldór eldri * Jónsson frá Reykjahlíð í Vogum.   Hann
vakti opt yfir Illuga á nóttum, þegar aðsóknin var sem mest.   Eina nótt,
þegar Illugi vaknaði með miklum andfælum, hljóp Haldór út, af því hann
ætlaði, að Skotta mundi vera á glugganum yfir Illuga.   Þegar Haldór
kom út, sá hann, að Skotta var að glíma við strák einn, sem dáið hafði á
Neslöndum um haustið, og Illugi hafði opt ávítað fyrir strákapör sín.
Haldór var óhræddur, og kvað vísu um Skottu, og skipaði henni að snauta
burtu.   Hvarf hún þá þegar, en kom sömu nóttina við í Vogum, fór inn
í baðstofu, og æpti svo hátt, að heimafólk heyrði, og sagði: "Haldór er
kjaptfortur." (?)   Síðan tók hún til og kitlaði þar stúlku eina, svo hún
sýktist af því, en batnaði þó aptur, þegar Haldór kom heim.   Hún drap og
beztu kú Haldórs og nokkrar ær.—Einu sinni meðan Skotta fylgdi Illuga
eldra, kom hún að Grásíðu í Kelduhverfi, þegar fólk var háttað.   Þar var
vinnumaður á bænum, sem Asmundur hèt, sem sagt var að færi með
kukl.   Skotta snaraði sér upp fyrir hann í rúmið og sagði: "Nú er lúinn
Asmundur."   Hann spurði, hvað henni væri að því.   "Að fylgja austur
yfir hálsana og norður yfir skörðin," sagði hún; því að jafnan sýndist hún
á ferð með þeim frændum Illuga á Arnarvatni.

* Haldór Jónsson ýngri frá Reykjahlíð bjó í Borgarseli í Skagafirði.   Eptir
honum áttræðum hefir Gísli Konráðsson tekið sögu þessa 1848.   Sá Haldór hafði
þreifað á Skottu í úngdæmi sínu í föðurgarði, og ætlaði vera systur sína.   En
Björg móðir hans, sem var ramskygn, sá að það var Skotta.

XII. EXTRACT FROM
CHRONICA SEM KALLAÐER ERU ODDA ANNALAR
ÚR LATINU UTLAGÐIR AF SÆMUNDI FRÖÐA.

XII. Extract from Chronica

ANNO MUNDI 3430 var TARQUINIUS DRAMBLÄTE kongr hiñ siöunde Romanorum Rykte 25 är, hann flutte þä siðe iñ i Romam að binda menn i myrkva stofu, hann kom eiñ dag iñ i eitt hus hvort ätte Collatinus Riddare sa same Collatinus ätte þa hæverska quinnu Lucretiam, eñ að fullkomnuðu synu verke gieck hann heim Eñ Lucretia sende boð epter synum bonda, Eñ hann var i strÿðe hiä kongenum, nu sem Collatinus fieck bref frä siñe konu beiddest hann orðlofs að Rÿða heim og for heim iñan farra daga Eñ ä meðan hafðe Lucretia til bueð með giesta boð og er Collatinus kom sende Lucretia efter sÿnum föður og moður og öllum ætt mönnuñ sÿnum og svo bonda sÿns Og er þier voru aller komner og sester til borðs og er miçið var liðeð ä mältyð stoð Lucretia upp fra borðuñ og seiger við bonda syñ, þu skallt vita Collatinus að seinast er þu forst heim an skilder þu mig eina hreinferðuga kvinnu epter heima i þinu husi huer aldrei hafðe saurgast af neinum utan þier Eñ nù ä meðan þu hefur á burtu vereð hefur miñ heiður mig ræntr vereð suo eg er nu horkona orðeñ, Og það hefur Sextus Tarquinius gert eñ með þuy þier somer eige að hafa hooru i sæng hiä þier þa vil eg þig þess biðja og þina ættmeñ að hefna þinar svyvirðingar, en eg vil sialf straffa mig fyrir mitt brot, og með þessum orðum greip hun eiñ knyf og rak iñ i sitt hiarta og fiell strax niðr dauð en Collatini og Lucretiu ættmenn upp vöktu almugañ i Rom mote Sextus Tarquinius suo hann var drepeñ Og . . . . kom Collatinus þvy til leiðar að Tarquinius hann saklaus var i þessu varð og lyka drepeñ og . . . . kongs rykenu og þar með aller hans ættmeñ suo ei lifðe eiñ maður epter af kyne Tarquini, so grimlega varð ei nockurs morðz i Rom hefnt so sem Lucretiu dauða.

Anno Mundi 3449 varð Oðin kongr i Danmörk, sä framðe forneskiur með mesta galldre og giörningum og nefnde folkeð börn efter honum, hann var drepeñ og heigður þar sem nú heiter Oðins ey ä Fione.

Anno 3506 Toku Romveriar QUINTUS CINCINATUS eiñ kotkall og settu hann ypparstan höfuðsmann yfer allañ Romaborgar lyð, hann frelsaðe þa af öllum ägange þeirra ovina og eiðelagðe alla motstöðumenn þeirra eñ efter þann sigur villde hann ei annað eñ fara i sitt kot aftur, til sins fätæklega buskapar og sat þar til dauðadags efter þenañ Quintum settu Romveriar X menn i hans stað og kölluðust Tribuni.

Anno 3518 varð ØRVENDILL kongr i Danmörk.

Anno 3585 var ä dögum PLATO höfðinge allra lærðra manna, þesse Plato var kallaður Divinus hann do þa hann var að skrifa 81 ars gamall.

Anno Mundi 3588 var AMLODE kongsson i Danmörk, það seigest af honum i fyrstu að Feggi kongr drap broður siñ Órvendil føður Amloða og eignaðist Geyrlögu, broðer konu sýna moður Amlöða, en er Amloðe sa þetta liest hann fyfl vera, þä giörer Amloðe kroka af sterkum Eyke spýtum. Fege kongr efaðe að Amloðe munde heimskr vera og liet til bua Hest og Reiða og bað Amloða fara ä bak og Rýða til skoogar eñ hann hliop a bak og snere aftur fangenu eñ kongr sende niosnar mann með honum huort hañ talade nockut af vite, og Hier með hafðe hañ lateð konu i skogeñ að hún skylde Reina sañleikañ eñ Aml. hafðe vine með ovinum og eiñ hans vin tok breñ flugu og batt Gras strä um hana og liet hana fliuga þar að hann Aml. var og konan, Og strax formerkte Aml. að svik voru under. Sýðan profaðe kongureñ eñ ä aðrañ výs Aml. hann læste hann i ein hyse einu siñe hia moður siñe og liet eiñ svein aa laun i husinu að heyra hvað þau töluðu Eñ Aml. for upi sængena þar maðuriñ lä og niður under føteñ og stappaðe með fötunum og fañ so mañiñ og liest skiella höndum saman og Galaðe sem Hane, eñ moðer hans griet og visse ei að niosnar maðuriñ var þar iñe, Hañ Seigir hún griete, þuy sonur honnar være fyfl, og skiftingur. Eñ Amloðe sagðe af vite og bað hana að grata sýna sköm er hun fremðe með broður bonda syns, og mañs bana og stöck hann ur sængeñe og drap niosnar mañiñ og hio hañ i stycke og kastaðe styckiunū i setu hans eñ þar komu svýn og atu upp stycken. Eñ þa kongr spurðest um mañiñ svaraðe Amloðe af vite og ei af vite að hañ sa að maður fiell ofan i giegnum seturnar og þar að svýn kiæme og æte hañ upp og þa hlo kongriñ og aller sem til heirðu og colluðu Aml. meður þetta af ovite tala. Eftir þetta sende kongriñ þenañ Aml. með tveimur mönnum til kongsins af Englande og skrifaðe bref með þeim að Einglands kongr skylde lata heingia Amloða og skrifa sier aftur til með mönunum eyrindis

R

lokeñ öll eñ er Aml. og hans fylgiarar komu a veigeñ komst Aml. að brefunum braut þau upp eñ er hann hafðe yfer leseð brefeñ, skrifaðe hann öñur bref og setur svo iñ i brefeð og lagðe i sama stað að þegar kongriñ aa Einglande fær þesse bref skylde hañ gefa Aml. dottur sýna eñ heingia hina tvo meñina og bio so um brefeð og lagðe i sama stað og hin voru aðr greind Eñ er þeir komu til Einglands geingr þeir fyrer kong og voru til borðs af honum setter en Aml. sat og villde huorke eta nie drecka og suo leið allt kvölldeð. Eñ er menn voru til sængur leidder sette kongriñ mann eiñ til niosnar i herbergeð að heyra hvað þeir hialaðe og er lios var slöckt tala þeir fylgiarar Amloða til þuy hañ villde ei neyta eñ hann seiger að brauðeð lyktaðe af manna beinum og kiöteð af manna hollde en Biöreñ af Rið Järnum, þar með hefr kongr þræls yferlit og með þetta sofnuðu þeir eñ niosnar maðuriñ giec leynelega ut og til köngs og seiger honum þesse orð, strax liet kongriñ spyria hvar korneð hefðe vaxið fañst það aa þeim Akre sem korneð hafðe gröeð að forðum hafðe strýð vereð og lau þar dauðra manna bein ogryñe, Eñ kiöteð var af svýne huort eteð hafðe dauðan mañ, up var grafiñ eñ biöreñ var bruggaður af bruñe þeim er fullur lä af sverðum og oðrum Rið Jarnum og er kongr fieck þetta svo i sañleika reint spurðe hañ Amloða hueriu giegnde þræls yferlitur ä sier. Eñ Aml. bað kongeñ að spyria moður syna að þuy en það fanst að kongrinn var þræls son, Og er kongriñ formerkte vysdom Aml. gifte hann honum strax dottur syna eñ liet heingia hina baða stallbræðr hans eñ þegar Aml. verður þessa výs liest hann mioc reiður vera og þar fyrir gaf kongrinn honum mikeð Gull og það liet Aml. smella i tvo stafe og seiger nu þetta skylde vera syner stallbræður og suo for hañ heim til Danmerkr eñ er hañ kom heim hafðe kongrinn lateð til bua mikla veitslu er vera skylde erfe efter Aml. og er hann spurðe þetta gieck hann inn i höllina og tok til að skeinkia boðsmönum eñ konguriñ spurðe hvar stallbræðr hans væru hann riette fram baaða stafena er aður greinðe og hlo kongriñ að orðum hans, Sýðan giec Aml. að skeinkia og rañ sverð hans ur slýðrum og skarst hann ä hende og giec hann strax til smiöz og bað hañ drepa ä gat og slä nagla i giegnum huortveggia sverðeð og balcd og gieck suo iñ aftur og gierðe gestina svo druckna að þeir sofnuðu þar hver sem var komiñ eñ Aml. tok nu spytu kroka og krækte þa saman og fötiñ giestaña niður með þeim. Og sette so eld i husið og brende upp allt saman, gieck so þar að sem kongriñ lä og tok sverðeð kongsins eñ feste sitt sverð i staðeñ ä stolpañ og vakte suo kongeñ og sagðest nu vilia hefna föður sýns en kongriñ hliöp upp og greip sverðeð og ä meðañ hann gieck að toga sverðeð þa drap Amlöðe kong og varð syðañ kongur efter hañ og Rykte ei miög leinge.

Anno Mundi 3603 varð Philippus faðer Alexandri Magni kongr i Macedonia, seirna varð sä landskialfte i Rom að þar varð eitt hol a miðiu torgenu af huoriu hole giec upp Reikur og so ill lyckt so að plaga varð af so margt folk doo en Romveriar spurðu sÿna guðe um hiälp eñ goðeñ svöruðu að þetta hol munde ei aftur lukast nema eiñ Eðalboriñ maður steipte sier þar ä höfuðeð ofan i eñ þar eiñ Riddare sem hiet *Marcus Curtius* ungur og værn, hann seigest helldur vilia deyia eñ borgiñ og moðurland hans fordiarfest og biö sig með herklæðum og stie ä sinn hest og reið ofan i þetta gap og strax byrgðest aftur holeð, er það nu kallað Locus Curtius.

259

XIII.

EPITOME OF SAXO'S DANISH HISTORY,

FORMERLY ATTRIBUTED TO THOMAS GHEYSMER, MONK OF ODENSE,
WHO PROBABLY MERELY TRANSCRIBED IN 1431 THE WORK OF
AN UNKNOWN EPITOMIST OF THE FOURTEENTH CENTURY

RORICUS 14TUS.

XIII. The Gheysmer Epitome

ORTUO HÖTHERO, *Cureti, Sweci,* & *Slavi,* qvi prius tributarii erant, *Daniam* infestare ceperunt, propter qvod RORICUS, congregato exercitu, contra *Slavos* venit. *Slavi* autem in duobus locis insidias posuerant, ut *Danos* incautos opprimerent. Sed RORICUS hoc intelligens, socios ordinavit, qvi eos omnes in insidiis occiderent. Cumqve RORICUS venisset ad exercitum *Slavorum,* videntibus *Slavis* turmas *Danorum,* unus ex eis corpore magnus, officio magus, singulare certamen expetebat. Cui qvidam *Danus* fortis magis mente qvam corpore occurrens, ad primum ictum *Slavi* occisus est. Gaudentibus igitur *Slavis* de victoria, seqventi die idem *Slavus* duellum petiit, credens jam, nullum superesse, qvi sibi resistere potuisset. Cui cum occurrisset qvidam *Danus,* nomine *Ubbo,* ambo in certamine moriuntur. Igitur *Slavi* petunt pacem, manentes tributarii, sicut prius. Eo tempore *Horwendillus* & *Fengo* fratres patri suo a RORICO in prefecturam *Jucie* subrogantur. Porro *Horwendillus* tam preclara opera fecerat, ut *Collerus* Rex Swecie, fame ejus invidens, decorum sibi putaret, si eum armis superare posset, & dum pro hoc *Norwegiam* exisset, accidit, ut ad qvandam insulam, in medio mari positam, *Collerus*

XIII.

𝕯𝖞𝖙 𝖎𝖘 𝖉𝖊 𝖉𝖊𝖓𝖘𝖈𝖍𝖊 𝖐𝖗𝖔𝖓𝖊𝖐𝖊 | de Saxo grammaticus de poeta
ersten gheschreeff | in dat latine vñ daer na in dat dudessche
ghesettet | is vnde inholt dat van Abrahams tyden is danne |
marken eyn konninkryke ghewezen vñ sodder hefft | eghene
konninghe vñ heren alletyd ghehat vñ dar | tho van vele groter
manheyt starke vnde vele grote | werke myt vele meer wunders
de ghescheen syn by | dessen konninghen vñ dat densche volk.

Fol. 20ᵛ.

Van Konnink Korico [Cvᵛ–Diijᵛ].

XIII. Low-
German
version

𝕬LSE Hotherus doeth was do vormanneden syck de sweden (fol. 21ʳ)
Vnde de wenden Wente de ghenen beyde schat dē denen de
beghunden Do antouechtende dannemarken Darumme samelde Korius(!)
de nye konen syne schare to hope toghen de wenden Wente se anlagheden
dat land in twen enden vp dat se mochten so de denen bedroghen hebbē
Vnde vordrukket mit vnuorsichticheyt Sunder Koricus de bekande dath
vñ schikke daer syne ghesellen tho de des waer nemen vnde slughen se
alle dar ouer Do Koric' quā tho der schare der wende vnde de wende
seghen syne schare Do was dar eyn mank dē wendē de was groet van
lychamme Vnde mechtych van werken de warde daer na dat he alleyne
vechten wolde De | me leep eyn dene entyeghen de daer was mer
starch van herten wē van lichāme de van deme ersten slaghe des groten
wendes doet bleeff Des vrouweden sik de wende ghās sere dat ere
man stāde bleeff Des begherde de grote went Enes de mit em eynen kāp
vechtede Wēte he mende dat dar nu nemēt mer we | re de em wedder stan
mochte Des quā dar eyn dene | em entieghē de het Vbbo de kempede
mit em so dat se beyde döt bleuē Dar vmme beden de wende vm | me
vrede vñ bleuē vort vnder den denen so dat se dē denē schat geuē vort an
To der suluē tijd eyn de het Horwendill' de bedreeff so mechtighe werk
Dat de konnink van norweghen Collerus hatede sin ruch | te vñ duchte
dat he daer mochte grote ere vñ vroude vā hebbē efft he ene kōde ouer-
wynnē Vñ alze he dar vmme vuer vth norweghē so vyl yd sik Dat se sik

261

ex una parte & *Horwendillus* ex alia applicarent, dumqve insulam intravissent, contigit, illos duos solos sibi mutuo obviare. Tunc *Horwendillus* prior Regem interrogat, qvo genere pugne sibi libeat decertare. Ille vero duellum elegit, facta mutua paccione, ut victor victum sepeliat, ac exeqviis honoret. Qvibus congressis, *Horwendillus* nimia aviditate hostem impetens, clypeum proprium neglexit, ac utraqve manu gladium arripiens, clypeum *Colleri* crebris ictibus assumpsit, atqve pede ejus absciso cadere coëgit. Qvo mortuo, corpus ejus regio tumulo ac solempnissimis exeqviis honorabant. Deinde sororem ejus bellicis rebus peritam persecutus occidit. De talibus pugnis victoriosis RORICO sollempnia spolia apportavit, per qvod RORICUS in tantum eum honorabat, qvod filiam suam *Geruth* uxorem ei daret, de qva ille *Ambletum* filium suscepit. Tot ejus successibus prosperis frater suus *Fengo* invidens, occasione habita, fratrem occidit, uxorem fratris sibi assumens, incestum fratricidio adjecit.

Ambletus considerans, qve fiebant, ne patruo propter prudenciam suspectus esset, stulticiam simulavit. De qva ut eo magis fidem aliis faceret, sordibus domus se inqvinavit, ita ut in facie monstro similis videretur. Qvidqvid dicebat, deliramentum videbatur : qvidqvid agebat, insaniam pretendebat. Interdum foco assidens, favillasqve manibus verrens, ligneos facere uncos igniqve durare solitus erat, ac in angulis sibi notis conservare. A qvo cum qvereretur, qvid ageret, acuta spicula ad ulcionem patris se formare dicebat. Qvod factum cum aliqvi subtilius advertentes, dicebant, eum astuciam prudencia occultare. Facto igitur consilio, pulcherrimam juvenculam sibi anteponi in rubetis clanculo ordinabant, ut si eam per venerem attemptaret, utiqve expers stulticie videretur. Vadunt secum statim aliqvi, qvi ipsum in eqvo ferrent ad profunda nemoris, & predicto modo ipsum temptarent. Cumqve eqvum ascendere deberet, ita se super eum posuit, ut faciem ad caudam eqvi versam haberet. Qvod factum omnibus risum ingessit. Procedens *Ambletus,* cum lupum obvium haberet, sociiqve dicerent, esse eqvum

262

wundē vp eynē werdere middē in dem mere   Alze se quemen vp dat
werder so ghinghen de twe alle | ne to samēde   Do vraghede Horwendill'
dē kōnink erst mit wat wapen em lustede to vechtende Vn̄ in | | (fol. 21ᵛ)
welker mate em lustede   Doeschede he den kamp vn | de makeden eyn
loffte vnd' sik we den anderē ouer wūne de scolde den anderē begrauen
vn̄ scolde sine bygrafft eren   Alze ze do to hope gingen do was Horwendill' siner so gyrich dat he sinen schylt vorgat vn̄ greep sin swert in beyde
hande vn̄ how Colleri sinē schilt in alle stukkē vn̄ how em vort dē eynē
vot aff Dat he stortede so sluch he en vort döt vn̄ make | de em dar
eyn konninklik graff vn̄ grueff en dar in Vn̄ dede em eyne erlike bygrafft
Vn̄ sluech vort sine suster de ok gelert was to vechtende mit den
wape | nen van den erliken vnde mechtighen stryden broch | te he
Koriko dem konninghe van dannemarken dur | bare goue   Dar vmme
erde ene Koricus so hochliken dat he em sine dochter Gherud ghaff to
eyner husvrouwen mit d' teelde he eynen sone den hete he Ambletū   Do
hadde Horwendill' enen brod' de het Fengo de hate de lucksamicheyt sines
broders vtherma | ten sere Vnde nam der tyde ware dat he stede vnde
stunde dar tho mochte kryghen Dat he en mochte morden   Alze he dede
vn̄ nā dar to syn wyff Ambletus de merkede vul wol wat dar schen was vp
dat sin vedd' nene acht vp em en ghene so likende he sik | enem doren vn̄
vp dat de anderen sik des ock scholden dunken laten so nam he drek vā
der erdē vn̄ besmerde sik dar mede dat he was gheschapen in de | me
antlate alze ein dē mē holt vor ein wytwūder vn̄ allēt dat he dede dar terde
he sik io dorlikē to vn̄ allēt dat he sprak dat duchte en wesen gabberye
vnd' stundē sath he in dē schorstene vn̄ kokede in d' aschē vn̄ makede
hakē van holte vn̄ leet de so by dem vu | re herden vn̄ lede de denne wech
in hemelike winkel daer he se bewart wuste wen he denne ghevraghet | |
(fol. 22ʳ) wart wat he dar mede doen wolde vn̄ wat he makede so sede he
he makede scharpe schote dar he sinē vader mede wreken wolde   Dar
merkeden etlike vul behendeliken vp wat he dede vn̄ seden vnderstundē
he were nicht al dore he schulde grote wyszheyt vn | der der doetscop So
ghinghen se to rade wo se dat voruaren mochten so vundē se dat men
scholde ne | men eyne iuncvrouwen vn̄ setten de in den busch were id
zaze dath he sik myt er bewerde so mochte men dat wol weten dat he
neen dore were   So tho | ghen alke vort etlike mit eme hen alze he scholde
vp dat pert stighē so sette he sik dath he syn antlat kerde to des perdes
sterte des lachedē se altomale   Alze se do henne toghen do quā en eyn
wulff entieghen so sedē sine kumpane dat were eyn iunck pert Do se | de
he wedder He hedde der nicht vele gheseen rydē in synes vaderen schar
Vortmeer quemen se by en ouer des meres Dar vunden se eyn ruder
van enem schepe Dat seden sine kumpane dath se hadden eyn mest
gheuūden   Do sede he plecht men dar dat water mede to snidende   Do
seghen se dat wytte sand in dem mere vnde se zeden dat were meel do
zede he ya dat is van deme storme der bulghen dar to hope woltert   Do

tenerioris etatis, nimis paucos hujusmodi in *Fengonis* grege militare dicebat. Idem litus preteriens, cum socii, invento navis gubernaculo, cultrum maximum invenisse se dicerent; eo, inqvit, pregrandem pernam secari oportet, mare signans, cujus magnitudinem gubernaculo dividi satis est notum. Cumqve arenam albam dicerent farinam, ait, eam commolitam impetu procellarum. Cum igitur ad nemus venissent, ut eo audacius veneri indulgeret, ipsum ex industria reliqverunt. Inventaqve femina, ex insperato subito fecisset, nisi qvidam ex eis, ejus collactaneus, ipsum sagaci signo de cavendis insidiis premonuisset. Nam inventum stramen oestri pretervolantis caude submisit, ac in eum locum, qvo *Ambletus* erat, ad volandum direxit. Nec callidius hoc signum datum qvam cognitum fuit. Nam *Ambletus*, videns oestrum cum stramine volantem, insidias metuit, ac amplexans mulierem, ad palustria longe deduxit, factoqve concubitu, exegit ab ea, ne cui rem proderet. Qvod & illa fideliter repromisit, nam educata fuerat cum *Ambleto*. Domum igitur reductus, cum interrogaretur, an puellam cognovisset, sic se fecisse fatetur. Rursum interrogatus, qvo loco rem egerit, super ungulam eqvi, cristam galli ac laqvearia tecti fecisse dicebat; horum enim particulas secum tunc habebat. De qvo dicto cum omnes risissent, interrogata puella, nichil talium ipsum fecisse, dicebat. Tunc ille, qvi sibi oestrum direxerat, ut se coram eo monstravit, dixit, se solum de eo solicitudinem habuisse. Qvi ad mentem ejus & factum subtiliter respondens: Vidi, inqvit, qviddam subvectum alis stramen in posterioribus gestans. Qvod dictum sicut alii risum ita fautori *Ambleti* gaudium fecit. Dum igitur solercia juvenis sic deprehendi non posset, habito alio consilio, *Fengo* se absentavit, interimqve *Ambletus* & ejus mater in uno cubiculo includuntur: ut si qvid prudencie ei inesset, coram matre aperiret, ac ambobus insciis, unus cum eis occultate latuit, qvi verba eorum diligencius adverteret, eratqve idem, qvi hoc consilium dederat *Fengoni*. Cumqve locum *Ambletus* intrasset, suspicatus insidias, complosis manibus ac concussis brachiis saltare cepit,

264

se quemen in den wolt Do lepen se van em vp dath he deste vryeliker syk
vor enighede mit dem wyne Do he dat wyff dar vant do wuste he des
nicht dat se dar vmme daer was dat se ene dar mede vorsoken wolden so
dat he vul na hadde sinē wyllē mit er vullenbrocht dat se id ghesen hadden
Men dar was eyn mede mank sinē kūpane De ene vorsoken scholden de
ghunde em woel de ghaff em des eyn teken dat se ene dar mede vor soken
wol | den vnde he vant eyn stro dath stak he in eynes vo | | (fol. 22ᵛ)
gels stert vn̄ leth den vleghē in de stede daer he myt deme wyue was do
sach Amblet' dat stro nicht so drade he bekāde dat dar by dat he dar mede
gewarnet was Vn̄ nā dat wyff in sinen arm Vn̄ ghynck mit er in de
dusternisse des woldes dar ene nemāt senen kōde Vn̄ hadde dar allikewol
sinē willē myt dē wyue vn̄ bat se do dat se dat nicht segghē scholde Vn̄
se louede em dat wyslikē to holdēde Wēte se | ghūde em ok wol vn̄ was
mit em vp gheuudet do wurdē se en wedder tho hus vn̄ vraghedē en io
efft | he de iunkvrouwē hedde ghetruwet do zede he al ia Se vraghedē
em in wat stede he sede vp enē perdes houe vn̄ vp dē helm tekene Vn̄ vp
dē dake vn̄ van dessen alle dren hadde he io ein merke mede bracht Do
he sodane wort sede Do lacheden se altomale Do vraghedē se de iūck-
vrouwē wer he so ghedā hed | de do sede se he hadde er nichtes nicht
ghedā Do se siner daer mede nicht konde wys werdē do bedach | tē se
enē anderē raet Dat Fengo sine veddere he hud | de sik oft he dat nerghē
were vn̄ se nemē se vn̄ beslotē Ambletum in eyner kamerē mit siner moder
vn̄ ein de hudde sik vp de kamerē dat se yd beyde nycht en wustē dat he
scholde horē wat he to siner mod' spreke Wente se mendē were dar noch
wat wyszheit in | ne dat wyszede sick yo vth wē he by sine mod' queme vn̄
de sulue de vp d' kamerē mit behud was de hadde Fengoni dē raet
ghegheuē Do Amblet' vp de kamerē quā do merkede he vn̄ dachte vul
woel dat se em echter haddē gelaget Do sprāk he vp vn̄ clappede mit dē
hendē vn̄ sloch to hope mit den armē vn̄ begūde to kreyēde alze eyn hane
alze he stech vp dat stro do vulde he vn̄ vornā dat dar sik ein gehut hadde
vn̄ greep en vn̄ to how ene so degher dat eimlyt | | (fol. 23ʳ) nicht by dē
anderē bleff vn̄ warp en so dor de hemlicheyt vn̄ dar etē ene de swyne vp
do he do alleyn mit d' mod' was Do bewēde syne mod' sine dorheyt Do
sede he to d' mod' Bewene di suluē du boze sno | de wyff de du lichst
alze ene schöke mit dynes mannes brod' dat vntēlit is vn̄ drifst mit eme
dyne boszheit Jk do dat nicht sund' sake dat ick mi so dorlikē there wēte
ik wet dat wol de sines egenē brod' nichᵗ en schonede De scolde vul luttek
medelidinge hebbē mit sines brod' kinde Mē ick scal mines vad' doet
nicht vorghetē Wē id ik alzo valt so wyl ik des nicht vorsumen du schal
dar nemāde vā segghen Do se ene wedder aff letē Vn̄ Fengo quam do
wedder to hus vn̄ se sochten vuste na deme de daer ghehuch was vp de
kamerē Vn̄ se ene yo nicht en vundē do vraghede Fengo eins in schimpe
Ambletum efft he en nicht ghesen hadde Do zede he dat he were steghē
dor dar huszeken Vn̄ vyl in de schitē so eten ene de swyne vp vn̄ makede
265

ad modum galli cantum edendo. Dumqve stramenta conscenderet, perpendit pedibus subtus aliqvem latitare. Qvem confossum membratim divisit, ac per cloacam dejecit, qvi a porcis devoratus est. Cumqve cum matre esset, ipsa ejus insaniam deploravit. Cui ille, deplora te ipsam, turpissima mulier, inqvit, scorti more incestum faciens, fratrem viri tui turpi concubitu amplexaris. Ego enim non sine causa stoliditatem simulo, sciens, qvod, qvi fratri non pepercit, nec eciam filio fratris compateretur, necem patris mei non neglexeram, qvam tempore oportuno vindicare propono, hec sub silencio tene. Reversus *Fengo*, cum dictum insidiatorem diu qvesitum nusqvam reperiret, per jocum qverebat *Ambletum*, si eum vidisset. Qvi respondit, eum cloacam intrasse ac in cenum cecidisse, sicqve a suibus devoratum. Qvod dictum omnibus cachinnum fecit. Cumqve *Fengo* omnino eum prudencia suspectum haberet, nec tamen eum propter Roricum Regem avum ejus interficere auderet, ipsum *Regi Britannie* misit occidendum. Discedens *Ambletus*, matri latenter jubet, ut anno revoluto aulam cortinis ornet ejusqve exeqvias faciat, promittens, se eo tempore rediturum. Vadunt cum eo duo satellites *Fengonis*, habentes *literas ligno insculptas*, ut tunc moris erat, qvibus *Regi Britannie Ambleti* occisio mandabatur. Qvibus dormientibus, *Ambletus* eorum loculos perscrutatus, literas invenit, qvibus lectis, literas ibi positas abrasit aliasqve posuit, qvibus sociis suis mors, sibi autem connubium filie *Regis Britannie* petebatur. Cum autem *Rex Britannie* literas legisset, recepit eos convivio. Sed *Ambletus* tam cibum qvam potum regium fastidivit. Dum autem dormitum irent, premisit Rex qvendam, qvi latitans intus verba colloqvencium auscultaret. Interrogatus *Ambletus* a sociis, cur sic in mensa abstinuerit, dixit, panem cruore respersum, potum autem habere saporem ferri, ac carnes humani cadaveris habere odorem. Addidit eciam, Regem habere serviles oculos, Reginam vero tria ancillaris ritus officia peregisse. Exprobrantibus sociis ejus vesaniam, qvod laudanda vituperaret. Ille, qvod latebat, reversus, Regi omnia enarravit, qvi ultra modum

266

dar ene gabberye aff dat se alle nuch to lachende haddē   Do hadde Fengo **XIII. Low-**
allyke wol grote var vor sine wysheyt   Wēte em mistuchte vnderstundē **German**
an eme Vn̄ he endorste ene doch nicht dodē vor deme Forico de syn **version**
grote vad' was van der mod' weghē Vn̄ sande ene to dem hertoghe vā
Britanien dat de en doden scolde   Do nā Amblet' syne moder hememelikē
to sik vn̄ sede er wen eyn iar vmme ghan were vā der tijd an so scolde
se dē hof al vmme behenghē mit vmmehāgen schonlikē vn̄ de gheliken
Vn̄ scolde laten sine begrafft eren vn̄ begā so wyl ik wedd' komē   So
toch Amblet' hen vn̄ Fēgo sende twe schildknechte mit em vn̄ dede den
eyn | holt mede daer in gheschreuen was alze do de zede was Dat de
hertoge vā Britanien scolde Ambletū | | (fol. 23ᵛ) doden   Alze do sine
kūpane slepen so besochte he ere budele vn̄ vant daer de breue inne Vn̄
las dat dar inne schreuē was vnde scrapede dat aff vn̄ schreeff ander
wedder in de stede Dath de twe worden ghedodet vn̄ scholde hebbē des
hertoghen dochter vā Britanien dar lede Fengo vrūtlyken vmme bydden
Do de Hertoghe vā Britanien de breue las do bat he se to gaste men
Ambletus de wolde des herthoghe spysze nicht ethen   Do se slapen ghinghen do let de hertoge hemeliken dar na horen wat se to hope spreken
Do vragheden de twe Ambletum wor vmme dat he alzo sath ouer der
tafetē vn̄ wolde nicht eten zede he dat brot were besprenget mit bluede vn̄
dat beer hadde enē smak na yserne vnde dat vlesch roke alze eyn as van
eynē minschen Vnde sede noch dar to dat de konnink hadde knechtlike
oghen Vn̄ | de hertogh innē hadde dre magetlyke werk ghedan   Do straff-
eden ene sine kūpane vnde seden He laster | de de he louen scholde vn̄ dat
were dorheyt   De yen|nede ene behorkede de zede deme hertoghen
alle desse stukke Vnde de konnink konde dat merken dath he konde
smekken bouen de rechten mynsliken na | ture Vnde vunden dat dat
korne daer dat brot van was dat wus vp eynem acker daer vele doder
myn | schen knoken leghen Wente vp der stede hadde eyn grot strijd
ghewezen dar vele lude ane gheslagē worden Vnde de swyne dar dat
spek van was he hadden enen Rouer in ghegheten Vnde dat water dar
dat beer van ghebruet was Daer leghen vele swer | de inne dede rust
ghegheten hadde Dar vmme besinnede dat de hertoghe wol dat de
iunghelink hadde al rechte ghesecht vnde nam sine moder to sik
vnde bedrouwede de so langhe dat se em moste segghen | | (fol. 24ʳ)
we syn vader was Do sede se id em dat is was ein knecht   Do shemede
sick de konink dat yd so was vmme zyne zake Vn̄ vraghede do dē
iūghelink vmme de konninghinne wath maghetlike werk dat se | ghedan
hadde   Do zede he se pleghe eren hoykē vp dat houet to henghēde Vn̄
pleghe ere cledere vp to schortēde Vn̄ se pleghe de tenē to stokēde mit
eynem stocke Vn̄ dat se dar vth stockede dat ete se denne achter na Vn̄
sede dar noch tho des kōninghes moder wart to eyner tijd gheuanghē dar
van wart se alze eyne maghet   Dar vmme erde de konnink sine wyszheyt
efft he eyn god were Vn̄ gaff eme sine dochter vn̄ sine kumpane de leeth

267

humanum sapere vel desipere juvenem indicavit. Inventumqve est, qvod panis factus fuit ex segete, qve creverat in campo repleto ossibus mortuorum, eo qvod illic strages belli ante fuerat maxima, & qvod porci, ex qvibus lardum erat, corpus unius latronis devorassent, & qvod aqva, unde potus factus fuit, habebat in fundo plurimos gladios jam fere ferrugine consumptos. Igitur Rex animadvertens, eum de istis subtiliter judicasse. Cum a matre per minas extorsisset, qvis pater suus fuerit, servum fuisse cognovit. Erubescens autem Rex de sua condicione, qvesivit a juvene, qvaliter in Regina facta servilia denotasset, eo, inqvit, qvod more ancille pallio caput obduxit, qvod vestem ad gressum succinxit, & qvod reliqvias cibi inherentes dentibus stipite eruit & erutas comedit : addidit, qvod mater Regis per captivitatem in servam aliqvando redacta fuisset. Cujus industriam Rex qvasi aliqvid divinum veneratus, filiam suam ei donavit, ac socios ejus seqventi die suspendio consumpsit. *Ambletus* contra Regem conqverens, qvod socios suos occiderit, aurum a rege composicionis nomine recepit, & postmodum igni liqvatum latenter duobus baculis cavatis infudit. Anno fere revoluto, de licencia Regis solus in *Daniam* rediit, nichil secum de regiis opibus habens, preter duos baculos supradictos. Ut autem in *Juciam* venit, statim ut prius vesaniam pretendebat. Cumqve triclinium, in qvo sue fiebant exeqvie, intravit, stupor omnes invasit, qvod, qvem mortuum credebant, vivum viderent. Interrogatus de sociis suis, ostendit baculos, qvos gerebat : Ecce, inqviens, hic & unus & alius est. De qvo dicto ridentibus convivis, pincernis se junxit : Et ne gressum laxior vestis impediret, gladio se cinxit, qvem plerumqve de industria extrahens, supremos digitos vulneravit, propter qvod gladium cum vagina clavo perforante confixit. Adeo autem cunctos inebriavit, ut nullus aulam exire posset, sed ubi comederant, ibi sopori se dabant. Cernens autem, cunctos profundius obdormire, cortinas superius solvit, extunditqve eas super proceres in pavimento dormientes, atqve inexcogitabili modo hamis ligneis, qvos aliqvando fecerat, eos ligavit, sicqve ignem imposuit ac cunctos cum aula cremavit. Accedens eciam ad cubiculum *Fengonis*, gladium ejus lectulo herentem arripuit, ac suum loco ejus fixit. Demum patruum excitans, proceres ejus igne perire refert, & adesse Ambletum, trucidatur. Occiso *Fengone*, *Ambletus* latitabat, qvousqve intelligeret,

268

he des anderen dages henghen   Ambletus de claghede ouer den konninck **XIII. Low-**
wor vmme dat he sine kumpane ghemordet hadde So langhe dat em de **German**
konnink vele goldes gaff to zone vor sine kumpane Vñ he nam dat golt **version**
Vñ leet weik werdē in deme vure vñ makede twe hole stokke Vñ goet id
dar hemeliken in Do dat iaer vul na vmme komen was   Do nam he orloff
van dem konnighe Vñ quā alleyne wedder in dannemarken Vñ nā nicht
mit sik van des konninghes ryke daghen ane de twe stokke   Alzo vort
alze he in Jutlande quā Do nā he sine dorheyt wedd' vor   Alze he quam
to d' wert | schop dar mē sine bygrafft beghink do wūderdē se sik altomale
Dat se den luendych dar seghen den se menden dat he langhe döt hadde
ghewezē   Dē vragheden se na sinem kumpane do wyzede hede twe stokke
Vnde sede dyt is de eyne dath ys de andere dar van worden se altomale
lachende   Do makede he sik by yewelken schenken vñ halp en dat se io
vul scholden schenken vñ he halde vul beer Vñ he gink los ghegordet vñ
de kled' hinderdē eme dat he nicht | | (fol. 24ᵛ) so wol konde helpen
schenkē alze he gherne dā hadde do nam he vñ gordede sik mit sinē
swerde vnde toch do dat swert io vaken vth vñ to sneet buten sine
vinghere dat se em bloddē daerūme nam he eynen nagel vñ sluch dor de
scheden vñ dor dat swert vñ neghelde id so to hope vp dat mē en io
scholde vor eynen doren holdē vñ vp dat sik nemāt vor em warde wēte
he wuste alrede wol eyne andere wysze dar he se mede vor deruen wolde
wē mit dē swerde vñ he halp dar alzo to mit siner wūderlicheyt dat se
altomale so drunkē worden dat daer nicht eyn kōde vth deme houe komen
Sund' dar se gheten had | dē dar ledē se sik slapen alze he sach dat se
altomale harde slepen do lozede he de vmmehanghe bouen althomale vñ
toch de ouer de eddelinghe de dar leghen vp d' dele vñ slepē vñ makede
darso wund'liken eyn strijck vñ eynen hamen van vñ beknuttede vñ
bestrikkede se darso inne mit den haken de he oldinghet ghemaket hadde
dat id vnsprekelyck vñ vndenkelik was vnde stack do vuer in den hoff
vnde vorbrande allent dat dar inne was   To deme lesten ghink he to
Fengonis bedde vñ nam sin swert dat by synem bedde stūt vñ sette sin
in de stede vñ wekkede en do vp vñ sede sine gudē lude weren altomale
vorghan in dē vure vñ he were Amblet' de hedde dat ghedan vñ sluch en
do ok So ghink he do vth deme weghe so langhe dat he horde wo dat
volck wolde laten vmme Fengonis döt   Do horde he dat etlike sik bed-
rouedē vmme synem döt   De anderen de he wuste dat sines vader vrunt
weren vñ leth dat volk to hope vorboden vñ claghede vñ sede vā synes
vad' vnschuldyghē dode vñ vā siner eghenē bedroffnisse vñ iamericheyt
de he ledē hadde mēnych | | (fol. 25ʳ) yar vñ claghede dat so iamerlike
dat mē nicht quā to groter medelidinghe vñ dat mēnich weende vā barm-
herticheyt   Do lesten nemē se en mit enem ghemenen rade vñ koren en
to konninghe vñ vorhopeden sik altomale ghudes van siner grotē wijszheyt
vñ vorsichticheyt   Do so mennighe yar lykende sych | enem doren vp dat
he mochte vullen bringhen sine begheringhe do dyt ghescheen was do nam

269

qvaliter populus mortem ejus ponderaret. Dum igitur aliqvi mortem ejus dolerent, alii laudarent, vocatis ad se, qvi amici patris fuerant, populum congregari fecit, coram qvo de injusta patris sui nece ac de propria calamitate, qvam pluribus annis pertulerat, tam motive perorabat, ut multos ad miseracionem, plurimos eciam ad lacrimas commovit. Tandem finito merore, alacri omnium acclamacione in Regem sublimatur. Nam omnibus de ejus industria maxima spes accreverat, qvi tot annis simulate se gesserat, ut ad intentum perveniret. Hiis gestis, cum tribus navibus adornatis, assumptaqve probissima societate, in *Britanniam* est reversus. Inter cetera vero sollempnia, qve secum habuit, gessit clypeum, in qvo omnes eventus sui & notabilia, qve fecerat, de qvibus jam dictum est, mirabili ingenio depicti erant. Sed & comites ipsius tantum deauratis clipeis utebantur. *Rex* vero *Britannie* eos letissime suscepit, atqve de statu amici sui *Fengonis* inter epulas interrogans, interfectum ab *Ambleto* intellexit. Qvo audito, obstupuit propter id maxime, qvod ejus mortem in proprium generum vindicare deberet. Condixerant enim inter se *Fengo & Rex Britannie*, qvod superstes necem alterius vindicaret. Excogitato igitur consilio, rogavit *Ambletum*, ut ad *Reginam Scocie* legacionem sibi assumeret, eam pro ipso procuraturus, eo qvod uxor ejus noviter jam fuerat defuncta. Sciebat enim dictam Reginam omnes procos suos odio habere, nec aliqvem superesse, qvin per eam capite truncaretur. Assumptis igitur sociis, *Ambletus* proficiscitur, atqve dum prope curiam Regine esset, in pulchro prato ad qviescendum se deposuit. Audito hospitum adventu, Regina X. juvenes emisit, qvi hospites & eorum apparatum explorarent, qvorum unus clipeum *Ambleti* ad caput ejus positum, ac *literas legacionis* ejus de loculo callide receptas ad Reginam deportavit. At ipsa diligenter clipeum & literas considerans, eos referri precepit. Evigilans interim *Ambletus*, iterum sompnum simulavit, atqve exploratorem clipeum referentem subito vinculavit, sociisqve excitatis ad curiam accessit. Cui cum caussam legacionis dixisset, literasqve tradidisset, respondit illa, se multum mirari, cur homo tam nobilis tantorumqve operum vellet legacionem sumere pro viro de servili condicione nato, licet in Regem sublimato, ac filiam ejus accipere in uxorem : addiditqve, se *Ambleti* amplexibus dignam, utpote qve Regina esset, ac per thorum suum Regem facere posset. Sic dicens, ipsum amplexata est, qvi e contrario in ejus ruit oscula, sibiqve, qvod virgini erat placitum, protestatur.* Deinde fit convivium, convocantur amici, nupcie peraguntur. Qvibus expletis, in *Britanniam* cum

* Pro *protestatur* Apographum Magnæanum legit *porrigebat.*

he dre | schepe vn̄ tzyrde de schonliken vn̄ nam dar yn mit sik de alder-
menlikesten vn̄ beddernesten selschop de he konde vinden in sinē lāde vn̄
toch so wedder in Britanien Mank anderē hochtichlikē dynghē de he
mit sik hadde so droch he enē schilt dar alle de stukke de em to komē
weren vn̄ alle de merkeliken dynk de he bedreuen hadde inne stundē myt
vntelliker behendycheyt ghemalt Sunder sine kumpane haddē altomale
vorguldede schylde Do se dar quemē do entffenk se de konninck ghans
leeffliken vnde do se ouer maltijd seten do vraghede he na deme state synes
vrundes Fengonis vn̄ vnderstūt wol dath he ghedodet was van Ambleto vn̄
vnderquam des dat he sinen dȯth scholde wrekē in sinē eghenē swaghere
wente Fengo vn̄ he de haddē dat to hope gelouet welk er des anderen dȯt
leuede de scholde den anderen wreken vn̄ dachte eynē raet dat he bat
Ambletū dat he wolde vmme sin werff varē to der kȯninghinnē vā schot-
lande vn̄ wernē em de wēte syne vrouwe were nyens ghestoruē De kȯnink
mende dat dar vp he wuste wol al de iēne de to d' kȯniginnē quemē vn̄
woruē vmme vrye de leth se altomale dodē So nā he sine kūpane vn̄ vur
daer hen do he quā by d' kȯnighinnē hoff do lede he sik in eyne scoue
wysch rouwē do de kȯnighinne horde d' geeste to | | (fol. 25ᵛ) kumpst
Do sande se vth teyn iunghelinge de ere verde vnde ghelate vorspeen
scholden Do quā eyn vn̄ sach den schylt Ambleti ligghen tho sinem
houeden vn̄ he nam den schilt vnde sine breue dar sine bode schop ane
stund vth sine budele vn̄ brochte dat d' konninghinnen Do se hadde den
schylt vul wol beseen vn̄ de breue Do bat se en dat he dat dar wolde wedder
bringhen De wyle wakede Amblet' vp vn̄ vornam wol wo dar gheuaren
was Do lede he sik wedd' efft he slepe vn̄ greep dē vorspeer De dē schilt
wedder brochte vn̄ venk en vn̄ bāt en al harde vn̄ wekkede do sine kūpane
vn̄ ghinck vp dē hoff vnde warff sin werff Vn̄ wyzede sine breffe Do sede
se dat er dat ghās sere wunderde dat alzodanich eyn eddel man de alzodanich werk bedreuē hadde Dat de wolde alzodanych eynes mānes bode
vezen De dar were van enem knechte boren Woldoch dat he were
vorhoghet to eynē konninghe Vn̄ dat he wol de syne dochter nemē to
eyner huszvrouwe Vn̄ sede vort Jk were werdych dyner De ik eyne
kȯninghin byn Vn̄ vormiddelst mynem bedde mach eynen kȯnink maken
Alze se to em sprak so grep se ene in den arm Vn̄ he kussede se vn̄ hadde
alle synen wyllen mit er Darna makeden se brutlacht vn̄ vorbodeden ere
vrūt Do de hochtijd vthe was Do toch he mit siner nyen brued wedder
in Britanien Vn̄ nam mit sik enen starkē hupē vā den schotten Do he
dar quā do lep des kȯninghes dochter sine andere huszvrouwe entieghen
Vn̄ bath ene woldoch dat he hadde noch eyne ghenomen Dat he se doch
nicht scholde leuer hebbē wen se Vn̄ lete er des gheneten dat se em hadde *
eynem sone teelt Vnde se warnede ene vort dat he sik yo warde vor der
bedrechnisse eres vaders | | (fol. 26ʳ) Do leep em ok de hertoghe van

* *Dadde* in the old text.

XIII. The Gheysmer Epitome. conjuge *Hermintruda* redit, valida manu *Scotorum* secum sumpta. Cui occurrens uxor sua prior, Regis filia, rogabat, ut, qvamvis uxorem aliam superduxerit, non tamen eam preamaret, caussam pro se allegans, qvia filium secum jam habebat. Insuper admonuit, ut patris sui insidias precaveret. Occurrit autem *Rex Britannie*, generumqve amplexatus, dolose ad convivium invitavit. *Ambletus* autem, licet sciret fraudem subesse, tantum receptis secum CC. eqvitibus, paruit invitanti. Sed dum essent inter portas ad curiam ducentes, Rex eum jaculo perfodisset, nisi ferrum, qvod *Ambletus* sub toga habuit, obstitisset. Igitur festinus rediit ad locum, ubi *Scotus* jusserat expectare. Rex vero fugientem insecutus, majorem partem sociorum ejus trucidavit : ita ut, dum seqventi die *Ambletus* pro salute preliari deberet, adjutorium de interfectis mutuatus est. Nam qvosdam eorum stipitibus affixit, qvosdam ad lapides erexit, aliqvos in eqvis posuit, adeo ut hospitibus videbatur, qvod nullum dampnum habuisset, propter qvod territi Britannici fugam inierunt. Qvorum Rex, dum segnius fugeret, ab inseqventibus est occisus. Victor igitur *Ambletus* jam *Rex Britannie* ac *Scocie* factus, cum ingenti preda in *Juciam* cum utraqve conjuge est reversus.

Interea defuncto RORICO Rege Danorum, avo *Ambleti*, WICLETUS vitricus *Ambleti* in regno successit. Qvi qverebatur, qvod *Ambletus* fraudulenter *regnum Jucie* usurpasset. Sed *Ambletus* dissimulans, splendidissima dona de suis spoliis *Wicleto* transmisit. Qvem tamen postea, publicus hostis effectus, bello devicit. Sed WICLETUS iterum congregans exercitum, *Ambleto* bellum denunciat. Qvi periculum ejus imminere considerans, plus dolebat de uxoris sue *Hermuntrude* viduitate, qvam de proprie necis respectu ; tantum enim eam amabat. Cumqve de hoc cum ea loqveretur, promisit, se futuram cum eo in acie, detestabilem asserens feminam, qve cum viro mori non auderet. De qva promissione parum tenuit ; nam interfecto *Ambleto*, statim iniit amplexus WICLETI occisoris. Tanta est mulierum fides. WICLETUS autem senex est defunctus.

Britanien entyegē mit bedrechnisse vn̄ nam en in dē arm vn̄ bath ene wȫl dȫn alze he em bat mē do se werē tusschen dē portē de vp dē hoff ghinghē do hadde Amblet' de kōnik aldoct gheschotē hadde he nicht dat yserne hat vn | der dē hoykē dar van wende he sick varlozē vn̄ quā dar he de schotten ghelatē hadde vn̄ de hertoge volghede em vn̄ vorderuede em dē grotestē deel vā sinē kūpanen des anderē daghes do Ambletus scholde stridē vor sinē heyl vn̄ salicheyt do nā he hulpe van dē dodē Eyn deel rychtede he vp byde stene eyn del stak he stakene in de erdē vn̄ bant se dar to eyn deel sette he vp de perde so dat he britanier seghē sinen hupē allike grot vn̄ dat he nenen schadē ghenomen hadde vn̄ wordē dar mede vleende vn̄ de konninck was vā dē de achter na vloghē vn̄ wart so gheslaghē So wart Ambet' kōnink ouer britanien vnde ouer schotlande vn̄ quā so mit eynē mechtyghē roue vn̄ mit sinen twen huszvrouwen wedder in syn eghen lant Vnder des wart konnink Rorikus van dannemarken begrauen vn̄ Wicletus de ambletum ouerwā de volghede em in dat ryke de claghede do ouer Ambletū dat he mit bedrechnisse hadde sik vnderbrokē Jutlande sund' Amblet' wolde en bewekē vn̄ sande em de ald' durbarsten ghaue vā sinē eghenen dat he gherouet hadde de doch allike woel syn vyent wart vn̄ ouerwā ene wente Wiclet' de sam | melde vnder des sine schare to hope vn̄ kundyghede Ambleto enen strijd do dat Ambletus horde do vruchtede he alzo vort sinē schaden vn̄ dachte wol | | (fol. 26ᵛ) dat he den dȫth nicht entghan konde vn̄ sorghede do meer vor sin wyff de kōnighinnē vā schotlande dat se scholde wrdewe werdē wen he sorghede vor sinē eghenē doet do he mit er darūme sprak do louede se em dat se wolde mit em bliuen vor in d' spijsse vn̄ sede dat were en vnardych wyff de nicht dorste steruē mit ere mānе dar se doch suluē vul luttich aff helt wente do Amblet' doth was do ghink se alzo vort hen vn̄ leet sik helsen Wicletū de eren man slaghen hadde Alzodane is der wyue loue Do de Wycletus olt wart so starff he.

XIV. HAMLET DANAPRINS.

ÍSLENZKRI ÞÝÐINGU EPTIR *MATTÍAS JOCHUMSSON*,

REYKJAVIK, 1878.

ACT III. SCENE IV.

PÓL. Þ Ú er hans von. Þér vægið honum ekki,
en segið að hans ærsli ekki kunni
hið minnsta hóf og þolist því ei lengur.
Og að þér sjálfar hafið einatt hlotið
að vera hlíf í milli hans og bálsins.
Eg ætla hér að halda mig í tómi.
Þér hlífið honum ekki.

HAMLET [*úti fyrir*]. Móðir! móðir!

DROTTN. Nei, því sé fjærri, verið þar um vissir,
en farið því eg heyri hvar hann kemur.

[HAMLET *kemur;* PÓLÓNIUS *felur sig.*

HAMLET. Nú móðir góð, er nokkuð nýtt í efni?

DROTTN. Þú, Hamlet, hefur stórum styggt þinn föður.

HAMLET. Þér, móðir, hafið stórum styggt minn föður.

DROTTN. Fý fý, þú svarar furðu léttúðlega.

HAMLET. Fý fý, þú talar furðu syndsamlega.

DROTTN. Nú hvernig, Hamlet?

HAMLET. Hvað er nú að gjöra?

DROTTN. Þú manst ei hver eg em?

HAMLET. Jú, mildi Guð minn!
þér eruð drottning, bóndans bróðurkona,
en líka—því er miður—móðir mín.

274

DROTTN. So veit eg þá, sem við þig geta talað.

HAMLET. Kom! sezt nú hér og hreif þig ei úr stað,
eg fer ei burtu fyr en eg hef sýnt þér
í spegil þann sem sýnir í þér hjartað.

DROTTN. Hvað ertu að hugsa; viltu myrða mig?
Æ, hjálpið, hjálpið!

PÓL. [bakvið]. Þey! þey! hjálpið, hjálpið!

HAMLET. Hvað? valska! drepst hún? já, eg veðja dúkat,
hún drepst.   [Bregður sverði og rekur í gegnum tjaldið.

PÓL. Hann drap mig, æ, æ!   [Deyr.

DROTTN.   Hvað er þetta?
Hvað gjörðir þú?

HAMLET.   Eg veit ei; vóg eg kónginn?
        [Lyptir upp tjaldinn og dregur fram PÓLÓNIUS.

DROTTN. Ó mikil blóðug ófyrirsynju-ódáð!

HAMLET. Já, blóðug víst og nær eins markverð, móðir,
og morð eins kóngs og samlag við hans bróður.

DROTTN. Og morð eins kóngs?

HAMLET.   Já, mín orð voru það.

[Við PÓLÓNIUS.] Þinn veslings flysjungs-garmur, vertu sæll!
eg hélt þú værir herra þinn; tak kaup þitt!
Árveknin, sérðu, hentar bezt í hófi.
Gnú þú ei hendur, haf þig kyrra, sittu,
og lof mér gnúa hjarta þitt, því það skal
nú kenna til, ef annars bítur á það,
og vana-fjandinn hefur ei um það hamrað
eirbrynjustokk gegn öllum tilfinningum.

DROTTN. Hvað hef eg gjört, að þú með þessum ofsa
eyst gífuryrðum yfir mig?

HAMLET.   Þá ódáð,
sem flekkar sæmdar-feimni hverrar konu,
umbreytir tryggð í tál og grípur blómstrið
af hreinnar ástar yndisbjörtu enni
og gjörir það eitt graftarmein og breytir
hjúskapar eið í flárra spila falseið.
Ó, ódáð, þá er hrífur glóðheitt hjartað
úr barmi sáttmálans og gjörir guðsorð
og góða siði að tómu hræsnis-skrumi.

275

Já, himinsins hin háa ásýnd roðnar,
og gjörvöll þessi þétta, rekna hvelfing
fær hræðslusvip sem dómsins dagur ógni,
og sýnist sjúk af sturlun.

DROTTN.   Æ, mig auma !
og hvílík synd er þetta þá, sem hljóðar
og þrumar gegn mér ?

HAMLET. Lít á þessa mynd
Og þessa ; vel þær líkjast báðum bræðrum
Ó skörungs-tign sem skín úr þessum svip !
Apollós lokkar, ennisprýði Jóvis,
herguðsins ægu ógnar-snöru sjónir,
og vaxtarlagið líkt og sendiguðinn
nýstiginn niður, gnæfi hátt á gnýpu !
því slíkan hafði hann vöxt og vænleiks-prýði,
að sýnast mátti, svo sem allir guðir
sitt smiðshögg hefði sérhver á hann sett,
að sanna heiminum að þar var maður.
Og þennan áttir þú.   En lít nú hinn :
nú áttu þennan : eins og eitrað brandax,
síns bróður forsmán.   Áttu auga í höfði ?
Gaztu þá kvaðt svo fagran fjallahaga
og velt þér niðr í þrílíkt forarfen ?
svei ! áttu augu ?   Nefn það aldrei ástir ;
á þínum aldri er blóðið stillt og staðnað
og stjórnast þá af viti, en hvaða vit
kýs þennan fyrir þennan ?   Vitin áttu,
því ella bærðist' ekki úr stað, en rænan
er eflaust úr þeim vitum ; vitfirringin
er ei svo vitskert, engin ráðdeild getur
svo þrælkað undir ærslum, að hún hafi
ei eptir enn það korn af frjálsu vali,
að geta gert sér grein á slíkum mismun.
Hver fjandinn bjó þig í þann blindingsleik ?
Tilfinning sjónlaus, sjón án tilfinningar
eyru án handa og augna, ilman smekklaus—
einn minnsti angi einhvers heilbrigðs vits
gat aldrei hafa farið flatt sem þetta.

276

Ó, skömm, hví roðnar þú ei ? Vargólmt viti !
æsir þú bál í beinum settrar konu ?
má skirleiksdygð hins unga verða að vaxi
og brenna á sjálfs sín báli ? Nefn ei skömm,
hvar hamslaus lostinn steypir allri stilling
og elli-frostið logar eins og æskan
og vit og græðgi haldast beint í hendur.

DROTTN. Æ, Hamlet ! hættu, les ei þetta lengur !
þú hringsnýrð inn til hjartans augum mínum ;
eg sé þar inni svarta vonzku-bletti,
sem lit sinn vilja ei láta.

HAMLET.   Og að dúsa
í frillulífsins viðbjóðslegu velgju,
í syndarinnar ýldu, kjassa og kyssa
á þessu fúla fleti.

DROTTN.   Hættu, hættu !
Hvert orð þitt sker mín eyru líkt og knífur.
þey, Hamlet !

HAMLET.   Þetta hrak og manndrapsmaður
og tuttugu sinnum tuttugu verri maður
en þinn hinn fyrri ; þetta kóngafífl,
og rummungsþjófur ríkisstóls og tignar,
sem konungsdjásnið hrifsaði ofan af hyllu
og stakk í vasann !

DROTTN.   Þey ! þey !

                                        [VOFAN kemur.

HAMLET. Þennan konung
úr tötradulum.—Drottins náðarskarar !
Æ, hjálpið mér og veifið líknarvængjum !—
Hvað viltu hingað helgi voða-svipur ?

DROTTN. Æ, hann er ærður !

HAMLET. Seg ertu kominn til að saka son þinn
um seinlætið að nota ekki tímann
né hafa hugmóð til hins stóra starfs
er stranglega þú bauðst mér, seg mér, seg mér ?

VOF. Gleym þú því ei. Eg kem að kveikja aptur
upp áform þitt, sem þegar er á förum.
Sjá móðir þín er lostin stórri sturlun ;

277

veit henni hjálp í hennar sálarstríði ;
vit, ímyndun er skæðust breysku blóð ;
Ó mæl til hennar Hamlet !

HAMLET.   Hvað er að
þér drottning ?

DROTTN.   Eg spyr hvað er að þér, Hamlet,
því horfir þú svo fast á ekki neitt,
og heldur hróka-ræður út í loptið ?
Úr augum þínum horfir sálin hamslaus,
og hár þitt rís úr rekkju líkt og liðsmenn
sem heyra heróp, stendur upp með endum
sem fjöri fyllt.   Æ kældu, kæri sonur,
með kaldri stilling ofsahuga skaps þíns !
Hvað horfirð' á ?

HAMLET. Á hann ! á hann !   Ó sjáðu,
hve náfölur hann starir ! sök og svipur
í sameiningu hrópa hér svo hátt
að steinar mættu stökkva.—Horf ei á mig !
því hryggðarmynd þín kynni að sjúga krapt
og líf og lit hins voðastranga verks míns,
svo ausi' eg tárum út en ekki blóði.

DROTTN. Seg til hvers ertu að tala ?

HAMLET.   Sérð' hann ekki ?

DROTTN. Nei, eg sé ekkert, og þó allt sem er hér.

HAMLET. Og heyrirð' ekkert ?

DROTTN.   Ekkert nema þig.

HAMLET. Þey, lítt á ! hér ! nú læðist hann á bust
Faðir minn, alveg eins og þá hann lifði !
Sjá þarna fer hann, þarna út um dyrnar.

[VOFAN *fer.*

XV. SUMMARY OF MANUSCRIPTS.

AMBALES-SAGA. AI.

1. A.M. 521c, 4to paper, seventeenth century, written by Arni Gislason : "Saga af Ambulo eður Amloða enun keymska." Arni Magnússon writes in a note that Arni Gislason got his copy from Pál Bjarnarson; yet different from 521B, which also came from Pál Bjarnarson.

The saga, re-told in Danish by Steingrímur Thorsteinson *circa* 1870, is found in the same MS. at the end. Written *circa* 1670–80; divided into forty chapters. (*Cp.* Specimen, Appendix VI.)

2. ISL. BÓKMENTAFÉLAG, 108, 4to : "Sagan af Ambales Konge ;" later half of eighteenth century; very similar to 1; differs occasionally in phrases and words.

3. ISL. BÓKMENTAFÉLAG, 116, 4to : "Sagan af Ambales Kóngi ;" written *circa* 1800; much like 1, but defective at the end, and varying slightly in phraselogy.

4. ISL. BÓKMENTAFÉLAG, 165, 4to : "Af Ambales ;" in a very contracted hand; written 1778; evidently written from a good original; differentiated in phraseology from the 1, 2, 3.

5. ISL. BÓKMENTAFÉLAG, 185, 4to : "Af Ambales og Köppum hans ;" written after 1850; very like 1; slightly different in wording.

6. ISL. BÓKMENTAFÉLAG, 309, 4to : "Sagan af Ambölis Konge ;"

written 1788; illegible for the most part.   At the end of the saga, which resembles 1, the following lines occur :—

> " Æðis mikell Amloode,
> Ungdoms Tyð fram geck slungeñ,
> Fifl, syndest fimur að Able,
> Frækeñ var og vel sprækur.
> Fodur leifd fieck með Raadum,
> Fliott unned Ny Aars Noottu
> Braadt komst burt ur Hættu
> Bloomgadest og varð kongur." *

7. Isl. Bókmentafélag, 368, 4to : "**Af Ambales Konge** ;" late eighteenth century; thirty-nine chapters; similar differences in diction.

8. Isl. Bókmentafélag, 175, 8vo : "**Sagan af Ambolis Kongi** ;" copied from 6.

9. Isl. Bókmentafélag, 700, 8vo : "**Sagan af Ambales eður Amlöða** ;" *circa* 1750; thirty-nine chapters; similar differences.

10. British Museum, xi. 158 : "**Saga af Amboles edur Amloðe** ;" forty chapters; written in three different hands; *ff.* 71–122; thirteenth century; with the verses at the end, as in 6.

11. A manuscript in the possession of Dr. Jón Thorkelsson, of Reykjavik, Iceland : "**Sagan af Ambales eður Amlóða** ;" nineteenth century.

12. A modern manuscript, formerly the property of Gisli Brynjulfsson, of the University of Copenhagen.   At his death it passed into the possession of the editor of this volume, and has been used for the present

---

* "Fierce-tempered was Amloði ; in his youth he was cunning ; a fool he seemed, yet endowed with strength ; he was valiant and skilful ; his father's heritage he got with his wiles ; he won them soon on New Year's night ; anon he escaped from danger, flourished, and was king."

edition. It was written by Pétur Jónsson of Arneskofar, near Húsa- **XV.**
víkurbæ. The volume (which contains also "Sagann af Falentin og **Summary**
Ourson Græna Riddara og Fleiri Koppum") was a gift to Gisli from **of MSS.**
Kristján Jónasarson; previously it had belonged to Guðný Bjarnardóttir.
The title is as follows: — "**Sagann af Ambales Salmans Syni,** er
kalladur var Amlode." There are forty-one chapters; the verses are
not found. The former owner of the MS. has drawn, at the end of the
MS., a genealogical tree of the persons of the saga.

AMBALES-SAGA. Aɪɪ.

13. A.M. 521ʙ, 4to paper, seventeenth century: "**Saga af Amloða
eður Ambales.**" Note by Arne Magnússon that the MS. came originally
from Pál Bjarnarson of Unnarholt. This is the oldest MS. of this class;
the writing is very contracted, and in places illegible; forty-one chapters
in all; in many minor respects different from Aɪ.

14. A.M. 521ᴀ, 4to; well written, and not contracted; *circa* 1700;
evidently copied from 13, or both are from the same original. Its descrip-
tion is as follows:—"**Saga af Amloða eður Ambales.**" An important
note by Arne Magnusson states that it came from the widow of Torfæus,
1720.

15. Nʏ Kɢʟ. Sᴀᴍʟ., 1719, 4to; a poor copy of 14. (*Cp.* Specimen,
Appendix VI.)

B. SAGAN AF AMLODA HARÐVENDELS SYNE.

16. A.M. 521ᴅ, 4to; 14 pp.; written *circa* 1700. Arne states in a
note:—"Amloda saga, komin til min frä Jone Thorlaks syne 1705. Er
tekin ur Saxo Gramatico, og er ölik Amloda Sögu Pals Biarna Sonar:
añars skrifaði Jon Thorlaksson mier með henni 1705, 12 Junii: Eg læt
hier með fylgja *amloda sögu*, sem mig minner þier beiddud mig um ä ärunum.

281

Eñ eg ätti hana þa eigi til, og eigi hefir hun mier iñ borist fyrr eñ i vetur. Svo dyliast sögurnar riett upp undir mier, þö til sieu.

> me, nimirum decipere voluit vir bonus, et persvadere, se
> rem vetustam
> mihi mittere. Sed non ego credulus illi."

(See Specimen, Appendix VI.)

C. RÍMUR.

17. Isl. Bókmentafélag, 8vo, 273: "**Rímur af Ambáles eptir Hallgrím Haldórsson.**" Imperfect at the beginning, but authorship attested by runic passage at the end of the work. The author flourished during the first half of the eighteenth century. Twenty-five sections. (*Cp.* Appendix I.)

18. A.M. 521e, 4to: "**Ríjmur af Ambalez eða amloða;**" in the same hand as No. 13; twenty-five sections; half of last ríma wanting; seventeenth century. Note by Arne Magnusson states that these rímur were sent him by Jón Thorláksson. Dr. Kålund points out that, as Pál Bjarnarson of Unnarholt is known to have composed Ambales-Rímur, perhaps these are his; but the MS. seems to be a copy (an imperfect copy, due to inability on the part of the scribe to read what was before him), and cannot well be the author's autograph. (*Cp.* Appendix II.)

19. Ny Kgl. Saml., 1719, 4to; clearly a copy of the previous MS.; similarly defective at the end.

20. MS., 4to, in the possession of Dr. Jón Thorkelsson, Copenhagen: "**Rímur af Ambalis kveðnar af Illuga Helgasyni.**" In tattered condition; composed *circa* 1690–1700; written about the middle of the eighteenth century, or later; twenty-four sections; defective at the end. (*Cp.* Appendix III.)

21. Isl. Landsbókasafn, 72, 4to: (*a*) "**Ambáles Rímur Salmanssonar,** ortar af Thorvaldi Sigmundarsyni;**" written in three hands; *circa* 1750–1800; ends in the eleventh ríma, the rest wanting; 28 pp. (*b*) Another MS. of the same; part of the first ríma missing; ends in the middle of

the nineteenth ríma; 36 pp., in same handwriting; earlier than the the former. (*Cp.* Appendix IV.)

22. MS., 4to, belonging to Dr. Jón Thorkelsson, Copenhagen; brought from Iceland, 1894, and recently discovered among his papers: "**Ríjmur af þeim nafnfræga konungi yfir Vallandi Ambales Salmans Syni ordtar af**

a Þ Lágafelli E í mikla S hrepp;"

i.e., Þórður Einarsson á Lágafelli í Mikla [holts]hrepp. Lágafell is a farm three hours' ride from Snæfellsjökul, in the west midland of Iceland. The MS. is certainly the author's autograph.

D. ANNALS.

23. BRITISH MUSEUM, Finn Magnusson's MSS., No. 375 (= xi. 153): " **Fiesjöör margra loflegra fräsagna, annäla, æfintyra, &c.; samantekinn af Magnúse Joonssyne í Vigur.**

"(M. J.) Magnate Islandiæ, *circa* 1550. Ipsius autographum et verisimiliter unicum quod jam existit exemplar. Ineditus. In Annalibus antiquioribus, oddensibus dictis occurrit, ad annum mundi 3588, singularis narratio de Amlodo (Amleto sine Hamleto), Danico principe, alioquin a Saxone Grammatico et posterius a Guilielmo Shakespeare celebrato. Adscribuntur hi annales celeberrimo *Sæmundo* dicto *fróði*, Eddicorum carminorum primo collectori in Islandia defuncto 1133 (ante nativitatem Saxonis in Dania; hic Sæmundus dictos annales e latino sermone transtulisse perhibetur)."—Note by F. M.

The volume is certainly written at the end of the seventeenth century, as Finn Magnusson must have known. The writer states the date clearly at the end of one of the sections (1694); he must have known, too, the date of Magnus Jonsson í Vigur. (*Cp.* Introduction.)

24. There is a much later MS. of these "Odda Annaler" in NY KGL. SAML., 1703, 4to, written *circa* 1770: "Argi" is given as the wicked uncle's name instead of "Feggi."

E. BÁLANTS EÐA FERACUTS RÍMUR.

25. Of these Rímur, closely connected with the Ambales Saga and Rímur, there are many MSS., more especially in the Bókmentafélags-

283

Safn (*e.g.*, Nos. 174, 176, 200, 278, 297), and in private hands. Dr. Thorkelsson, of Copenhagen, possesses two MSS. One of these, written in Snæfellsness, *circa* 1760, is here described :—

"**Hér byrjar rímur af Bálant admiral, kveðnar af Guðmundi Bergþorssyni.**"

The author, a cripple, was evidently a professional composer of rímur; in the Mansöngr to the fifth Ríma he enumerates no less than thirteen other rímur-cycles.

The name of the author of the present Rímur, the date (1701) and place of composition, and the name of his patron (Arnljotur), are thus indicated at the end of the twenty-fourth Ríma :—

> Snekkjur dverga tvennar tólf
> tókst mér nú að skapa
> nýbangaðar náms um gólf
> nú á *Arnarstapa.*

> *Árferð,† vinda agg ‡ og lögur,§
> ís ‖ yfir skarði landa,¶
> týr,** úr,†† reið,‡‡ sá beiddi um bögur
> brjótur kennist landa.

> Valdráður §§ og vífa fé ‖‖
> vakti Kvásis dreyra
> óliðlegast ort þó sé
> ekki er nafnið meira.

> Ártal hef eg í ljóðin leitt
> lesarann á þó furði
> seytján hundruð alls og eitt [= 1701
> eru frá Christi burði.

* = ár = a.	† ferð = reið = r.	‡ = nauð = n.	§ = l.	‖ = i.
¶ = ós = ó.	** = t.	†† = u.		‡‡ = r, *Arnljótur.*
§§ Guð.	‖‖ mundur, Guðmundur.			

Printed by BALLANTYNE, HANSON & Co.
Edinburgh & London